# A HISTORY OF
# SHIPBUILDING
# AT LYTHAM

Lytham Shipbuilding & Engineering Comp.ʸ

*A perspective drawing of the yard about 1899.*

# A HISTORY OF SHIPBUILDING AT LYTHAM

## By Jack M. Dakres
(Author of "The Last Tide")

World Ship Society
Kendal LA9 7LT
1992

# CONTENTS

| | | | |
|---|---|---|---:|
| Acknowledgements | | | 5 |
| Chapter 1 | The Early Years | | 7 |
| Chapter 2 | The Founding Years | - Richard Smith & Company | 8 |
| Chapter 3 | | - Lytham S.B. & E. Co. Ltd | 10 |
| Chapter 4 | Pre 1914-18 War | - The Rubber Boom | 16 |
| Chapter 5 | | - Into Africa | 18 |
| Chapter 6 | The 1914-18 War | - The War Effort | 21 |
| Chapter 7 | Post 1914-18 War | - The Vital Link | 25 |
| Chapter 8 | The 1939-45 War | - Another War Effort | 31 |
| Chapter 9 | Post 1939-45 War | - The Decline | 32 |
| Chapter 10 | | - The Closure | 34 |
| Bibliography | | 35 | |
| Chapter 11 | The Vessels | | 36 |
| Appendix I | Ships built at Lytham by early builders | | 127 |
| Appendix II | Ships built by Smith, Preston | | 128 |
| Appendix III | Ships built by R. Smith & Company, Preston | | 129 |
| Index I | Alphabetical list of owners or agents of vessels built at Lytham by Richard Smith & Co. and by Lytham S.B. & E. Co. (Ltd.) | | 132 |
| Index II | Alphabetical list of vessels built at Lytham by Richard Smith & Co. and by Lytham S.B. & E. Co. (Ltd.) | | 136 |
| Index III | Text | | 143 |

*Rear cover:*
*The builders' plate of FRESHSPRING.* 	*B. Phillips*

**ISBN 0 905617 71 1**

# ACKNOWLEDGEMENTS

It is with the greatest of pleasure and appreciation that I record my indebtedness to the many individuals, companies and authorities who have so willingly given of their time to assist me in my long and detailed research, so necessary for a book such as this.

Without the cooperation of the Friedenthal family this book would have been impossible to complete. My thanks go to Mr. and Mrs. G. L. Friedenthal, Mrs. Betty Sayers, Mr. L. Cochrane, Mr. and Mrs. R. Twittey and their son David. Mr. R. Twittey was especially helpful over a long period and there is no doubt that his invaluable assistance made a significant contribution to the completion of the book. He must have spent many hours, which he would otherwise have spent on his yacht, meticulously copying information from the late Richard Friedenthal's records for me, as well as supplying me with most of the photographs, many of which have never been published before.

The Science Museum Library at South Kensington, London, has always been most helpful as has the World Ship Society. These authorities are always most cooperative and my thanks go to them. I would specifically thank Michael Crowdy, Chairman of the World Ship Society for his support, Viscount Leathers of Purfleet, Commander G.I. Mayes, R.N., Roy Fenton, Clifford Parsons, Kevin O'Donoghue, Dr. G.S. Wilson, Harold Appleyard, Rowan Hackman, Peter Kenyon, Brian Hillsdon, Historian of the Steam Boat Association of Great Britain and the late Ian Hazlett and Jim Sawbridge for their help. The cooperation of the Goethe-Institut, Manchester is acknowledged and my grateful appreciation goes to Herr Werner Herzog of the Werner Herzog Filmproduktion, Munich, for providing details about the ship(s) used in his film 'Fitzcarraldo'.

Many others have contributed in various ways and their interest and support is gratefully acknowledged. They are my neighbour and friend Colin Dickinson for his help with engine details and photographs, Peter White, Gloucester, M. Colley, Birkenhead, C. McCarthy, Dundalk, Harley Crossley, Dorset, Keith Ingham, Lancaster, P.J. Tebay of the Liverpool Nautical Research Society, M.D. Dorth, Devon, Percy Dunbavand, Runcorn, Freddie Johnson, Freckleton, Barry Phillips, Bristol, Mr. and Mrs. L. Jones, Preston and Peter Sharman of the Lytham Heritage Group and late of Lancashire Libraries.

Finally, and by no means least, my sincere thanks go to the President of the Lytham Heritage Group, my good friend Stanley Brown, for his invaluable help, advice and support throughout the production of this record, and for allowing me access to the Group's archives whenever it was sought.

*Frederick Francis Joseph Friedenthal 1850-1928.*

*John Alfred Friedenthal 1882-1960.*

*Richard Ernest James Friedenthal 1891-1987.*

# SHIPBUILDING AT LYTHAM

## 1: The Early Years.

There is little doubt that ships have been built at Lytham for a very long time but it was not until the predecessors of the Lytham Shipbuilding and Engineering Co. Ltd., founded a works at Lytham, that this became a major industry in the town. Wherever water was present, no matter where in the world, ships were built as a matter of necessity. This was as much true at Lytham as anywhere else in ancient times, especially as water provided the most convenient and labour saving form of transport. The first vessels built on the river were canoes cut out of tree trunks (there was no shortage of trees in the area) and other similar craft. Two such canoes were recovered during the excavations for Preston Dock in 1885 and can be seen at the Harris Museum and Art Gallery at Preston where they are occasionally displayed. These of course were used as ferries for crossing the river, for the transport of domestic goods and animals as well as for fishing. During their occupation of this country from the 1st century A.D., onwards, it is known that the Romans used the river for the transport of goods, but only scant evidence of this has been unearthed at Ribchester and Walton-le-Dale, near Preston. Nothing has been discovered to suggest that any form of shipbuilding by the Romans took place on the River Ribble nor has any evidence of the presence of Roman vessels been found.

The first recorded trading on the River Ribble was in the early 14th century, but it is certain that trading took place well before that. Lytham, situated as it is on the estuary of the river immediately opposite to Southport, and nearer to the more populated hinterland, no doubt played an important role in these trading activities, and it is known that Lytham provided a calling place for vessels if only for the transfer of cargo from the large seagoing sailing ships to smaller lighters. Lytham was also a popular stopping place for small passenger steamers plying between Liverpool, Southport, Blackpool and Preston. The first steamship service is recorded as having started in 1835 when the wooden paddle steamer ENTERPRISE operated excursions in the summer season. She had been built at Preston and was launched on 23rd May, 1834 for Hugh Williams of Woodside for the Mersey ferry service which he ran between Woodside and Liverpool. Many other such pleasure ships provided a very pleasant relaxation for both holidaymakers and locals alike and this continued until the early 1920s.

The first vessel which is recorded as having been built at Lytham was the brigantine GRACE as late as 1818, a vessel of 98 tons old measurement which was still sailing in 1882 for Preston and Lytham owners. Many others must have been built but details of them do not appear in such records as Lloyds Register of Shipping, the Mercantile Navy List and Maritime Directory or the Preston Register, and, in the absence of shipyard records, nothing is known of them or their builders. A short list and details of those vessels which were registered appears at Appendix I.

In 1841 the Second Ribble Navigation Company, based at Preston and having quays there alongside the river, entered into an agreement with Thomas Clifton of Lytham for the making of a dock and wharves at Lodge Pool near Lytham. This was mainly to afford an inducement to foreign vessels of a large class to enter the River Ribble knowing that if the wind was unfavourable or there were adverse weather conditions, they could lie safely in port at Lytham, and not aground in the estuary as had been the practice. Under the terms of this agreement the Second Ribble Navigation Company leased the dock for 20 years from its completion in 1843 at a rent of £150 per annum, but did not renew the lease in 1863 for financial reasons. However, the Second Ribble Navigation Company had other obligations and in 1883 these were ratified by the Ribble Navigation and Preston Dock Act, whereby the Corporation of Preston, among other things, agreed to keep the access to the Lytham Dock "as convenient for vessels as it now is and shall keep the drainage outfall of such dock and also of the brook or watercourse called Warton Brook below the respective flood gates as properly and efficiently open for the purposes of drainage as at present." This is the agreement to which Richard Friedenthal referred when explaining some of the reasons for the closure of the shipyard some seventy years later, an agreement which seems to have ended only when Preston Dock was finally closed in 1981.

## 2: The Founding Years - Richard Smith & Company.

The forerunner of the Lytham Shipbuilding and Engineering Co. Ltd., was Richard Smith and Company, a company which had been founded at Ashton Quays, Preston in about 1869 but possibly ten years earlier. The actual date is uncertain, but what is certain is that John Abel Smith purchased the Ashton Quays, including the wet dock, from John Bolton sometime between 1842 and 1854, and this gentleman entered into an agreement with the Third Ribble Navigation Company in 1854 whereby they purchased the quays from him in perpetuity together with a portion of the adjacent Preston Marsh for the residue of a 75 year lease at rents amounting to £250.5s.9d. per annum. Part of this property was let to Thomas Smith in 1855 and included the wet dock mentioned previously, which had been constructed by John Bolton in 1843 the year after he had purchased the quays, together with a portion of land on the west side. He converted the wet dock into a graving dock and this was said by the Port Authority 'to be a very desirable facility for those engaged in the shipping trade'. In addition he erected extensive buildings for his occupation as a ship builder and ship repairer. He carried out repair work at this yard and also built several vessels of both iron and wood, but there is no evidence to suggest that he built anything other than sailing ships, mainly schooners and barques, and up to 1869 these were accredited in what records are available merely to 'Smith, Preston'. See Appendix II.

This site at Ashton was later occupied by Richard Smith and Company, and one can only assume that Richard was a relative of Thomas. However, under this trade name he built some 140 ships at Preston, the first ones being recorded in 1869. These included sailing ships, steam yachts, paddle steamers, steam tugs and screw steamers, almost all being built of wood or iron, only the odd one being built of steel. It appears that very few, if any, were built for foreign owners although some did eventually find their way abroad. A couple of steam tugs were built for the Peninsular and Oriental Steam Navigation Company together with several small ones for the Bridgewater Canal Company. See Appendix III.

Unfortunately for the company, this activity was brought to an abrupt end in 1888 when the River Ribble was diverted to accommodate the new Albert Edward Dock which was then under construction. This left Richard Smith and Company with a shipyard at Preston but with no water into which to launch their ships, the river having been filled in from just seaward of the Ashton Quays to just east of the Victoria Quays. Accordingly the company had to seek a site elsewhere and chose one not far away at Lytham where they were able to continue their business, leaving William Allsup and Sons as the only shipbuilders of note still at Preston. This company was completely unaffected by the new diversion and, if anything, enjoyed much improved launching facilities. They were to have their own problems later but remained at Preston for another twenty years before finally going out of business in about 1908.

The site chosen by Smith, known as Lytham Creek, was to the east end of Lytham Promenade on the south side of the road to Preston and extended to about nine acres, the shipyard being built on the Lytham side of Liggard Brook. The first vessel completed at this yard was the twin screw steamer SUNLIGHT, Yard No. 141, built in 1889 for Lever Brothers, a company which was to become one of the largest and most successful trading undertakings in the world and one which was to have a lasting association with the Lytham shipbuilders. In fact William Lever, who founded the business along with his brother James, had an interest in the sea from a very early age. In 1865, at the age of 13, he paid a visit to Blackpool with his family for a holiday and records his disappointment on a trip to Fleetwood, when he complained that 'only a few Irish steamers were to be seen'. On Good Friday he went for a sail on a pleasure steamer and said in a letter to a friend that 'it would be very nice sailing to Egypt if there was no such thing as seasickness'. On the Monday he went to Lytham to see Mrs. Clifton of Lytham Hall open the pier. It is most unlikely that this visit had any influence whatever on Lever to build his first ship at Lytham, although he was certainly well acquainted with the area.

This first vessel, SUNLIGHT, named after a famous brand of Lever's soap, was to be used in a service to his new soap works at Port Sunlight where manufacture had started in January 1889. The Port Sunlight development took place on 52 acres of land on the south side of the River Mersey which had been purchased by William and James Lever in 1887. The site was carefully chosen to allow steamers direct access to the factory at high tide and it was here that the first sod of the site for the new works was cut by William's wife Elizabeth on 3rd March, 1888. William, who had been brought up in a strict business environment, realised early in his career that if maximum sales were to be achieved the way in which a product was presented to the customer, both as regards its name and visual appearance, was just as important as the quality of the product itself. Accordingly he had selected and registered the trade name 'Sunlight' for his soap as far back as 1884 when he was a retail grocer, and at that time he had the soap manufactured for him by well known soap companies to his own specification. Lever Brothers became a private limited company in 1890 and four years later a public company.

## 3: The Founding Years - The Lytham S.B. & E. Co. Ltd.

With a sternwheel steamer as a trade mark, Richard Smith and Company continued to trade at Lytham under that name until 1893 when the business was being carried on by Thomas Edmondson and Frederick Bracewell. In that year the partners changed the name of the company to the Lytham Shipbuilding and Engineering Company, a company which became a limited liability company when it was incorporated in February 1904. It was dissolved in February 1957, two years after it had ceased trading. This is the only information available from Companies House but by the late 1920s it is known that the Share Capital consisted of 6,500 Ordinary and 300 Preference Shares. These were not fully paid up and were held by or on behalf of 26 individuals and the Orme Shipping Co. Ltd., all the members of the Friedenthal family being shareholders. During the nineteenth century shipyards in Britain constructed some 80% of the world's shipping, and enjoyed an almost captive market for shallow draft river craft for service in Africa, Burma, India, and South America, and it was in this type of vessel that the company specialised. As early as 1894 river steamers were being built for the rivers of Brazil, and already the company was becoming well known and respected in such places as Madagascar and Bombay as well as in South America. Soon it was to embark on a long and profitable relationship with the river trading companies in both East and West Africa, particularly the latter.

The site of the shipyard extended to about nine acres, two thirds of which eventually became occupied by buildings. From an early date these were of a substantial construction, being built partly of brick and partly of timber and corrugated iron. The workshops were fitted with the most up to date machinery and accordingly the company was able to turn out the highest class of work, specialising in sternwheel, screw and light draft craft. Many were constructed under cover, dismantled for delivery in pieces and reassembled at their destination. The buildings had an approximate floor area of 110,000 square feet and were, in the main, lofty and single storey. Provision was made for at least six vessels to be on the stocks at the same time, on shipbuilding berths fitted with concrete keel blocks and, in addition, there was an area set aside for smaller craft such as launches. All the larger ships which were built on the stocks were constructed in the open but many smaller vessels were built in the ship erecting shops.

*Engines for the paddle steamer WINIFRED, 1893.*

By 1893 the layout of the shipyard was very similar to a drawing of it which appeared in the company's illustrated brochure, a reproduction of which forms the frontispiece of this book. There was an overhead travelling crane which ran between the workshops and the fitting out berth on Liggard Brook, whilst a forge, a blacksmith's shop and offices, completed the buildings running alongside the roadway. At right angles to this complex ran another workshop block between the road and the brook. During the following thirty years or so many extensions and

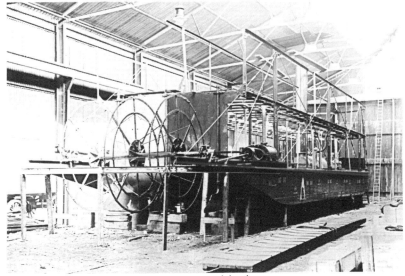

*A sternwheel steamship building on a covered berth.*

11

*A locomotive type boiler in the workshop, showing the overhead crane.*

improvements were carried out. A large boiler shop was built and a new engine shop with an overhead travelling crane was erected whilst the fitting out quay was extended and provided with a fixed 35 ton crane in place of the original overhead crane. A tramway was built for a travelling steam crane, which ran between the engine shop and the boiler shop, with branches to the fitting out and building berths. This tramway was also used for moving heavy components and equipment on low bogies. Other improved or new buildings included offices, mould loft, forges and covered berths designed for the construction of the smaller ships mentioned previously. One interesting piece of equipment which the company acquired was a steam lorry. The driver's cab was fitted off centre to allow the carriage of long lengths, such as steel angle. The maximum speed of this vehicle was 10 miles per hour, a round trip to Liverpool taking three days, the driver living in the lorry and cooking his meals on the boiler fire.

The Friedenthal family was perhaps the best known of those associated with the Lytham Shipbuilding and Engineering Co. Ltd., and it was members of this family who provided the technical skill and expertise for more than half a century - a skill which was so essential in such an enterprise. The first member of the family to be involved with the company was Frederick Francis Joseph Friedenthal, an engineer who was born at Kutna Hora, (the German version of which is Kuttenberg), Bohemia, in 1850, came to England in 1877 and settled in Preston. Here he joined the firm of shipbuilders, Richard Smith and Company, at their Ashton Quay shipyard. In 1884 he commenced in business as a consulting engineer on his own account, having offices at 18, Chapel Walks, Preston. From these premises he advertised his 'Friedenthal's Patent Circle Propellers', and indicated that he was the sole manufacturer. He described himself as a practical shipbuilder, engineer and surveyor and offered his services as an agent for the sale of sailing ships, steamers and engines as well as for the preparation of plans and specifications for all manner of ships, marine engines, pumps and boilers. He later

12

accepted the position of managing director of Messrs. Stevenson and Co. Ltd., propeller and engine builders, who were based at the Canal Foundry, Preston, a company which also advertised and manufactured his 'Patent Propeller'.

## FRIEDENTHAL'S PATENT PROPELLERS.

### OVER 2,200 IN USE.

GREATER SPEED ——·—— LESS COAL ——·—— RESULTS GUARANTEED.

*These blades are formed by a combination of curves so proportioned that each part cuts into the solid; the curvature towards the tip counteracts the centrifugal tendency of water (which no other Propeller of helical construction can do)—namely, the work begins at the root, and every portion of the blade sends water aft nearly parallel with the keel, and not along the blade, which simply means so much less slip or of power.*

SOLE MAKERS:

# STEVENSON & Co. LTD., PRESTON.

In the spring of 1888 he opened the Ribble Engine Works in Brieryfield Road, Preston, where he manufactured his patent propeller, steam engines and boiler feed and general service pumps for the marine service. By this time he had become well known in this country as a very successful and respected marine engineer and, in due course, he decided to settle permanently in Preston. His Certificate of Naturalization is dated the 5th of February, 1890, when he was the father of five children; three more were to be born later. The eldest, Frederick John Joseph, was 9 years old in 1890 and in due course he entered the service of the company with his father and was joined a few years later by Albert Louis, the third son. Subsequently the fifth and youngest son, George Charles, took over the business when his brothers died, and was assisted by the fourth brother, Richard Ernest James, who attended to the technical and design side, in addition to his work at Lytham. This family business, Friedenthals Ltd., is in existence today and still manufactures the propellers which were patented so long ago. The workshops occupy the same premises, which lie between Brieryfield Road and Croft Street, the only major change being that the main entrance and offices are now situated in Croft Street. The company remains under the control of the same family and George's son, George Leonard, is now the managing director, his father having been tragically killed in a motor car accident in 1950 when he was only 51 years old. Whilst never having any direct financial connection with each other, the two companies were nevertheless very closely connected through their management structures, the Preston company contracting for the supply of propellers, steam engines and steam pumps.

Frederick Francis Joseph died in 1928 leaving five sons and two daughters, a daughter having died in 1919. The second son, John Alfred, was managing director of the Lytham Shipbuilding and Engineering Co. Ltd., after initially serving the company as chief draughtsman in charge of the Drawing Office. Richard Ernest James succeeded him in the latter position and these two brothers had a long association with the company, a relationship which went back to well before the First World War. Richard had joined the firm in 1911 as an apprentice and subsequently assisted John, his elder brother, to run the business. Both lived at Lytham where John died in 1960 whilst Richard died at his daughter's residence in Oxfordshire in 1987.

The shipyard at Lytham was unique for such a small business in that all the work necessary to construct a vessel, from design to completion, was all carried out at Lytham. The hull, boilers, engines, steering gear and deck machinery were all produced and fitted at the same premises, the only exception being the manufacture of heavy castings. The company did not have its own foundry, although there was a small one at the propeller works at Preston, and accordingly this work was put out to contractors who supplied castings to the company's own specifications. Plans to build a foundry were considered but unfortunately the sub soil of the site was found to be unsuitable. After a ship was launched she was towed over to the engineering yard where the machinery was installed and the vessel made ready for sea. At their peak the company employed some 400 men who, when necessary, worked round the clock to produce ships of all sizes and descriptions. Accordingly the Government took full advantage of the company's expertise during the First World War when production was almost entirely given over to the war effort, but more of this later.

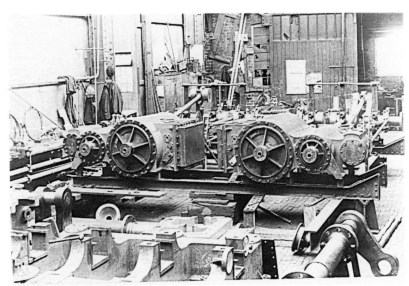

*Twin side by side compound horizontal steam engines for a quarterwheel steamer in the Engine Assembly Workshop.*

*Side by side compound steam engines for a sternwheel steamer in the Engine Assembly Workshop.*

*bottom left*
*Vertical cross compound 2-cylinder steam engine in the Workshop.*

*bottom right*
*Triple expansion inverted vertical steam engine in the Workshop.*

## 4: Pre 1914-1918 War - The Rubber Boom.

During the prewar period the company produced all manner of ships, from small poling canoes for use on the upper reaches of rivers, such as the River Niger, to twin screw coasters and side and stern wheel paddle steamers. The order book was always full and what was more, production was evenly spread over the years. Vessels were constructed for such well known companies as Lever Brothers Ltd., Niger Co. Ltd., F. and A. Swanzy and Co. Ltd., the Rea Transport Co. Ltd., the Pacific Steam Navigation Co. Ltd., the Antofagasta Railway Company in Chile and such authorities as the Brazilian Government, the Egyptian Delta Light Railway, H. M. Indian State Government, the Bombay Port Trust and many other companies, authorities and agents. One of these agents, Jones, Burton & Co. Ltd., of Liverpool even produced a comprehensive catalogue of marine machinery, steam and motor boats and other equipment, quoting prices for all the items offered including sternwheel steamers, steam tugs, steam launches, small cargo steamers, dumb barges, grab dredgers, motor lighters, motor cruisers and even floating cranes. Some of these vessels were offered for delivery in pieces or sections and many of them were supplied by the Lytham company.

Between 1894 and 1912 the company built upwards of thirty river steamers for South American owners. The exact number is not known as many were supplied to agents such as Jones, Burton and Co. Ltd., mentioned previously, who were acting on behalf of foreign owners. Most of these river steamers plied the River Amazon and its tributaries, collecting latex from the trading posts during the rubber boom of that period, as well as carrying passengers who described them as 'gaiola' or bird cages, because of their appearance. This rubber was carried by porters through thick jungle along barely discernible tracks from the rubber estates whose owners made handsome profits, whilst the porters were lucky even to survive. According to the diaries left by the explorer, Lt. Col. P. H. Fawcett, these tracks were strewn with the carcases and bones of both man and beast.

The rubber boom lasted from 1900 to 1912, being ushered in by the appearance of the motor car, and this boom soon became nothing more than an orgy of greed, blood and lust, the like of which had not been seen by the civilised world for decades. The Amazon was the sole producer of rubber during this period and it was estimated that for every ton of rubber produced, two human lives were lost as a result of violence, ill treatment or ill health, in that order. By the year 1910 the Amazon was still supplying 80% of the world's rubber but by 1913 this had decreased to 42% and by 1952 to 1%. The reason for the dramatic decline over a period of three or four years was that a supply of rubber tree seeds had been smuggled out of the country and planted in Ceylon and Malaya. Here civilisation was more stable and the general conditions in these countries, both as regards to the availability of labour and the mode of transport, made it possible to organise and control the cultivation and collection processes.

The Amazon is 4000 miles long and, apart from Brazil, enters Bolivia, Peru, Ecuador, Colombia and Venezuela. It is a vast network of rivers, having no less than 1,100 tributaries, seven of which are over 1,000 miles long. The River Madeira is 3,000 miles in length and the River Negro 1,500, being 20 miles wide before joining the Amazon. Ocean going ships can ascend the Amazon as far as Iquitos in Peru, a river journey of some 2,400 miles, where even at Iquitos, the river is 120 feet deep and wider than the Mississippi at its mouth. At Manaos, 1,000 miles

16

up river from Belem, the difference between high and low water is 60 feet. The vastness of the Amazon and its network is difficult to imagine, ocean going ships having an astounding 30,000 miles of river available for navigation, whilst light drafted vessels have 50,000 miles without ever leaving Amazonia.

This then is the labyrinth into which the sturdy little vessels from Lytham disappeared to earn their keep, navigating the often snag filled and sometimes narrow rivers far from civilisation. Unlike their counterparts in Africa, none of the Lytham built ships were sternwheelers and none of those ordered direct from the company were delivered in pieces. They were either single or twin screw steamers (only one ship being a side paddle steamer), and this was to help counteract the dangers from the vast amount of debris in the form of uprooted trees, always found floating just below the surface of many rivers. This hazard was to cause severe problems even for propeller driven craft, where broken propellers were a common occurrence.

Vessels built for South America had fascinating names and most sailed out on their delivery voyages under their own steam, although some of the smaller ones went out as deck cargo. These delivery voyages were not always without incident; for example one of them, the twin screw steamer CHRISTINO CRUZ was badly damaged when she ran aground on the Isle of Man very early on her delivery voyage to Brazil in 1912. This stranding was said to have been caused by the captain, presumably not relishing the prospect of such a long journey in so small a river craft, opening the bottle too soon. The vessel was returned to Lytham where she was hauled out of the water and had several steel plates replaced in her bottom before being allowed to proceed on her voyage. Other ships such as the BARAO DE URUSSUHY, ARIPUANA., FREIRECASTRO, MUCURIPE, ALTO ACRE, RIO ARIPUANA, CASSIO REIS and many others sailed out without incident.

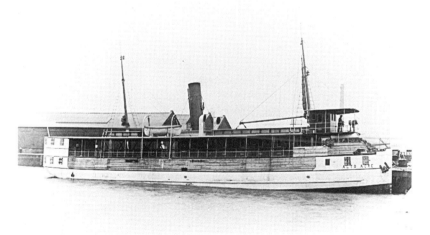

*ALTO ACRE.*

17

Many of these ships were named after tributaries of the River Amazon or after areas of South America. All were built to a strong specification to withstand extreme conditions and, strange as it may seem, often had an elaborate and sometimes ornate internal design. They were equipped with revolving chairs and amusingly, dozens of mirrors for the passengers, who enjoyed nothing more than to admire themselves. There is no doubt that this diversion had been carefully thought out by the shipowners in an effort to protect their property in such a volatile and often violent environment. Life was not easy on the rivers in those days, but at least these vessels built at Lytham offered some degree of comfort for the crew, who enjoyed the provision of comfortable cabins, whilst the vast majority of passengers were left to their own devices. They had to provide their own food and bedding and sleep anywhere they could on what was often a long and tiresome journey.

Were some of these vessels still plying the Amazon and its tributaries more than half a century after leaving Lytham? The answer may be found in the film 'Fitzcarraldo' which was shot in Amazonia in 1982. Made by the German film company Werner Herzog Filmproduktion of Munich, it featured a river passenger steamer identical to those built at Lytham prior to the First World War. Some interesting facts have been revealed by Herr Werner Herzog who says that he used three ships in the film as follows -

**Ship One** - Named NAVINHO, built in 1902 or 1904 probably on the River Clyde. She was found lying derelict ashore on an Amazon tributary in Colombia. Completely beyond repair, she was used only in the early part of the film.

**Ship Two** - The hull of an old ship was acquired into which his film company built the decks and engines. She had almost the same dimensions as ship number one and was only used in the scenes where the ship was hauled overland.

**Ship Three** - Built by the film company, which took two years. She was identical to ship number two and was used in the river travelling shots. Herr Herzog explains that in the film it looks as if an old ship is found, repaired, sailed on the Amazon and hauled overland. He cannot remember the original name of ship number two, so it will never be known if a Lytham vessel was involved.


## 5: Pre 1914-1918 War - Into Africa.

The outbreak of the First World War, coupled with the end of the rubber boom in South America effectively ended the firm's association with this continent, apart from two tugs which were built in 1931 for the Argentine Navigation Co. Ltd., and shipped as deck cargo from Liverpool to Buenos Aires. During this prewar period, production was by no means concentrated on the South American market, vessels also being delivered to Cape Town, Egypt, India, Madagascar, Mozambique, Indonesia, Nigeria, Portuguese Guinea, Uganda, Mexico and the Belgian Congo. Some sailed out under their own steam, some were delivered as deck cargo, whilst others were completed on the stocks and, after careful testing, the parts were marked and numbered before the vessel was dismantled and packed in cases ready for delivery to the export steamer, usually at Liverpool. They were then re-erected at their destination under the supervision of Company staff who had been specially

*Typical hull markings on a vessel to be dismantled for shipment. These are on KWILU (see also page 27) which was shipped out to H.C.B. (Huileries Du Congo Belge) at Matadi.*

sent out for the purpose and often stayed there for two or three years. Vessels sent to such destinations as Uganda were packed in cases small enough to be carried manually overland from their port of arrival to Lake Tanganyika, Lake Kioga or Lake Victoria. The boilers, however, created a technical problem as they could not be dismantled once they had been built. The company surmounted this problem by fitting four wheels to the boilers or building special trailers for them so that they could be hauled manually across, very often, rough and hilly terrain.

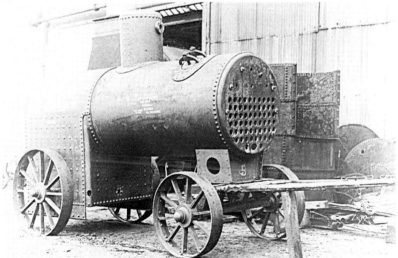

*A locomotive type boiler mounted on wheels ready for hauling across country in East Africa. (The "delivery instructions" stencilled on it are O.H.M.S. His Excellency The Governor Entebbe Uganda via Kilindini.)*

19

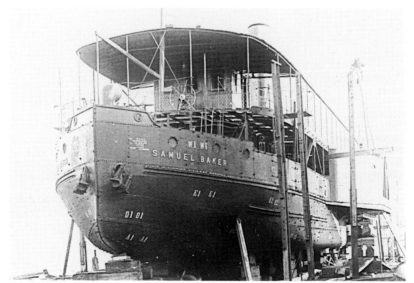

*SAMUEL BAKER under construction. Note the section numbers painted on the hull and how it is temporarily bolted together. She, too, was to be shipped to Uganda via Kilindini.*

Some of these small ships carried the names of famous explorers, such as LUGARD, a 145 foot sternwheel steamer, delivered in 1926 from Lytham in no less than 274 packages. Others included SAMUEL BAKER (1909), SPEKE (1909), MUNGO PARK (1912), and GRANT (1925). Swim-ended barges were sent to Uganda in sections and all these small craft plied the lakes referred to above for many years. In fact Henry Morton Stanley was the first man to introduce a European ship to the middle reaches of the Congo when he had a small army of porters carry a 45 foot barge overland in five sections. She was the LADY ALICE, not however, built at Lytham.

In these days the foundation was laid for many long and lasting associations, and the company made every effort to preserve their reputation for a first class product promptly delivered, a reputation so painstakingly earned and one which was never questioned. The Rea Transport Company ordered their small steam tug AYSGARTH in 1900 and this was followed by orders for many others. The Zillah Shipping and Carrying Co. Ltd., placed an order for the steam coaster ASHFIELD in 1914 and this business association lasted until after the Second World War. The Niger Company, Levers and Swanzys all ordered vessels of various types and sizes, and this trade, although interrupted by the First World War, was to continue until the company went into liquidation many years later.

## 6: The 1914-1918 War - The War Effort.

The company played a prominent part in building small craft for the Government in the First World War. This started towards the end of 1914 at which time the company had a small single screw steam launch on the stocks named PIONEER which they were building for the African Transport Company. The War Department requisitioned the vessel and took over the contract, minor alterations were made and she was handed over as the tug A.54 a few weeks later. As this was the first vessel to be completed to the order of a Government Department, an extra special effort was made to complete her in record time and as a result, orders for many more ships and barges followed. She was not, however, the first Lytham built vessel to serve her country as that honour must go to the single screw steam tug TOILER, built in 1894 and taken over by the Admiralty in 1896. Yet another, the single screw steam tug MYSTIC, built in 1899, was requisitioned by the Admiralty in 1916 and renamed H.T.12. In fact from mid 1915 to the end of 1919 the whole of the company's production was to the order of various Government Departments. Over thirty twin and single screw steam tugs, a

*A44, the first of the small War Office tugs.*

telegraph repair ship, four minesweepers of the 'Dance' class, three larger rescue-type tugs, five hospital ships and some sixteen dumb barges were all built for the Admiralty or the War Office. A dozen of these dumb barges were specially designed by the shipyard to carry ammunition and explosives in maximum safety, their holds being lined with pinewood. These barges were towed across the channel and along Continental waterways by tugs, which had also been designed and built at Lytham, delivering their lethal cargoes to the British Army. Complete plans and specifications were prepared at the yard for these vessels, and some were used by shipyards on the Clyde and on the East Coast when fulfilling Government orders for similar ships.

In 1916 the responsibility for river transport was placed under the newly created Inland Water Transport Department of the War Office., and this new department was given ample funds with which to operate. Under its management new steamers and other vessels were ordered, many from the Lytham shipyard, and are included in those mentioned above. However, in 1917 the Department was experiencing a great deal of trouble with its hospital ships on the River Tigris in Mesopotamia. These were side paddle steamers and were proving to be too wide for the narrow winding channels that they so often encountered. As a result many of them sustained damage to their paddles and this inevitably led to an interruption in the service. The Lytham company had a reputation for building craft suitable for such conditions and accordingly, were approached by the War Office as a matter of some urgency, to design a quarterwheel river steamer capable of both carrying troops and doubling as a hospital ship on the River Tigris, without sustaining, or at least substantially diminishing, the damage which was so far being experienced.

The company submitted a design which was based on vessels supplied to the Niger Company before the war, and this was accepted by the War Office who immediately placed orders at Lytham for five vessels. Additional orders were also placed at other yards and all the vessels were to be built using the Lytham drawings and in some cases incorporating engines, boilers and machinery built at Lytham. By the end of 1917 the five quarterwheel river steamers had been built and were in service on the River Tigris. In addition, the company had completed the machinery and boilers for a number of similar vessels constructed elsewhere. These troop transporters were 150 feet long and were fitted with twin horizontal compound surface condensing engines each driving a paddle wheel housed in the stern 14 feet in diameter and fitted with eight floats. This considerably reduced the width of the vessel to 33 feet and offered some protection against damage from hitting the banks. They were fitted with twin rudders and equipped with an oil fired boiler, 12½ feet in diameter and 11 feet long, the engines producing 500 i.h.p. The first one to be completed was the S.40 and she sailed

*The model of S40 at the Ribble Cruising Club.*

22

from Preston to Basra, planked up for the voyage, in order to test the seagoing ability of the vessels. The remaining four were all dismantled and shipped as cargo to the Middle East where they were re-erected at an independent dockyard just above Basra, a yard which had been specifically built by the Inland Waterway Transport Department for the re-erection of river craft.

These five vessels replaced some of the side paddlewheel steamers then in use and served with distinction as troop and hospital ships until the end of the war. In 1920 one of them was transferred to the Bengal Marine in India and sent to Burma where she was subsequently acquired

*CANMORESK.*

by the Irrawaddy Flotilla Co. Ltd., at Rangoon in 1929 and renamed CANMORESK. She was an extremely good looking ship, especially with regard to her fittings, but proved to be a commercial failure. Accordingly, she was demoted and used as the Pilot Commander's residence at both Prome and Magwe in Burma before finally being turned into a stores hulk at Prome in 1934. Her end came in 1942 when she was scuttled at Thongine, Burma, to avoid being captured by the invading Japanese army.

As mentioned previously, the company had already completed several quarterwheel river steamers for the Niger Company prior to the war and these had sailed to Nigeria under their own steam. They had originally been introduced by Colonel H. E. Ratsey, a member of a family well known at Cowes on the Isle of Wight as sail makers. He was the Marine Superintendent of the Niger Company which he joined in 1893, serving that company and its successors for forty seven years, and early in his career had experienced great difficulty with the navigation of the company's side paddle steamers and full sternwheelers on the Rivers Niger and Benue in Nigeria. These vessels were hard to control in narrow and tortuous channels and often sustained damage to their paddle wheels. In order to overcome this problem he introduced quarter wheel steamers to these rivers for his company with a great deal of success and it was in the knowledge of this success that the War Office made a special request for his services. With the rank of Colonel,

23

he served with distinction in the Middle East where he applied the methods he had worked out on the Nigerian rivers to the Rivers Euphrates and Tigris, and it was in accordance with his advice that the War Office placed orders for this type of vessel. Shortly before he retired in 1940 his company honoured him by naming one of their quarterwheel river steamers COLONEL RATSEY after him. She was built at Lytham, launched and named by his sister Mrs. E. Coltar in his presence and sailed from Preston to Burutu in convoy in July 1939.

Towards the end of the war the company built six twin screw tunnel tugs for the Admiralty. The first to be delivered was the E.T.7 in 1918.

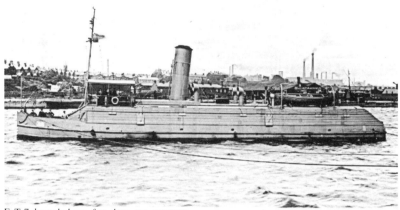

*E.T.7 boarded up for deep-sea passage.*

She sailed direct from Preston to Alexandria and is still there today, named MISR, undergoing restoration. Four of them were converted to minesweepers of the 'Dance' class before delivery and were named FANDANGO, MORRIS DANCE, STEP DANCE and SWORD DANCE. They

*The model of a "Dance" Class Minesweeper at the Ribble Cruising Club.*

were all used extensively for clearing away wartime minefields, the first-named falling victim to a mine herself on 3rd July, 1919. A fine builder's model of one of these vessels can be seen displayed in a glass case at the Ribble Cruising Club, Lytham as well as one of a hospital ship mentioned above. Both models were presented to the club by Richard Friedenthal when he was Commodore.

The last vessels to be built for the Admiralty during this period were three larger and more powerful rescue type-tugs completed in 1919, named ST.FAGAN, ST.FAITH and ST.HILARY. According to Richard Friedenthal, these were built specifically for towing large German vessels back to this country from the United States where they had been immobilised by their German crews during the War.

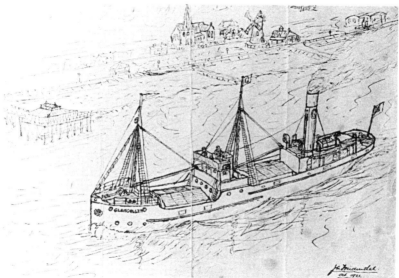

*A sketch of GLENCULLEN made in October 1921 by J. A. Friedenthal.*

## 7: Post 1914-1918 War - Lever Brothers, the Vital Link.

Since 1916 the whole of the company's production had been taken up by the Government and there is no doubt that this had made a significant contribution to the country's war effort. By 1919, when the last Government vessels were on the stocks, it became essential for the firm to readjust and re-establish itself in a peacetime environment if it was to remain in the forefront of the small-ship building industry. The management, of course, had seen this situation arising when the war ended in 1918 and was not slow in taking steps to seek orders in the commercial market, but it was not until 1920 that the first order was completed for a private company. This first order came from the Alliance and Dublin Consumers Gas Company for a steamer to be used in the British coal trade. She was named GLENAGEARY and a sister ship, the GLENCULLEN was delivered the following year. These vessels were very similar to those built for the Zillah Shipping and Carrying Co. Ltd., who renewed their prewar acquaintance with the company when the BRIARFIELD was ordered in 1920.

The Niger Company remained loyal, although their name was becoming increasingly linked with that of Lever Brothers Ltd. This company finally purchased the Niger Company in 1920, the price offered and accepted for its 1,250,000 shares of £1 each being £6.10s. per share which became payable on 1st July, 1920. Levers had already gained a foothold in the West African trade through W. B. MacIver and Company, an old established firm with considerable business interests in Nigeria and the Cameroons. This was further extended by the purchase of John Walkden and Co. Ltd., R. & W. King in the Ivory Coast and Cameroons (one of the oldest companies in Africa), P. Ratcliffe and Company in Sierra Leone and the Cavalla River Company in Liberia. The position of the Niger Company in West Africa had been unique, for whilst it was a trading company, it had received a Royal Charter on the 10th July, 1886 and from that date had become responsible for the administration in Nigeria. One of the Government's conditions was that the flag of the newly incorporated Royal Niger Company Chartered and Limited, should indicate the British character of the company. The flag which was chosen strongly resembled the White Ensign flown on British naval vessels, with the addition of a circle containing three arms which represented the main waterways of Nigeria. On each arm was a single word, Ars, Jus and Pax and in 1925 three of the company's sternwheel steamers carried these names. This charter was revoked as from 1st January, 1900 when the company became known simply as The Niger Co. Ltd. It had many trading stations throughout Nigeria with its headquarters at Burutu on the mouths of the Niger and had a large fleet of sternwheelers and other craft. It owned several associated companies with interests in the Gold Coast, Senegal, French Guinea, the Sudan and the Seychelle Islands. The Niger Co. Ltd., continued to trade under that name until merging with the African and Eastern Trade Corporation as equal holding companies in a new trading company called the United Africa Co. Ltd., which commenced trading on 1st May, 1929.

During the First World War Lever Brothers had experienced difficulty in getting supplies of raw materials from their plantations in West Africa to their factory at Port Sunlight. They overcame this problem by buying a small steamship company, Herbert Watson and Company of Manchester, which owned eight vessels with names derived from villages in Shropshire and Cheshire. This small fleet was formed into the Bromport Steamship Co. Ltd., and soon achieved its objective of clearing the large backlog of goods awaiting shipment to the Mersey. This was not without incident however, as in two years half of the ships were lost through enemy action. There seems little doubt that this shipping company had taken its name from a company incorporated by Levers in 1908, the Bromborough Port Estate Ltd., which was formed to develop 800 acres of land with a one and a half mile deep water frontage to the River Mersey, purchased in 1904. This is the site where the world's largest private dock was to be found. Bromborough Dock was completed in 1931 and closed its gates to commercial traffic for the last time in the spring of 1986. The shipping company did not last long, however, just long enough to have six dumb barges built at Lytham in 1923. Four were delivered to Liverpool under tow by way of the River Douglas to Tarleton and thence along the Leeds and Liverpool Canal to their destination.

In 1923 William Lever ordered two semi tanker sternwheel steamers, KWANGO and SANKURU, from Lytham for his Belgian company in the Congo. They were both named after tributaries of the River Congo and were shipped out in pieces after first being built and then dismantled at

Lytham. This was the first order to be received since before the war from this company which had been established in the Congo in 1911 when William Lever was approached by, and entered into an agreement with, the Belgian Government to form a joint stock company specifically for operations in that country. It is interesting to note that in 1905 he had tried to negotiate concessions in the Colonies with the British Government, but he was unsuccessful in the attempt as the British Government proved to be opposed to such alienation of land. This Belgian company, La Societe Anonyme des Huileries du Congo Belge (for convenience this was often abbreviated to H.C.B.), was to undertake development work in the Congo, was to erect mills at five centres for the production of palm oil, and in return was to enjoy certain rights and privileges. William Lever was elected President of the new company. The five areas covered by the convention were

**Lusanga,** the first site to be developed with its centre at Leverville, which stood at the point where the River Kwenge joins the Kwilu. Two of the first vessels to be delivered to H.C.B., from Lytham in 1912 were appropriately named KWILU, a single screw steam launch, and LEVERVILLE a sternwheel steamer of 350 tons gross.

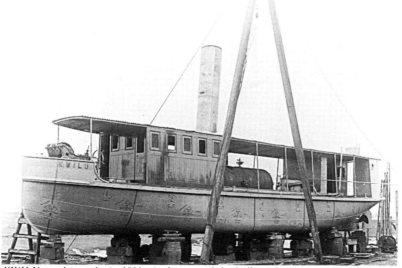

*KWILU on the stocks in 1911. A close-up of the hull markings appears on page 19.*

**Basongo,** with its centre at Brabanta, named after the Duc de Brabant, the Belgian Crown Prince. Appropriately enough another vessel delivered from Lytham in 1912 was the DUC DE BRABANT, a sternwheel steamer of 415 tons gross. Two smaller vessels, the WAMBA and MOLUA, followed in 1914.
**Ingende,** with its centre at Flandria, named after the Comte de Flandre, King Albert's younger son.
**Bumba,** with its centre at Alberta, named after King Albert.
**Basoko,** with its centre at Elizabetha, named after the Queen of the Belgians.

Lever exercised the closest personal control and vigilance over this company, not a building being erected nor a vessel purchased without him first having agreed to the specifications and plans. As a result, the first machinery was despatched to the Congo for his new mills as early as the 12th August, 1911 and the first consignment of palm oil reached Antwerp on 20th March, 1912. Soap made from this oil by the Savonneries Lever Freres in Brussels was ready by the 27th March. In April, Sir William Lever, as he had become, was received by King Albert, when a casket made from Congo ivory, enclosing the first tablet of soap, was presented to His Majesty. At the same time a fine working model of the company's first sternwheeler, the DUC DE BRABANT, mentioned previously, was presented to his elder son, Prince Leopold. This is the steamer that King Albert used some time later when he toured the Belgian Congo. For the occasion she was fitted with luxurious staterooms specially constructed at Lytham and shipped out to the Congo.

The shipyard continued to enlarge its share in the post-war market, especially with companies engaged in the West African trade and to a lesser extent with Uganda. The Lytham company's reputation for the design and production of specialised craft was well known and it was not long before the Crown Agents for the Colonies approached them with an invitation to design and build a number of shallow draft barges. These barges were to be capable of carrying some 200 tons of large stones and were to be used on the construction of two breakwaters at Takoradi Harbour, West Africa, then being built.

This was in 1923, when work on the breakwaters was in its early stages and normal barges, with doors in the bottom, were used to release the stone. However, as the work proceeded and the breakwaters neared the surface, these doors were unable to open and it became obvious that a special type of barge was needed. Accordingly the company designed a shallow draft barge capable of carrying about 200 tons of large stones on a deck which was slightly concave. A series of water ballast tanks was built along each side of the vessel and, as the tanks on one side were flooded with water, the vessel listed to that side and so discharged the cargo. The tanks were so situated that after dumping the cargo, the sluices were left open to allow the tanks to empty automatically by the time the barge had been towed back to the reloading berth. Before finalizing the design a scale model was constructed and tested in the photographic developing tank in the Drawing Office! Later, when the first barge was completed it was towed up to Preston, loaded with stone and underwent successful tests on the River Ribble. Four of these vessels were built, named G.C.H.1 to 4, and two were towed out to the Gold Coast by tug from Lytham. A good view of one of them on the stocks can be seen on another page. The letters G.C.H. probably stood for Gold Coast Hopper.

Many other dumb barges of all sizes and descriptions were built. These included some interesting looking 'double decker' passenger dumb barges built for the Niger Co. Ltd., (see photograph opposite) and it is not difficult to imagine them on the rivers of Africa when fully loaded with hundreds of passengers and their belongings. Poling canoes, which were used for the transport of merchandise on the shallower upper reaches of rivers, anchor boats and lighters, combined to form a large proportion of the company's output in the ensuing years. They were all built to meet the specific requirements of companies and authorities such as J. Holt and Co. Ltd., the African and Eastern Trade Corporation Ltd., the Niger Co. Ltd., the Crown Agents for the Colonies and later the United Africa Co. Ltd. Delivery was usually made by road or rail to Liverpool but others sailed under tow to their final destinations or to Liverpool for shipment. The smaller vessels were shipped as deck cargo in one piece but the larger ones were either built in two halves or completely dismantled at Lytham and shipped in boxes. The method of delivery adopted depended largely on the location of the final destination which was sometimes far inland from the port of disembarkation. In either case they were re-erected when they reached their owners.

*PASSACEIRO, one of the passenger barges built for the Niger Co. Ltd.*

During the period 1920 to 1939 it is interesting to note that no less than 88% of all the vessels completed at Lytham were delivered to Africa for trading on the rivers and lakes of that continent. (This compares with a figure of 50% for the whole period under review.) The remaining 12% were built for a wide variety of owners, only the Zillah Shipping and Carrying Co. Ltd., placing regular repeat orders. In fact Richard Friedenthal mentioned this when discussing the company some years later. He went on to say that Zillahs were 'very decent shipowners' and that they attributed their success to a policy of trying to have a new vessel on the stocks every year. This, of course, was very much to the advantage of the builder.

In addition to building ships, vessels were accepted at Lytham for either major or minor repair and very often for complete overhaul. Engines were supplied to other shipbuilders such as the Hansen Shipbuilding Co. Ltd., of Bideford, Devon, and J. Crichton & Co. Ltd., of Chester ready for installation in their completed hulls. Boilers, engines and other machinery were delivered to customers, both at home and abroad, for their vessels, workshops, cotton plants and even laundries. An engine for a laundry as far away as Valparaiso was shipped in 1913, and it was not an uncommon occurrence for the company to receive enquiries from all corners of the world for spare parts or for specific information relative to vessels built by them many years previously.

29

The period between the wars was particularly notable for the contribution which the ships built by the company made to the development of trade and commerce in Africa, just as they had done a decade earlier in South America. This naturally led to the publication of all kinds of stories about the activities of the company's vessels. Whilst many of these stories emanating from the very depths of Africa were, without doubt, founded on fact, others were merely figments of the imagination and will not be repeated here. Only one story can be substantiated by a reliable source, Richard Friedenthal himself, when he confirmed in an interview that one of the ships built at Lytham was used in the film 'Trader Horn'. He saw the film along with his brother John at Lytham and both agreed, after seeing the film a second time at a private showing and having it stopped in order to study the vessel which was featured more closely, that it was indeed one of their ships. They did not, however, name the vessel but this is not surprising as many vessels were built to the order of shipping agents and only named by the eventual owners some time later. Richard was not sure whether she was built for the Congo or Lake Kioga in Uganda.

Many stories were published about the small steam launch AFRICAN QUEEN, an insignificant little vessel which found fame in 1951 when she featured in the film of that name starring Humphrey Bogart and Katherine Hepburn. Years later she was the centre of attraction when she was exhibited at the London International Boat Show in 1987 by her American owner, James W. Hendricks. He explained that the Boat Show coincided with the vessel's 75th birthday and that he had purchased her in 1982 for $65,000. She was said to have been built at Lytham in 1912, a date which is confirmed by another source which simply says that 'she was built on the North East Coast in 1912 as the LIVINGSTONE' and that she was found by the film makers on a river bank in Uganda. Whilst not being specific about her origins, it can be assumed that this source referred to the North East Coast of England where many builders were located at that time. In any case, there is no doubt that this launch was owned by the British East Africa Railway in Uganda and that she, in partnership with a larger vessel, the SAMUEL BAKER, a side paddle steamer built at Lytham in 1909 for the Crown Agents for the Colonies, Uganda, opened up a service on Lake Albert, which at that time formed the international frontier between Uganda and the Congo. It is also known that she was still afloat in 1928, although by then she was only employed occasionally to carry tourists and hunting parties. There is no evidence at all to suggest that the AFRICAN QUEEN was built at Lytham, although many unnamed vessels similar to her were. In support of this is the fact that the Lytham company always dealt directly with the Crown Agents for the Colonies, never through a third party or with the British East Africa Railways, and the company's records show that they only built one steam launch for this authority. She was the 45 foot single screw steel steam launch TANA, which was delivered to Kenya at the end of 1917, taking up her duties the following year. In fact, Richard Friedenthal stated categorically that the AFRICAN QUEEN was not built at Lytham and wrote accordingly to the Commodore of the Ribble Cruising Club, Lytham, at the time of the Boat Show.

## 8: The 1939-1945 War - Another War Effort.

As if in anticipation of the onset of the Second World War, the Government ordered a boom defence vessel named DUNNET from the company in 1936. She was launched in August of that year and proved to be the first of many more ships to be ordered by the Admiralty during the next few years. The COLONEL RATSEY, a quarterwheel river steamer, was the last ship to be delivered before the outbreak of hostilities in 1939 when she sailed from Preston for Nigeria on 3rd July. Soon afterwards a fresh water carrier of some 300 gross registered tons was ordered for the Royal Fleet Auxiliary Service and was named appropriately, FRESHWATER. She was delivered in September 1940

*The launch of FRESHWATER, 23.3.1940 by Miss Marjorie Friedenthal (Mrs. M. Twittey).*

and was to be followed by thirteen similar vessels of the 'Fresh' Class, all being fitted with coal fired boilers and steam engines driving a single propeller. By 1942 the whole of the company's output was in support of the war effort and this continued until 1946 when the FRESHSPRING was delivered.

Although production was concentrated on the building of the 'Fresh' ships during this period, an unusual order was received in 1944 for 'Bombardon Tanks'. Unknown to the company these units were intended to be used in the forthcoming invasion of Europe and accordingly, were built strictly to Admiralty instructions, none of the shipyard staff being aware of their eventual use. For such a confidential project the Admiralty chose the code name 'Bombardon Tanks' to describe the floating breakwaters destined to be moored just outside the artificial harbour which was to be built at Arromanches, on the coast of Normandy, in support of the invasion. They were designed to offer protection to the larger ships, which it was anticipated, would be unable to lie safely inside the harbour. However, they never reached their destination, being destroyed whilst under tow to Normandy by the adverse weather.

31

conditions which were experienced during the great storm 13 days after the assault which took place on the 6th June, 1944. However, the company's contribution to the invasion was quite considerable, as they had built many of the small cargo steamers which were used in support, including the coasters BEECHFIELD, BRACKENFIELD (sunk by a German E Boat on 10th June), BRIARFIELD, BROOMFIELD, GORSEFIELD, LARCHFIELD, MAPLEFIELD, ROWANFIELD and had built engines for many others. They also completed six Landing Craft Mechanised in 1945 to replace those lost in the conflict. These small vessels were designed to carry one 35 ton tank and deliver it directly onto the assault beach. They were an enlarged version of earlier British L.C.M.s., being almost eight feet longer and slightly wider. Manned by a crew of six, their twin screws were capable of producing a maximum speed of 9 knots.

## 9: Post 1939-1945 War - The Decline.

After this war, peacetime business was slow to recover, far slower than after the previous World War, but the company's sales efforts were rewarded with an order from an old friend, the United Africa Co. Ltd., for a couple of ferry pontoons in 1945. These were completed by 1946 and shipped to West Africa, thereby resuming a long established prewar relationship, but this business alone was not sufficient to sustain the company in a post-war market which was proving to be more and more progressive and competitive. However, work for the Admiralty was still in hand, but this was completed by the end of the year, at which time only one other vessel was building on the stocks. She was the single screw cargo steamer HAZELFIELD, under construction for the Zillah Shipping and Carrying Co. Ltd., and she was to have the distinction of not only being the largest ship ever built for the company at Lytham, but also their last. She was also the first of her owner's vessels to be oil fired and was launched in August 1947 at a time when the very future of the shipyard was most uncertain, making her maiden voyage from Preston to Belfast with a cargo of coal in April 1948.

Unfortunately for the Lytham company significant changes were taking place in Government policy towards the colonies. This was being reflected in a distinct decline in the number of orders being received from the company's major customers in Africa for the shallow draft craft in which the company specialised. This was a severe setback to a company, the bulk of whose peacetime output had previously been taken up by this continent. A rather lean spell followed which showed no sign of improvement, being aggravated by the poor state of the shipyard channel, which was very much restricting the company's activities, a handicap from which it never recovered. Only three light beacon boats were built in 1949 for the Mersey Docks and Harbour Board, six barges for the United Africa Company in 1950, two quarterwheel river steamers for the same company in 1951, the latter being shipped to Nigeria in pieces the following year, two lighters for Spillers in 1952-3 and finally a steam chain ferry for service on Lake Windermere in 1954. This was the last vessel to be constructed by the Lytham Shipbuilding and Engineering Co. Ltd.

Named DRAKE, she was transported to the British Railway's slipway at Lakeside by road in seven sections in June 1954 and assembled there by the company's staff. Fitting out at this slipway was completed on the 12th July, whereupon she was towed to the ferry site the following day, coupled up, tested and handed over, starting her service which lasted until 1990. The earliest record of a ferry between Ferry Nab and Swines Ness on Lake Windermere is in 1454 when passengers, goods and animals were taken across the lake by row boat. The first steam ferry appeared in 1870 and like the DRAKE, was a chain ferry. Other steam ferries subsequently operated the service, until the DRAKE replaced an earlier ferry which had been in service since 1914. This vessel had cost £3,600 to build, the DRAKE, capacity 10 cars, cost £22,500 in 1954 and her replacement, MALLARD, capacity 18 cars, cost £400,000 in 1990.

Although there was a big demand after the war for new tonnage to replace losses - Britain alone lost over 4,000 merchant ships during the war - the world's shipbuilding capacity was far greater than its need. So far as this country was concerned, the situation was further aggravated by a continuing decline in the number of vessels trading under the British flag. This number had gone down from 60% of the world's total in 1890 to around 25% in 1947 and was accompanied by a significant reduction in the number of vessels being ordered from British shipyards. There is no doubt at all that these circumstances made some contribution to the eventual downfall of the company, but another factor was to play an even more important part. Although the size of the vessels which were being demanded by owners was increasing, and significant improvements in the specifications were being made, especially in propulsion machinery and fuel, the company's technical expertise was still more than capable of keeping abreast of these developments. However, the one aspect which was beyond the company's control was the state of the launching facilities. This was a problem which was becoming more and more acute and very much reduced the size of vessel that could be built, further limiting an already declining market. Even as the steamer HAZELFIELD was slipping into the water at Lytham, discussions were taking place nearby at Preston with the County Borough Council (the Port Authority), regarding the rapid deterioration in the condition of the shipyard channel. This channel led from the shipyard into the main River Ribble channel and it was essential that a sufficient depth of water was maintained here for the successful launching of ships and their subsequent passage to sea. The depth was constantly being reduced by silting up, and this was causing grave concern for the future of shipbuilding at Lytham. The company held the Port Authority entirely to blame for this state of affairs which, in their opinion, was mainly brought about by the dredging of a new channel in the estuary. In addition they contended that it was the statutory duty of the authority, under an agreement entered into in 1843, to maintain the channel in such a condition as to allow the safe passage of vessels. As no satisfaction was obtained at this meeting, legal action was seriously considered as being the only remedy, but the directors finally came to the conclusion that if this was not successful, it could prove to be extremely expensive for the company. Accordingly, as an alternative to embarking on a very costly dredging programme themselves, and having in mind the current economic climate in the shipping industry generally, the board decided that there was only one course open to them and that was to close the yard.

## 10: Post 1939-1945 War - The Closure.

Consequently in 1955, the industrial premises situated in Dock Road, Lytham, as well as the plant, machinery and equipment together with the goodwill of the business, were put up for auction by the Joint Liquidators. This took place on the 26th to 29th July inclusive on the premises. The catalogue which detailed the items on offer ran to some 55 pages, and these items were offered as a whole in one lot on Tuesday 26th July. As little interest was shown in this offer, the land, buildings and goodwill were offered as separate lots whilst the plant, machinery and other equipment was sold piecemeal. The sale produced £29,150 for almost 1,600 lots, sadly bringing to an end an undertaking which had been a major employer in Lytham for over half a century and an industry which had thrived on the River Ribble for many decades.

Today the site of the shipyard is occupied by an industrial estate. Some of the original shipyard buildings and offices are still there serving other owners and their condition indicates that they will do so for some considerable time yet. However, the slipways have disappeared and the launching area is largely silted up, although there is sufficient water at high tide for very small pleasure craft and fishing boats.

*Looking over the site of Lytham Dock to the Liggard Brook, swinging away to the top right, and the site of the Lytham Shipbuilding and Engineering Co. Ltd. yard as it is today.*

# Bibliography

"Exploration Fawcett" by Lt.Col. P. H. Fawcett, Hutchinson, London, 1953.

"Henry Tyrer - a Liverpool Shipping Agent & His Enterprise, 1879 - 1979" by Peter N. Davies. Croom Helm, London.

"History of Nigeria" by A. C. Burns, George Allen and Unwin Ltd., London 1929.

Lloyds Register of Shipping.

Lloyds Register of Yachts.

Mercantile Navy List and Maritime Directory.

"Port Sunlight Factory - the First 100 Years 1888 -1988" Lever Brothers Ltd., 1988.

Preston Register of Shipping.

"Railway Across the Equator" by Mohamed Amin, Duncan Willets and Alistair Matheson. The Bodley Head, London 1986.

"The Amazing Amazon" by Willard Price. William Heinemann Ltd., London 1952.

"The Last Tide" by Jack Dakres. Carnegie Press, Preston 1986.

"The Lion and the Unicorn in Africa" by Frederick Pedler. William Heinemann Ltd., London 1974.

"Tigris Gunboats" by Wilfred Nunn.

"Viscount Leverhulme" by His Son. George Allen and Unwin Ltd., London 1927.

## 11: The Vessels.

The following details of vessels have been mainly extracted from shipyard records. Unfortunately no such records have been discovered before the year 1900. Accordingly, the following sources have also been consulted -

Mercantile Navy List & Maritime Directory
Lloyds Register of Shipping
Lloyds Register of Yachts
Preston Register of Shipping

The figures before the ships' name are the yard (contract) number given when the order was placed.
"ON" is the ship's Official Number in the British Registry. "grt" = gross registered tonnage; "net" = net registered tonnage.

All measurements are shown in feet and tenths of a foot except where an asterisk appears, then they are shown in feet and inches. Later names of vessels are given where known.

The following abbreviations have been used for details of the engines

| | |
|---|---|
| C. | Compound |
| C.I. | Compound Inverted |
| Cy. | Cylinder |
| C.D.J.C. | Compound Diagonal Jet Condensing |
| C.H.J.C. | Compound Horizontal Jet Condensing |
| C.N.C. | Compound Non Condensing |
| C.S.C. | Compound Surface Condensing |
| H.C.S.C. | Horizontal Compound Surface Condensing |
| H.H.P. | Horizontal High Pressure |
| H.P.I.D.A. | High Pressure Inverted Diagonal Acting |
| H.P.N.C. | High Pressure Non Condensing |
| I.D.A. | Inverted Diagonal Acting |
| I.C.D.A. | Inverted Compound Diagonal Acting |
| Osc. | Oscillating |
| T. | Triple Expansion |
| T.E.S.C. | Triple Expansion Surface Condensing |
| V.C.N.C. | Vertical Compound Non Condensing |
| V.C.S.C. | Vertical Compound Surface Condensing |
| 2S.C.S.A. | Two Stroke Cycle Single Acting |

The figures following the number of cylinders (Cy.) are the size of the cylinders x the length of the piston stroke. hp = horse power; ihp = indicated horse power; nhp = nominal horse power; rhp = registered horse power.

Because of the exotic nature of some of the vessels, the following explanations may be helpful -

| | |
|---|---|
| Sternwheel Steamer | Propelled by one paddle wheel mounted at the stern. |
| Quarterwheel Steamer | Propelled by two paddle wheels, one mounted at each quarter of the stern. |
| Paddle Steamer | Propelled by two paddle wheels mounted amidships. |
| Tunnel Tug | Propellers fitted in tunnels in the hull to give maximum protection against fouling. |
| Swim Ended Barge | A dumb barge fitted with a bowlike stern. |

## 11a. Vessels built by Richard Smith & Company, Lytham.

141 **SUNLIGHT** Twin Screw Steel Steamer.
Built 1889 Registered Liverpool.
Owners - Lever Brothers, Port Sunlight, Cheshire.
ON 96352 108 grt 64 net 93.0 x 19.6 x 6.6 ft.
2xC.2Cy. 10"-20"x14" stroke, 45 nhp by builder.

142-147 no record.

*An engraving of RODAS, "a first-class tug boat".*

148 **RODAS** Twin Screw Steel Steam Tug.
Built 1890 Registered Bilbao, Spain.
Owners - Mr. F. M. Rodas, Bilbao, Spain.
ON - 194 grt 56 net 111.0 x 19.0 x 11.0 ft.
2xC.2Cy. 16"-32"x21" stroke, 87 nhp by Clayton, Goodfellow & Co. Ltd., Blackburn. Later named M. PASTOR LANDERO.

149 **CECIL** Single Screw Iron Steamer.
Built 1890 Registered Runcorn.
Owners - The 'Cecil' S.S. Co. Ltd., Runcorn, Cheshire.
ON 97227 229 grt 75 net 130.2 x 21.1 x 9.5 ft
C.2Cy. 18"-36"x24" stroke, 60 rhp by Clayton, Goodfellow and Co. Ltd., Blackburn.

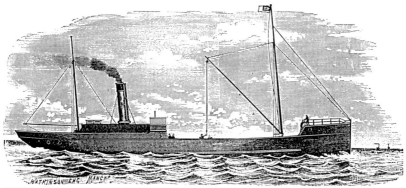

*CECIL, "a very strongly built Cargo Boat".*

150-173 no record but the following were built in the period.

**DAVY** Single Screw Steel Steamer.
Built 1891 Registered Liverpool.
Owners - The United Alkali Co. Ltd., Liverpool.
ON 99315 99 grt 52 net 75.0 x 19.6 x 8.0 ft.
Engine 28 nhp by builder.

**FARADAY** Single Screw Steel Steamer.
Built 1891 Registered Liverpool.
Owners - The United Alkali Co. Ltd., Liverpool.
ON 99327 102 grt 55 net 75.0 x 19.6 x 8.0 ft.
Engine 28 nhp by builder.

**LEBLANC** Single Screw Steel Steamer.
Built 1891 Registered Liverpool.
Owners - The United Alkali Co. Ltd., Liverpool.
ON 99301 109 grt 52 net 75.0 x 19.6 x 8.0 ft.
Engine 28 nhp by builder.

**HELVETIA** Single Screw Iron Steamer.
Built 1892 Registered Liverpool.
Owners - Monks, Hall & Co. Ltd., Warrington.
ON 99382 131 grt 78 net 90.0 x 21.4 x 9.1 ft.
C.2Cy. 13"-28"x18" stroke, 36 rhp by builder.

*PRINCE GEORGE, "constructed of Siemens-Martin mild steel throughout".*

**PRINCE GEORGE** Twin Screw Steel Passenger Steamer.
Built 1892 Registered Preston.
Owners - Preston, Lytham & Southport S.S. Co. Ltd., Preston.
ON 97445 78 grt 21 net 100.4 x 16.0 x 7.0 ft.
Two Compound Steam Engines by builder. Built to carry 400 passengers on the Ribble estuary service.

**SECRET** Single Screw Steam Tug.
Launched 22.10.1892.
Owners - Soundy & Son, London.
ON - 67.0 x 14.0 x 8.0 ft.
C.S.C. 200 ihp. Designed for towing on the River Thames and fitted with a lowering mast and funnel.

## 11b. Vessels built by Lytham S.B. & E. Company, Lytham.

**PROGRESS** Single Screw Steel Steamer.
Built 1893 Registered Runcorn.
Owners - Monks, Hall & Co. Ltd., Warrington.
ON 102367 65 grt 44 net 72.9 x 16.3 x 5.0 ft.
C.2Cy. 9″-18″x12″ stroke, 14 rhp by builder. (80 ihp).
Later named WESTON MAID.

*LUNA in frame.*

174  **LUNA** Single Screw Steel Steamer.
Built 1893 Registered Preston.
Owners - Thomas Edmondson, Lytham.
ON 97447 90 grt 30 net 76.9 x 19.6 x 8.2 ft.
C.2Cy. 13″-26″x16″ stroke, 25 nhp by builder. Delivered 1893 to Stephan Brothers
Ltd., Cape Town.

175-183 no record.

184  **LIFE BUOY** Twin Screw Steel Steamer.
Built 1894 Registered Liverpool.
Owners - Lever Brothers Ltd., Port Sunlight, Cheshire.
ON 102148 108 grt 64 net 76.5 x 19.8 x 8.1 ft.
2xC.2Cy. 10″x14″ stroke, 20 nhp by builder.

185  **SOCIAL** Twin Screw Steel Steamer.
Built 1894 Registered Liverpool.
Owners - Lever Brothers Ltd., Port Sunlight, Cheshire.
ON 102149 108 grt 64 net 76.5 x 19.8 x 8.1 ft.
2xC.2Cy. 10″x14″ stroke, 20 nhp by builder.

186-192 no record but the following were built in the period.

**TOILER** Single Screw Steel Steam Tug.
Built 1894 Registered Preston.
Owners - Thomas Edmondson, Lytham.
ON 97448 40 grt 21 net 61.5 x 14.2 x 5.1 ft.
H.P.I.D.A. 1Cy. 9″x9″ stroke, 30 ihp by builder. Delivered to the Admiralty in 1896.

**WATERWITCH** Single Screw Steel Steam Barge.
Built 1894 Registered Liverpool.
Owners - Brunner Mond & Co. Ltd., Northwich.
ON 120876 51 grt 28 net 69.8 x 15.2 x 6.1 ft.
Engine 16 nhp by builder.

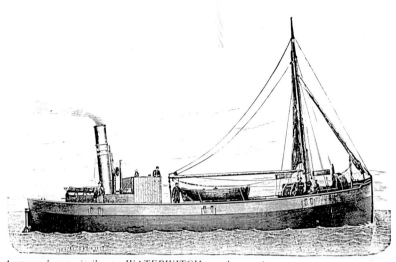

*A steam barge similar to WATERWITCH on the previous page.*

**193  FERNANDO DE NORONHA** Single Screw Steel Steamer.
Built 1894 Registered Pernambuco, Brazil.
Owners - The Brazilian Government.
ON - 124 grt 56 net 94.8 x 18.1 x 8.0 ft.
C.2Cy. 14″-28″x18″ stroke, 36 nhp by builder.

194-205 no record.

**206  CUMBRIA** Single Screw Steel Steam Tug.
Built 1895 Registered Southampton.
Owners - R. & J. H. Rea, London.
ON 105508 74 grt 1 net 73.1 x 16.2 x 8.4 ft.
C.2Cy. 14½″-30″x20″ stroke, 50 rhp by builder. Later named HALLGARTH.

207-215 no record.

**216  SANTO ANTONIO** Twin Screw Steel River Steamer.
Built 1895 Registered Manaos, Brazil.
Owners - A. de Miranda Araujo, Brazil.
ON - 360 grt 230 net 151.0 x 28.1 x 7.6 ft.
2xT.3Cy. 11″-17″-27½″x20″ stroke, 79 nhp by builder. Later named CARAMURA.

**217  DOURO** Twin Screw Steel River Steamer.
Built 1896 Registered Manaos, Brazil.
Owners - L. da Silva Gomes, Brazil.
ON - 120.0 x 25.1 x 5.8 ft.
2xT.3Cy. 9″-14″-24½″x18″ stroke, 63 nhp by builder.

218-233 no record but the following were built in the period.

**LILY** Single Screw Steel Steamer.
Built 1896 Registered Cork.
Owners - The Cork Harbour Commissioners.
ON 106279 23 grt 16 net 50.6 x 11.0 x 9.7 ft.
50 nhp by builder.

40

**NEW BOYNE** Single Screw Steel Steamer.
Built 1896 Registered Liverpool.
Owners - Grain Elevating & Automatic Weighing Co. Ltd., Liverpool.
ON 145908 42 grt 29 net 64.4 x 13.8 x 5.7 ft.
Engine 50 nhp by builder.

*KESTREL.*

234   **KESTREL** Single Screw Steel Steam Tug.
Built 1897 Registered London.
Owners - Kaiser Steam Tug Co. Ltd., London.
ON 108252 80 grt - net 70.0 x 17.0 x 9.0 ft.
T.3Cy. 11"-17¼"-29"x22" stroke, 50 nhp by builder.

235-237 no record.

238   **JOHN RICHARDS** Single Screw Steel Steam Tug.
Built 1897 Registered Liverpool.
Owners - Cleansing Department, Manchester Corporation.
ON - Invoice Price £1,100. 60.0 x 13.0 x 4.5 ft.
Named after the Chairman of the Cleansing Committee.

239-261 no record but the following was built in the period.

**OLD HOME** Single Screw Steel Steamer.
Built 1898 Registered Liverpool.
Owners - Lever Brothers Ltd., Port Sunlight.
ON 110570 108 grt 72 net 76.0 x 20.0 x 8.1 ft.
80 rhp by builder. Later converted to a sailing vessel.

262   **BARGE F** Steel Dumb Barge.
Built 1898 trials June. *120.0 x 26.0 x 8.6 ft.
Owners - Booth Steamship Co. Ltd., Liverpool.
ON - Displacement - Light 128 tons, Loaded 570 tons.

263 no record.

41

*MYSTIC.*

**264  MYSTIC** Single Screw Steel Steam Tug.
Built 1899 Registered London.
Owners - J. W. Cook & Co. Ltd., London.
ON 110067 75 grt 5 net 71.5 x 17.0 x 9.9 ft.
C.S.C.2Cy. 16"-34"x22" stroke, 50 rhp by builder.
Requistioned by the Admiralty in 1916 and renamed H.T.12. Later named
AVONCOCK.

265-266 no record.

**267-8  UNNAMED** Two Steel Dumb Barges.
Built 1899 50 grt.

**269  UNNAMED** Steel Dumb Barge.
Built 1899 90 grt.

**270  UNNAMED** Steel Passenger Dumb Barge.
Built 1899 80 grt 70.0 x 18.0 x 6.6 ft.

**271  UNNAMED** Steel Dumb Barge
Built 1899 264 grt.

**272  FYLDE** Single Screw Steel Steam Barge.
Launched 31.7.1899 Registered Preston.
Owners - Henry Alty, Brickmaker, Hesketh Bank, Nr Preston.
ON 105239 45 grt 31 net 62.0 x 14.2 x 5.9 ft.
C.S.C.2Cy. 8"-16"x10" stroke, 12 hp by builder.

**273  BARGE G** Steel Dumb Barge.
Built 1899 78 grt *120.0 x 26.0 x 9.3 ft.
Owners - Booth Steamship Co. Ltd., Liverpool.

**274  FYEDE** Single Screw Steel Steam Tug.
Launched 29.6.1899 50 grt.
Owners - Egyptian Delta Light Railways Ltd.

**275  UNNAMED** Steam Launch.
Built 1899 60 grt. Owners - Unknown Foreign.

42

276　**CLAUDE** Single Screw Steel Steam Tug.
Built 1899 Registered - Manchester 1924.
Owners - First owner not known.
ON 147396 15 grt - net 52.1 x 8.3 x 4.4 ft.
V.C.N.C.2Cy. 8"-15"x10" stroke, 45 ihp by builder. Later owned by the Manchester
Ship Canal Company and renamed M.S.C.CLAUDE.

277　**FULWOOD** Single Screw Steel Steamer.
Launched 4.12.1899 Registered Preston.
Trials April 1900.
Owners - S.S. Fulwood Ltd., (J. Pyke & Sons), Preston.
ON 112601 254 grt 76 net 120.1 x 20.6 x 8.8 ft.
C.S.C.2Cy. 16"-32"x21" stroke, 330 ihp by builder.

278-9 **UNNAMED** Two Single Screw Steel Steamers.
Built 1900 40 grt. Owners - Unknown Foreign.

280-1 **UNNAMED** Two Single Screw Steel Steamers.
Built 1900 60 grt. Owners - Unknown Foreign.

282-4 **UNNAMED** Three Single Screw Steel Steam Launches.
Built 1900 30 grt. Owners - Unknown Foreign.

*LEDA.*

285　　**LEDA** Twin Screw Steel Steam Pilot Boat.
Launched 29.6.1900 Registered Bombay.
Owners - Bombay Port Trust.
ON - 110 grt *99.6 x 16.0 x 8.0 ft.
2xT.E.S.C.3Cy. 9"-14"-24½"x18" stroke, 160 ihp by builder.

286-9 **UNNAMED** Four Single Screw Steel Steam Launches.
Built 1900 50 grt. Owners - Unknown Foreign.

290　**CHICA** Single Screw Steel Steamer.
Built 1900 Registered Liverpool.
Owners - Pacific Steam Navigation Co. Ltd., Liverpool.
ON 113437 44 grt 21 net 62.9 x 15.3 x 6.0 ft.
12 nhp by builder.

291 **AYSGARTH** Single Screw Steel Steam Tug.
Launched 9.10.1900 Registered Liverpool.
Owners - Rea Steam Tug Company, London.
ON 113428 20 grt 4 net 51.0 x 11.5 x 5.2 ft.
C.S.C.2Cy. 8″-16″x10″ stroke, 12 nhp by builder. Trials 8.11.1900.

292 **SOUDAN** Single Screw Steel Steamer.
Built 1901 152 grt. Owners - Unknown.

293 **LORRAINE** Single Screw Steel Steam Tug.
Built 1901 Registered Tamatave, Madagascar.
Owners - Hutton & Co. Ltd., Liverpool, Agents.
ON - *52.6 x 10.10 x 5.3 ft.
C.S.C.2Cy. 7″-15″x9″ stroke by builder. Built in three floatable sections.

294 **ALSACE** Single Screw Steel Steam Tug.
Built 1901 Registered Tamatave, Madagascar.
Owners - Hutton & Co. Ltd., Liverpool, Agents.
ON - *65.7 x 14.9 x 7.10½ ft.
C.S.C.2Cy. 10″-20″x14″ stroke by builder. Built in three floatable sections.

295-8 **UNNAMED** Four Sailing Lighters.
Built 1901 50 grt. Owners - Unknown Foreign.

*EBO.*

299 **EBO** Twin Screw Steel Steamer.
Launched 20.4.1901 Registered London.
Owners - Niger Co. Ltd., London.
ON 114693 97 grt 46 net 96.6 x 16.9 x 6.0 ft.
2xC.S.C.2Cy. 8″-18″x12″ stroke, 26 nhp by builder.

300 **WHELP** Single Screw Steel Steam Tug.
Built 1901 Registered London.
Owners - J. S. Morrison, London.
ON - 50 grt *54.6 x 12.0 x 5.9 ft.
C.S.C.2Cy. 8″-18″x12″ stroke by builder. Trials 1902. Weight complete in slings
in Natal 35 tons.

*WHELP.*

301 **SI THAN** Single Screw Steel Steam Launch.
Built 1901 20 grt. Owners - Unknown.
C.N.C.2Cy. 6″-10″x7″ stroke by builder.

302 **VICTORIA** Single Screw Steam Launch.
Built 1901 20 grt. Owners - Unknown.
C.N.C.2Cy. 5½″-10″x7″ stroke by builder.

303 **UNNAMED** Dumb Barge.
Built 1901 25 grt. Owners - Unknown.

*VICTORIA.*

304 **SEIONT** Single Screw Steel Steam Tug.
Launched 9.11.1901 Registered Caernarvon.
Owners - Caernarvon Port Trust, Caernarvon, Wales.
ON 109735 33 grt 15 net 56.4 x 15.1 x 6.0 ft.
C.S.C.2Cy. 8"-18"x12" stroke, 13 nhp by builder.

305 **LAMATANG** Steel Sternwheel Steamer.
Built 1902 60 grt. *70.0 x 15.0 x 4.0 ft.
Owners - Unknown Foreign probably Singapore.

306 **SIN HONG BIE** Steel Sternwheel Steamer.
Built 1902 60 grt. *70.0 x 15.0 x 4.0 ft.
Owners - Unknown Foreign probably Singapore.
Builder's drawing for this vessel quotes No.283 but does not say what this number is.

307 **FELLGARTH** Single Screw Steel Steam Tug.
Launched 10.5.1902 Registered Liverpool.
Owners - Rea Transport Co. Ltd., Liverpool.
ON 115302 67 grt - net 70.8 x 16.5 x 8.5 ft.
C.S.C.2Cy. 14"-30"x21" stroke, 52 nhp by builder.

308 **UNNAMED** Mersey Sailing Barge.
Built 1902 60 grt. Owners - Unknown.
Converted to a steamer in 1904-5 and named MERRILL.
Owners - John & Arthur Smith, Iron Merchants, Birkenhead.
ON 145909 47 grt 32 net 69.0 x 13.8 x 4.9 ft.
C.S.C.2Cy. 5½"-10"x8" stroke, 30 ihp by Caledonian Engineering Co., Ltd.,
Preston in 1905. Boiler by William Coltman of Loughborough in 1904. First
Registered Liverpool 1921.

309 **UNNAMED** Steam Pinnace.
Built 1902 10 grt. Owners - Unknown.

310 **UNNAMED** Steam Launch.
Built 1902 25 grt. Owners - Unknown.

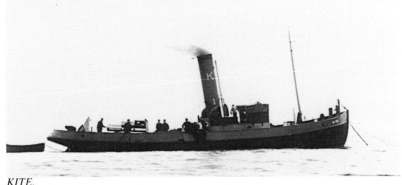

*KITE.*

311 **KITE** Single Screw Steel Steam Tug.
Launched 23.8.1902 Registered London.
Owners - Kaiser Steam Tug Co. Ltd., London.
ON 115949 69 grt 1 net 72.9 x 17.6 x 8.8 ft.
T.E.S.C.3Cy. 11"-17¼"-29"x22" stroke, 42 nhp by builder.

312 **UNNAMED** Steam Launch.
Built 1902 25 grt. Owners - Unknown Foreign.

*GOOD CHEER.*

313 **GOOD CHEER** Single Screw Steel Steam Launch.
Launched 4.10.1902 Registered Liverpool.
Owners - Mersey Mission to Seamen, Liverpool.
ON 115334 24 grt 4 net 50.8 x 12.0 x 6.3 ft.
C.S.C.2Cy. 8″-18″x12″ stroke, 13 nhp by builder.

314 **AUGUSTE BLANQUI** Single Screw Steel Steam Launch.
Launched 12.1.1903, trials 16.1.1903.
Owners - Hugo Brown & Co. Ltd., Liverpool, Agents.
ON - *54.6 x 12.0 x 6.9 ft.
C.S.C.2Cy. 8″-18″x12″ stroke, 13 nhp by builder.

315 **RIBBLE QUEEN** Twin Screw Steel Passenger Steamer.
Launched 14.4.1903 Registered Preston.
Owners - David & William Monk & William Preston, Preston.
ON 114911 100 grt 17 net*104.6 x 18.0 x 6.4 ft.
2xC.S.C.2Cy. 9½″-20″x14″ stroke, 33 nhp by builder. Later named CETINJE, NEPTUN and NETTUNO.

*RIBBLE QUEEN.*

316 **LETTEREWE** Single Screw Steel Steam Launch.
Launched 8.6.1903 Registered Loch Maree.
Owners - Marquis of Zetland.
ON - *30.0bp x 8.0 x 3.9 ft.
C.S.C.2Cy. 5"-11"x6" stroke by builder.
Letterewe is an isolated place on the northern bank of Loch Maree in the
Highlands of Scotland.

317 **COLOMBO** Single Screw Steel Steam Barge.
Launched 1.5.1903, trials 16.5.1903.
Owners - Valle Azevedo & Co. Ltd., Liverpool.
ON - *57.0 x 12.0 x 5.0 ft.
H.P.N.C. 1Cy. 9"x9" stroke by builder.

*DOM CARLOS.*

318 **DOM CARLOS** Twin Screw Steel Steam Tug.
Launched 14.5.1903 Registered London.
Owners - The Beira Boating Co. Ltd., London.
ON 118294 48grt 10 net 64.2 x 15.1 x 7.2 ft.
2xC.S.C 2Cy. 9½"-20"x14" stroke, 280 ihp by builder.
Trials 29.6.1903. Weight of hull in slings at London 40 tons. Beira is an important
port in Mozambique, East Africa.

319 **UNNAMED** Single Screw Wood Steam Launch.
Built 1903
Owners - G. Hepburn & Son, Liverpool, Agents.
C.S.C.2Cy. 7"-15"x9" stroke by builder.

320 **ROS-NA-RIGH** Single Screw Steel Steam Launch.
Launched 12.6.1903 Registered Drogheda.
Owners - Boyne Valley Launch Company, Drogheda.
ON - *60.0 x 8.6 x 3.6 ft.
C.S.C.2Cy. 5"-11"x6" stroke by builder.
Board of Trade Certificate for 71 passengers.

321 **EDWARD C. WHEELER** Single Screw Steel Steam Tug.
Launched 24.7.1903 Registered Liverpool.
Owners - Mersey Pilots, Liverpool.
ON 118042 46 grt 10 net 65.4 x 15.0 x 8.0 ft.
C.S.C.2Cy. 9½"-20"x15" stroke, 220 ihp by builder.
Named after the Superintendent of Pilotage on the River Mersey. Later names
SURVEYOR NO.5 and SNAPSHOT.

322 **FRANCIS** Single Screw Gal.Stl.Steam Launch.
Launched 13.8.1903 *54.0 x 9.0 x 4.8 ft.
Owners - F. & A. Swanzy & Co. Ltd., London.
C.N.C.2Cy. 8"-15"x9" stroke by builder. Trials 20.8.1903.

323 **SIN-YOE-SENG** Steel Sternwheel Steamer.
Launched 22.8.1903 Registered Singapore.
Owners - Jones, Burton & Co. Ltd., Liverpool, Agents.
ON - *74.0 x 15.0 x 4.0 ft.
C.N.C.2Cy. 9½"-14"x20" stroke by builder.

*EDENGARTH, 14.7.1955.*                                    *Dr. G. S. Wilson.*

324 **EDENGARTH** Single Screw Steel Steam Tug.
Launched 10.10.1903 Registered Liverpool.
Owners - Rea Transport Co. Ltd., Liverpool.
ON 118059 66 grt - net 70.9 x 16.7 x 8.4 ft.
C.S.C.2Cy. 14"-30"x21" stroke, 52 nhp by builder.
Trials 10.11.1903.

325 **ELSIE** Steel Sternwheel Steamer.
Launched 29.10.1903 Registered Addah.
Owners - F. & A. Swanzy & Co. Ltd., London.
ON - *42.9 x 9.0 x 2.9 ft.
H.H.P. 1Cy. 8½"x20" stroke by builder. Trials 31.10.1903 & shipped.

326 **TRADER** Single Screw Steel Steam Barge.
Launched 7.12.1903, trials 23.12.1903 and shipped.
Owners - Holt Brothers & Co. Ltd., Liverpool.
ON - 35 grt 23 net *60.0bp x 12.0 x 5.3 ft.
H.P.N.C.2Cy. 8½"-8½"x10" stroke by builder.

327 **MADRYN** Single Screw Steel Steam Tug.
Launched 2.8.1905, trials 9.8.1905.
Owners - Japp and Kirby, Liverpool, Agents.
ON - 50 grt *54.6 x 12.0 x 5.9 ft.
C.S.C.2Cy. 8"-18"x12" stroke by builder. Lines as WHELP (300).
Vessel built for South America and shipped from Liverpool.

328 **EGGA** Galvanised Steel Sternwheel Steamer.
Built 1903 Registered Burutu, Nigeria.
Owners - Niger Co. Ltd., London.
ON - *69.6 x 9.0 x 3.6 ft.
H.H.P.1Cy. 8½"x20" stroke by builder.
Shipped in pieces to Nigeria on 5.1.1904.

**11c. Vessels built by Lytham S.B. & E. Co. Ltd., Lytham.**

329 **UNNAMED** Galvanised Steel Dumb Barge.
Launched 20.2.1904 *70.0 x 10.0 x 5.3 ft.
Owners - Niger Co. Ltd., London.
Delivered 6.3.1904 to Liverpool for shipment.

330 **UNNAMED** Galvanised Steel Dumb Barge
Launched 5.3.1904 *70.0 x 10.0 x 5.3 ft.
Owners - Niger Co. Ltd., London.
Delivered 6.3.1904 to Liverpool for shipment.

331 **ISELGARTH** Single Screw Steel Steam Tug.
Launched 16.4.1904 Registered Bristol.
Owners - Rea Transport Co. Ltd., Liverpool.
ON 117714 93 grt - net 81.6 x 17.6 x 9.9 ft.
C.S.C.2Cy. 15"-32"x21" stroke, 314 ihp by builder.
Trials 28.5.1904. Later named CARDIFFIAN.

*SCARBROUGH.*

332 **SCARBROUGH** Steel Quarterwheel Steamer.
Launched 15.6.1904 Registered London.
Owners - Niger Co. Ltd., London.
ON 118480 468 grt 318 net 200.4 x 32.0 x 6.7 ft.
2xC.S.C.2Cy. 11"-24"x18" stroke, 46 nhp by builder.
Trials 20.8.1904. Twin engines combined gave 400 ihp.

333 **STURGEON** Steel Dumb Barge.
Launched 8.10.1904 Registered Liverpool.
Owners - Rea Transport Co. Ltd., Liverpool.
ON 118140 204 grt 201 net 120.0bp x 21.0 x 9.6 ft.
Trials 28.10.1904. 400 tons cargo on 8'9" draft.

334 **OCTOPUS** Steel Dumb Barge.
Launched 10.10.1904 Registered Liverpool.
Owners - Rea Transport Co. Ltd., Liverpool.
ON 118141 204 grt 201 net 120.0bp x 21.0 x 9.6 ft.
Trials 29.10.1904. 400 tons cargo on 8'9" draft.

335 **PORPOISE** Steel Dumb Barge.
Launched 10.11.1904 Registered Liverpool.
Owners - Rea Transport Co. Ltd., Liverpool.
ON 118147 204 grt 201 net 120.0bp x 21.0 x 9.6 ft.
Trials 25.11.1904. 400 tons cargo on 8'9" draft.

336 **NAUTILUS** Steel Dumb Barge.
Launched 8.12.1904 Registered Liverpool.
Owners - Rea Transport Co. Ltd., Liverpool.
ON 118148 204 grt 201 net 120.0bp x 21.0 x 9.6 ft.
Trials 11.12.1904. 400 tons cargo on 8'9" draft.

337 **KNIGHT ERRANT** Single Screw Steel Steam Tug.
Launched 23.3.1905 Registered Liverpool.
Owners - The Knight Errant Tug Co. Ltd., Liverpool.
ON 120861 148 grt 14 net 96.0 x 22.1 x 11.0 ft.
T.E.S.C.3Cy. 12"-20"-33.3"x22" stroke, 99 rhp by builder.
Trials 14.6.1905. 11½ knots achieved. Later named MONTORIOL.

338 **UNNAMED** Single Screw Steel Steam Tug.
Launched 9.1.1905 *56.0 x 8.0 x 4.10 ft.
Owners - North Staffordshire Railway Company, Stoke.
C.N.C.2Cy. 8"-15"x9" stroke by builder.

339 **HORNET** Single Screw Gal.Stl. Steam Launch.
Launched 5.4.1905 Registered Burutu, Nigeria.
Owners - Niger Co. Ltd., London.
ON - *68.0 x 10.0 x 4.6 ft.
C.S.C.2Cy. 7"-16"x10" stroke by builder. Trials 27.4.1905.

340 **WASP** Single Screw Gal.Stl. Steam Launch.
Launched 23.3.1905 Registered Burutu, Nigeria.
Owners - Niger Co. Ltd., London.
ON - *34.0bp x 8.0 x 3.9 ft.
C.N.C.2Cy. 5½"-10"x7" stroke by builder.

341 **MEJILLONES** Single Screw Steel Steam Launch.
Launched 18.5.1905 Registered Valparaiso, Chile.
Owners - Antofagasta Railway Company, Chile.
ON - *65.0 x 15.0 x 7.0 ft.
C.S.C.2Cy. 9½"-20"x14" stroke by builder. Trials 25.5.1905.

342 **BONITO** Steel Dumb Barge.
Launched 17.7.1905 Registered Liverpool.
Owners - Rea Transport Co. Ltd., Liverpool.
ON 120870 168 net 100.0 x 21.0 x 9.6 ft.
Trials 8.8.1905. Capable of carrying 330 tons of coal.

343 **BARRACOUTA** Steel Dumb Barge.
Launched 19.7.1905 Registered Liverpool.
Owners - Rea Transport Co. Ltd., Liverpool.
ON 120869 168 net 100.0 x 21.0 x 9.6 ft.
Trials 8.8.1905. Capable of carrying 330 tons of coal.

344 **ROSAMIRO** Steel Dumb Barge.
Launched 1.8.1905 and shipped.
Owners - John Lilly & Sons, Manchester, Agents.
ON - *65.6 x 16.3 x 5.0 ft.

345 **RAWAS** Steel Sternwheel Steamer.
Trials 14.10.1905 Registered Palembang, Indonesia.
Owners - C. Gill & Co. Ltd., London.
ON - *86.0 x 15.0 x 4.2 ft.
C.N.C.2Cy. 8½"-14"x20" stroke 321 ihp by builder.
Delivered for shipment 16.10.1905.

346 **KINGSWAY** Single Screw Steel Steam Trawler.
Launched 27.1.1906 Registered Fleetwood.
Owners - Fylde Steam Fishing Co. Ltd., Fleetwood.
Contract price £5,675.
ON 122938 247 grt 85 net 125.9 x 22.1 x 11.6 ft.
T.E.S.C.3Cy. 12"-20"-33½"x22" stroke, 55 nhp by W. Beardmore & Co., Ltd.,
Glasgow. Later named LA POINTE.

347 **RIO GUAMA** Single Screw Steel River Steamer.
Launched 2.10.1905 Registered Para, Brazil.
Owners - E. A. Da Costa & Company, Liverpool, Agents.
ON - 116 grt 79 net 90.7 x 20.0 x 6.1 ft.
C.S.C.2Cy. 11"-24"x18" stroke, 40 nhp by builder.
Trials 12.11.1905. Sailed for Brazil 17.11.1905.
Later named ALTAMIRA.

348 **WALLIN** Twin Screw Steel River Steamer.
Launched 31.10.1905 Registered Manaos, Brazil.
Owners - E. A. Da Costa and Company, Liverpool, Agents.
ON - 123 grt 83 net 95.9 x 20.1 x 6.2 ft.
2xC.S.C.2Cy. 8"-18"x12" stroke, 68 nhp by builder.
Trials 30.12.1905 and sailed for Para, Brazil on 8.1.1906 and arrived on 18.2.1906.

349 **LOWGARTH** Single Screw Steel Steam Tug.
Launched 29.3.1906 Registered Southampton.
Owners - Rea Transport Co. Ltd., Liverpool.
Contract price £3,575.
ON 119735 74 grt - net 76.2 x 17.2 x 8.9 ft.
C.S.C.2Cy. 15"-32"x21" stroke, 60 nhp by builder. Trials 19.5.1906.

350 **PORTADOR** Single Screw Steel Steamer.
Launched 24.2.1906 Registered Valparaiso, Chile.
Owners - Pacific Steam Navigation Co. Ltd., Liverpool.
Contract price £1,450.
ON 127913 31 grt 7 net 50.0 x 12.1 x 6.0 ft.
C.S.C.2Cy. 8"-18"x12" stroke, 12 nhp by builder. Trials 7.3.1906.

351 **ADDAH** Steel Sternwheel Steamer.
Built 1906 *50.0bp x 10.0 x 3.6 ft.
Owners - Rogers & Sons, Wolverhampton, Agents.
Contract price £700.
H.H.P.2Cy. 7½"-7½"x20" stroke by builder.
Trials May 1906, shipped from Lytham in pieces 11.5.1906.

352 **DRAGON** Single Screw Steel Steam Launch.
Launched 14.2.1906 Registered Burutu, Nigeria.
Owners - Niger Co. Ltd., London.
Contract price £1,030.
ON - 20 grt - net *48.0 x 10.0 x 4.8 ft.
C.N.C.2Cy. 7"-13"x9" stroke by builder. Trials 17.2.1906.

353 **UNNAMED** Steel Sternwheel Steamer.
Built 1906 *70.0 x 15.0 x 4.0 ft.
Owners - Constantine, Manchester, Agents, shipped in pieces.
Contract price £1,000.
C.N.C.2Cy. 8½"-14"x20" stroke, 32 ihp by builder.

354-9 **UNNAMED** Six Steel Dumb Barges.
Built 1906 Registered Calcutta.
Owners - Jones, Burton & Co. Ltd., Liverpool, Agents.
Contract price for the six £3,090.
ON -- *95.6 x 18.0 x 7.11 ft.
Three were shipped on 21.5.1906 and three on 28.7.1906.

360 **PACIFICO** Twin Screw Steel Steam Tug.
Launched 7.7.1906 Registered Valparaiso, Chile.
Owners - Antofagasta Railway Company, Chile.
Contract price £4,000.
ON - *76.0 x 17.0 x 8.0 ft.
2xC.S.C.2Cy. 9½"-20"xl4" stroke by builder. Trials 6.8.1906.
Shipped to Chile from Liverpool. Weight in slings 80 tons.

361 **ANASTACIA** Single Screw Steel River Steamer.
Launched 7.6.1906 Registered Iquitos, Peru.
Owners - J. Lilly & Sons, Manchester, Agents.
ON - 120 grt 79 net 90.0 x 20.0 x 6.4 ft.
C.S.C.2Cy. 11"-24"x18" stroke 40 nhp by builder.
Trials 10.7.1906 achieving 10½ knots. Sailed 25.7.1906 for Peru. Later named
URUBAMBA.

*ARGUS.*

362 **ARGUS** Single Screw Steel Steam Police Boat.
Launched 5.9.1906 Registered Liverpool.
Owners - Mersey Docks & Harbour Board, Liverpool.
ON 124002 29 grt 6 net 55.8 x 12.8 x 6.4 ft.
C.S.C.2Cy. 8½"-20"x14" stroke, 16 nhp by builder.
Trials 3.10.1906 achieving 10½ knots. Delivered 5.10.1906.

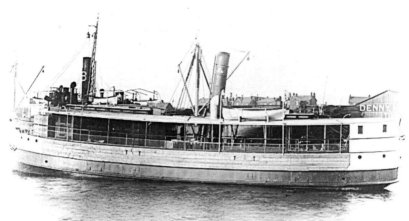

*MIRAFLORES.*

363 **MIRAFLORES** Twin Screw Steel River Steamer.
Launched 20.10.1906 Registered Iquitos, Peru.
Owners - E. A. Da Costa & Company, Liverpool, Agents.
ON - 135 grt 87 net 96.0 x 20.2 x 6.7 ft
2xC.S.C.2Cy. 9"-20"x14" stroke, 45 nhp by builder. Cost £4,402.
Trials 28.11.1906. Named after a lock in the Panama Canal.

364 **REPUBLICA** Single Screw Steel River Steamer.
Launched 8.6.1907 Registered Iquitos, Peru.
Owners - J. Lilly & Sons, Manchester, Agents.
ON - *79.4 x 17.0 x 5.0 ft.
C.S.C.2Cy. 9"-20"x15" stroke, by builder.
Trials 9.9.1907. Sailed from Preston September 1907 for Peru.

365 **NETHERGARTH** Single Screw Steel Steam Tug.
Launched 17.1.1907 Registered Bristol.
Owners - Rea Transport Co. Ltd., London.
ON 117732 96 grt - net 81.2 x 17.6 x 9.9 ft.
C.S.C.2Cy. 15"-32"x21" stroke, 60 nhp by builder.
Trials 7.3.1907. Later named PEAKE.

366 **UNNAMED** Steel Dumb Lighter.
Launched 29.12.1906. *60.0bp x 16.0 x 7.0 ft.
Owners - Arauco Company. Shipped.

367-8 **LIGHTER NO.5-6** Two Galvanised Steel Dumb Lighters.
Built 1907 Registered Burutu, Nigeria.
Owners - Niger Co. Ltd., London.
ON - *78.0 x 13.0 x 6.6 ft.
Both Shipped to Nigeria on 12.3.1907 from Liverpool.

369 **OVERGARTH** Single Screw Steel Steam Tug.
Launched 30.4.1907 Registered Liverpool.
Owners - Rea Transport Co. Ltd., London.
ON 124069 97 grt - net 81.6 x 17.6 x 10.0 ft.
C.S.C.2Cy. 15"-32"x21" stroke, 60 nhp by builder.
Trials 31.5.1907.

370 **UNNAMED** Steel Sternwheel Steamer.
Built 1907 *60.0bp x 14.0 x 3.0 ft.
Owners - Alex. Young & Company, London, Agents.
C.N.C.2Cy. 8½''-14''x20'' stroke by builder.
Trials July 1907, shipped from Lytham 2.8.1907 in pieces.

371-380 **UNNAMED** Ten Steel Dumb Barges.
Built 1907 *64.6 x 14.0 x 9.6 ft.
Owners - Jones, Burton & Co. Ltd., Liverpool, Agents.

381 **BANUM** Single Screw Gal.Stl. Steam Barge.
Launched 11.7.1907 Registered Burutu, Nigeria.
Owners - J. Holt & Co. Ltd., Liverpool.
ON - 75 grt *65.5bp x 12.6 x 5.0 ft.
C.N.C.2Cy. 8''-15''x9'' stroke by builder. Trials 27.7.1907. Cost £1,179.

382 **LIGHTER NO.7.** Galvanised Steel Dumb Lighter.
Built 1907 *50.0 x 12.0 x 4.9 ft.
Owners - Niger Co. Ltd., London. Shipped 10.7.1907.

383 **UNNAMED** Single Screw Steel Steam Barge.
Launched 10.12.1907 Registered Bolama, Portuguese Guinea.
Owners - Unknown *55.0bp x 11.0 x 5.0 ft.
C.S.C.2Cy. 7''-15''x9'' stroke by builder.

*The launch of BRITO, 10.9.1907.*

384 **BRITO** Single Screw Steel River Steamer.
Launched 10.9.1907 Registered Para, Brazil.
Owners - Brito & Company, Para, Brazil.
ON - 285 grt 194 net 141.0 x 28.1 x 7.6 ft.
T.E.S.C.3Cy. 12½''-21''-34''x24'' stroke, 81 nhp by builder.
Trials 12.10.1907, sailed for Brazil 20.10.1907.

385 **SOPHIA MARTINS** Single Screw Steel River Steamer.
Launched 11.10.1907 Registered Manaos, Brazil.
Owners - A. A. Martins (E. A. Da Costa & Company, Liverpool).
ON - 319 grt 217 net 142.1 x 30.1 x 7.6 ft.
T.E.S.C.3Cy. 12½''-21''-34''x24'' stroke, 81 nhp by builder. Trials 4.12.1907. Cost
£9,208. Later names RIO MURU, RIO ZINGU.

*JOSE MARTINS.*

386 **JOSE MARTINS** Single Screw Steel River Steamer.
Launched 23.11.1907 Registered Manaos, Brazil.
Owners - A. A. Martins (E. A. Da Costa & Company, Liverpool).
ON - 141 grt 83 net 101.1 x 20.1 x 6.6 ft
T.E.S.C.3Cy. 11''-17¼''-29''x22'' stroke, 56 nhp by builder.
Trials 16.3.1908, sailed to Brazil 22.7.1908.

387 **AQUILA** Single Screw Steel Steamer.
Launched 23.12.1907 Registered Liverpool.
Owners - Pacific Steam Navigation Co. Ltd., Liverpool.
ON - 33 grt 5 net 50.7 x 13.1 x 6.2 ft.
C.S.C.2Cy. 8''-18''x12'' stroke, 110 hp by builder.
Trials 21.1.1908, cost £1,362.

*The launch of ALVES DE FREITAS, 6.2.1908.*

*ALVES DE FREITAS fitting out.*

388   **ALVES DE FREITAS** Single Screw Steel River Steamer.
Launched 6.2.1908 Registered Manaos, Brazil.
Owners - J. M. de Freitas, Brazil.
ON - 383 grt 260 net 155.1 x 13.1 x 8.7 ft
T.E.S.C.3Cy. 14"-22"-38"x24" stroke, 100 nhp by builder.
Trials 7.4.1908, sailed to Brazil 24.4.1908.

*SANDBECK, see next page.*

389 **SANDBECK** Twin Screw Steel Steamer.
Launched 4.4.1908 Registered London.
Owners - Niger Co. Ltd., London.
ON 125689 401 grt 251 net 150.1 x 29.6 x 9.3 ft.
2xC.S.C.2Cy. 11''-24''x18'' stroke, 46 nhp by builder.
Trials 19.5.1908.

*NARAGUTA, boarded up amidships and aft for her voyage to Nigeria.*

390 **NARAGUTA** Steel Quarterwheel Steamer.
Launched 15.6.1908 Registered London.
Owners - Niger Co. Ltd., London.
ON 125713 642 grt 443 net 200.7 x 35.1 x 7.7 ft.
C.S.C.4Cy. 12½''-30''x24'' stroke, 70 rhp by builder.
Trials 28.7.1908, cost £13,209. Sailed from Liverpool 1.8.1908, on her delivery
voyage to Nigeria.

391 **SCORPION** Single Screw Gal.Stl. Steam Launch.
Launched 30.7.1908 Registered Burutu, Nigeria.
Owners - Niger Co. Ltd., London.
ON - *64.0bp x 13.0 x 5.6 ft.
C.S.C.2Cy. 8½''-20''x14'' stroke by builder.
Shipped from Liverpool 5.8.1908. Later named TARTAR.

392 **LYNN** Schooner Rigged Steel Cargo Barge.
Launched 26.9.1908 Registered Bristol.
Owners - Rea Transport Co. Ltd., Liverpool.
ON 127064 339 grt 306 net 125.7 x 24.2 x 11.5 ft.

393 **UNNAMED** Dumb Steel Barge.
Delivered 23.10.1908 90 grt*60.0bp x 14.0 x 6.0 ft.
Owners - F. & A. Swanzy Co. Ltd., London.

394 **SAMUEL BAKER** Steel Side Paddle Steamer.
Built 1909 Registered Entebbe, Uganda.
Owners - Crown Agents for the Colonies, Uganda.
ON - Cost £5,975 *124.0bp x 24.0 x 6.0 ft.
C.D.J.C.2Cy. 14''-28''x42'' stroke, 200 ihp by builder.
After trials at Lytham she was sent to Kilindini, Uganda in pieces, the last consignment leaving on 20.2.1909. She was reassembled by 1911 and served on Lake Albert where she forged the first international route to the Congolese ports of Mahagi and Kasenyi. One of her final duties was to carry the Prince of Wales across the lake in 1928 after visiting the Murchison Falls. Named after Sir Samuel Baker, born 1821, explorer and big game hunter who discovered a source of the River Nile on 14.3.1864 and named Lake Albert after Queen Victoria's husband.

*SPEKE. Note the section numbers and the temporary bolting of the hull and canopy.*

395 **SPEKE** Steel Sternwheel Steamer.
Trials 19.3.1909 Registered Entebbe, Uganda.
Owners - Crown Agents for the Colonies, Uganda.
ON - Cost £3,130 *100.0bp x 20.0 x 5.6 ft.
C.H.J.C.2Cy. 12''-24''x42'' stroke, 150 ihp by builder.
Named after John Hanning Speke, explorer, who died in 1864 aged 37. Together with two other sternwheelers, GRANT and STANLEY, she plied Lake Kioga, Uganda.

396-7 **UNNAMED** Two Gal.Stl. Dumb Barges.
Shipped March 1909 Registered Burutu, Nigeria.
Owners - Niger Co. Ltd., London.
ON - *78.0bp x 14.0 x 6.6 ft.

*VAMPIRE.*

398　**VAMPIRE** Single Screw Gal.Stl. Steam Launch.
Launched 8.5.1909 Registered Burutu, Nigeria.
Owners - Niger Co. Ltd., London.
ON - 60 grt *64.0bp x 13.0 x 5.9 ft.
C.S.C.2Cy. 8½"-20"x14" stroke by builder. Vessel cost £1,283.

399-400 **UNNAMED** Two Gal.Stl. Dumb Lighters.
Built 1909 Registered Burutu, Nigeria.
Owners - Niger Co. Ltd., London.
ON - 60 grt *78.0 x 14.0 x 6.6 ft.

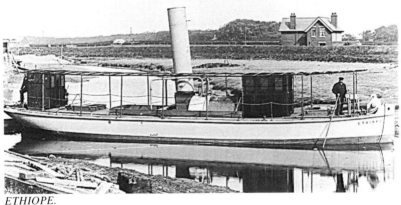

*ETHIOPE.*

401　**ETHIOPE** Twin Screw Gal.Stl. Steam Launch.
Launched 27.4.1909 *60.0bp x 13.0 x 5.9 ft.
Owners - Miller Brothers (Liverpool) Ltd., London.
2xC.S.C.2Cy. 7"-15"x9" stroke by builder. Trials 31.5.1909.

402　**UNNAMED** Gal.Stl. Dumb Lagoon Barge.
Shipped 7.6.1909 *55.0bp x 7.9 x 2.6 ft.
Owners - Miller Brothers (Liverpool) Ltd., London.

403　**UNNAMED** Gal.Stl. Dumb Lagoon Barge.
Shipped 7.6.1909 *54.6bp x 7.3 x 2.6 ft.
Owners - Miller Brothers (Liverpool) Ltd., London.

*BRIGG.*

**404 BRIGG** Single Screw Steel Steamer.
Launched 20.7.1909 Registered Liverpool.
Owners - J. Holt & Co. Ltd., Liverpool.
ON 127992 133 grt 51 net 88.8 x 21.1 x 5.4 ft.
C.S.C.2Cy. 9″-20″x15″ stroke, 16 rhp by builder.
Trials 9.8.1909.

**405 FORWARD** Single Screw Gal.Stl. Steam Launch.
Trials 10.8.1909 cost £648,*43.0 x 10.0 x 4.6 ft.
Owners - Miller Brothers (Liverpool) Ltd., London.
C.S.C.2Cy. 7″-15″x9″ stroke by builder.

**406-7 UNNAMED** Two Steel Sternwheel Steamers.
Trials 16.9.1909 Registered Rio de Janeiro.
Owners - Jones, Burton & Co. Ltd., Liverpool, Agents.
ON - *76.0 x 16.0 x 3.8 ft.
C.N.C.2Cy. 9½″-14″x20″ stroke by builder.
Delivered to Liverpool by rail 18.9.1909 for shipment.

*RIO MADEIRA (see next page) already renamed MOREY.*

61

408  **RIO MADEIRA** Single Screw Steel River Steamer.
Launched 30.10.1909 Registered Manaos, Brazil.
Owners - Gunzburger & Company.
ON - 312 grt 212 net 141.0 x 30.1 x 7.7 ft.
T.E.S.C.3Cy. 12½"-21"-34"x24" stroke, 81 nhp by builder.
Trials 29.12.1909, sailed to Brazil 6.1.1910, named after a tributary of the Amazon.
Later names MOREY and CAPITAO ASSIS.

409  **S'THOME** Single Screw Steel Steam Launch.
Launched 27.11.1909 *50.0bp x 12.0 x 6.9 ft.
Owners - J. Leone. Trials 15.12.1909. Cost £1,830.
C.S.C.2Cy. 8"-18"x12" stroke by builder.

410-2 **UNNAMED** Three Gal.Stl. Poling Canoes.
Delivered to Liverpool 11.11.1909 for shipment to Nigeria.
Owners - Niger Co. Ltd., London.*55.0 x 7.9 x 2.6 ft.

*OGUTA.*

413  **OGUTA** Twin Screw Steel Steamer.
Launched 15.1.1910 Registered London.
Owners - Niger Co. Ltd., London.
ON 129075 153 grt 62 net 110.8 x 20.1 x 6.6 ft.
2xC.S.C.2Cy. 9"-22"x15" stroke, 30 nhp by builder.
Trials 22.2.1910, cost £5,538. Named after a place in Nigeria.

414  **EDDA** Single Screw Galvanised Steel Steam Barge.
Trials 1.3.1910 Registered Burutu, Nigeria.
Owners - R. & W. King, Bristol, Agents.
ON - 75 grt *65.5bp x 12.6 x 5.0 ft.
C.N.C.2Cy. 8"-15"x9" stroke by builder. Delivered 29.3.1910.

415-6 **UNNAMED** Two Gal.Stl. Poling Canoes.
Delivered to Liverpool 5.1.1910 & 19.1.1910.
Owners - Niger Co. Ltd. London.*55.0bp x 8.9 x 3.0 ft.

*TUGWELL, boarded up prior to sailing to Nigeria.*

**417 TUGWELL** Steel Quarterwheel Steamer.
Launched 25.4.1910 Registered London.
Owners - Niger Co. Ltd., London.
ON 129098 188 grt 114 net 131.1 x 26.1 x 5.7 ft
H.C.S.C.2Cy. 17"-37"x48" stroke, 372 ihp by builder.
Trials 6.6.1910 before sailing to Nigeria.

**418 UNNAMED** Steel Dumb Barge.
Built 1910 90 grt *60.0bp x 14.0 x 6.0 ft.
Owners - F. & A. Swanzy Co. Ltd., London.

*EDDA, see opposite.*

*BRITANNIA.*

**419** **BRITANNIA** Single Screw Gal.Stl. Steam Launch.
Launched 12.5.1910 Registered Benin, West Africa.
Owners - McNeill & Scott, Liverpool, Agents.
ON - *43.0 x 10.0 x 4.6 ft.
C.S.C.2Cy. 7″-15″x9″ stroke by builder.
Trials 18.5.1910, shipped from Liverpool 19.5.1910.

**420** **STANEGARTH** Single Screw Steel Steam Tug.
Launched 25.6.1910 Registered Liverpool.
Owners - Rea Transport Co. Ltd., Liverpool.
ON 131276 45 grt - net 61.0 x 15.6 x 7.5 ft.
C.S.C.2Cy. 12½″-28″x18″ stroke, 39 nhp by builder.
Trials 25.7.1910.

*STANEGARTH.*

*FREIRECASTRO, boarded up prior to sailing for Para.*

**421 FREIRECASTRO** Twin Screw Steel River Steamer.
Launched 25.7.1910 Registered Para, Brazil.
Owners - F. Castro & Company, (E. A. Da Costa & Co., Liverpool).
ON - 297 grt 202 net 145.0 x 28.1 x 7.6 ft.
2xC.S.C.2Cy. 12½"-28"x18" stroke, 82 nhp by builder.
Trials 8.9.1910, sailed 15.9.1910 for Para, Brazil.

**422 ARIPUANA** Single Screw Steel River Steamer.
Launched 25.8.1910 Registered Para, Brazil.
Owners - A. R. Alves, Brazil.
ON - 214 grt 145 net 125.5 x 26.1 x 6.7 ft.
C.S.C.2Cy. 14"-30"x21" stroke, 57 nhp by builder.
Trials 8.9.1910, sailed 13.10.1910, arrived Para 11.11.1910.

**423 MUCURIPE** Single Screw Steel River Steamer.
Launched 5.10.1910 Registered Para, Brazil.
Owners - Mello, Frotas & Company, Brazil.
ON - 207 grt 141 net 124.0 x 24.1 x 6.2 ft.
C.S.C.2Cy. 14"-30"x21" stroke, 57 nhp by builder.
Trials 7.11.1910. Later names MIGUEL BITTAR and ALMERIM.

**424 ALTO ACRE** Single Screw Steel River Steamer.
Launched 3.11.1910 Registered Manaos, Brazil.
Owners - Tancredo, Porto & Company, Brazil.
ON - 248 grt 169 net 130.0 x 26.1 x 7.7 ft.
C.S.C.2Cy. 14½"-32"x21" stroke, 72 nhp by builder.
Trials 6.12.1910, sailed 23.12.1910 for Manaos.

**425 CASSIO REIS** Twin Screw Steel River Steamer.
Launched 17.12.1910 Registered Para, Brazil.
Owners - Roffe, Reis & Company, Brazil.
ON - 299 grt 203 net 145.0 x 28.1 x 7.6 ft.
2xC.S.C.2Cy. 12½"-28"x18" stroke, 82 nhp by builder.
Cost £9,277. Later names PARANA, PARA RIO, and ZEANTUNES.

*RIO ARIPUANA, boarded up for her voyage to Manaos.*

**426  RIO ARIPUANA** Single Screw Steel River Steamer.
Launched 1.2.1911 Registered Manaos, Brazil.
Owners - H. da Costa, Santos, Brazil.
ON - 210 grt 143 net 124.0 x 24.1 x 6.2 ft.
C.S.C.2Cy. 14″-30″x21″ stroke, 57 nhp by builder.
Trials 4.2.1911, sailed to Manaos, Brazil.

**427-8 UNNAMED** Two Gal.Stl. Dumb Lighters.
Delivered 1911 to Liverpool for shipment to Nigeria.
Owners - Niger Co. Ltd., London.
ON - 60 grt *78.0bp x 14.0 x 6.6 ft.

*RICHARD LANDER, similarly boarded up prior to sailing for Burutu.*

429 **RICHARD LANDER** Steel Quarterwheel Steamer.
Launched 13.3.1911 Registered London.
Owners - Niger Co. Ltd., London.
ON 132560 340 grt 235 net 150.2 x 30.0 x 6.2 ft.
H.C.S.C.2Cy. 17″-37″x48″ stroke, 55 nhp by builder.
Cost £8,612. Invoiced £10,390. Trials 29.6.1911. Sailed from Preston 5.7.1911 via
Falmouth and Las Palmas arriving Burutu on 29.7.1911. Named after an explorer
of the River Niger, 1830-1.

*BENI.*

430 **BENI** Single Screw Steel River Steamer.
Launched 29.5.1911 Registered Para, Brazil.
Owners - Amazon River Steam Navigation Co. (1911) Ltd.
ON - 469 grt 257 net 165.0 x 32.0 x 9.5 ft.
T.E.S.C.3Cy. 16″-26″-43″x24″ stroke, 90 nhp by builder.
Cost £14,476. Trials 12.8.1911. Sailed from Preston 26.8.1911 and arrived at Para
20.9.1911. Later names MARISE, FLAMENGO and RIO BRANCO.

431-2 **UNNAMED** Two Gal.Stl. Dumb Lighters.
Delivered 1.3.1911 & 18.5.1911 to Liverpool for shipment.
Owners - F. & A. Swanzy & Co. Ltd., London.
Shipped to Nigeria. *70.0bp x 16.0 x 6.0 ft.

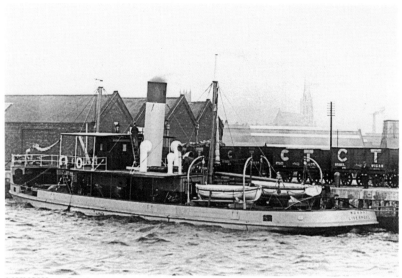

*MUNSHI at Preston.*

**433 MUNSHI** Twin Screw Steel Steam Tug.
Launched 29.7.1911 Registered Liverpool.
Owners - Miller Brothers (of Liverpool) Ltd., Liverpool.
ON 131385 177 grt 96 net 125.8 x 24.1 x 6.3 ft.
2xC.S.C.2Cy. 11"-24"x18" stroke, 46 nhp by builder.
Trials 21.9.1911. Sailed from Preston 30.9.1911 for Nigeria. Built as a combined tug and cargo boat. Named after an agricultural and warlike tribe in Nigeria.

**434 NIGRETIA** Single Screw Gal.Stl. Steam Launch.
Launched 28.7.1911 *64.0bp x 13.0 x 5.9 ft.
Owners - Niger Co. Ltd., London.
C.S.C.2Cy. 8½"-20"x14" stroke by builder. Trials 16.8.1911.

**435-6 K2-K3** Two Gal.Stl. Poling Canoes.
Delivered 1911 to Liverpool for shipment to Nigeria.
Owners - Niger Co. Ltd., London.*56.0 x 7.9 x 2.6 ft.

**437-8 K4-K5** Two Gal.Stl. Poling Canoes.
Delivered 1911 to Liverpool for shipment to Nigeria.
Owners - Niger Co. Ltd., London.*54.0 x 7.3 x 2.6 ft.

**439-440 K6-K7** Two Gal.Stl. Poling Canoes.
Delivered 1911 to Liverpool for shipment to Nigeria.
Owners - Niger Co. Ltd., London.*52.0 x 6.9 x 2.6 ft.

**441 LAHAT** Gal.Stl. Sternwheel Steamer.
Trials 8.9.1911. Delivered to Liverpool in pieces by rail.
Owners - Jones, Burton & Co. Ltd., Liverpool, Agents.
ON - *75.0bp x 16.0 x 4.0 ft.
C.N.C.2Cy. 10½"-19"x24" stroke by builder.

*The stern wheeler LAHAT under construction.*

**442  RIOZINHO** Single Screw Steel River Steamer.
Launched 26.9.1911 Registered Para, Brazil.
Owners - Pinho, Certo & Company, Brazil.
ON - 225 grt 153 net 112.5 x 27.1 x 7.7 ft.
T.E.S.C.3Cy. 11″-17¼″-29″x22″ stroke, 64 nhp by builder.
Trials 21.11.1911. Sailed from Preston 26.11.1911 calling at Las Palmas on 4.12.1911 and arriving at Para on 21.12.1911.

*RIOZINHO.*

*ACRE.*

**443  ACRE** Single Screw Steel River Steamer.
Launched 7.12.1911 Registered Para, Brazil.
Owners - Amazon River Steam Navigation Co. (1911) Ltd.
ON - 220 grt 115 net 120.0bp x 26.0 x 7.6 ft.
C.S.C.2Cy. 14½''-32''x21'' stroke, 39 nhp by builder.
Trials 14.6.1912. Sailed from Preston 22.6.1912 for Brazil.

**444  BELITI** Gal.Stl. Sternwheel Steamer.
Delivered 16 & 17.11.1911 in pieces to Liverpool by rail.
Owners - Jones, Burton & Co. Ltd., Liverpool, Agents.
ON - *75.0bp x 16.0 x 4.0 ft.
C.N.C.2Cy. 10½''-19''x24'' stroke by builder.

**445  KWILU** Single Screw Gal.Stl. Steam Launch.
Trials 2.12.1911 on the River Congo after shipment in pieces.
Owners - La Societe Anonyme des Huileries du Congo Belge.
ON - 27 grt 5 net *65.0bp x 12.0 x 5.0 ft.
C.N.C.2Cy. 9''-18''x12'' stroke by builder.
Named after a tributary of the River Congo.

**446  LEVERVILLE** Gal.Stl. Sternwheel Steamer.
Built 1912 Registered Kinchasa, Belgian Congo.
Owners - La Societe Anonyme des Huileries du Congo Belge.
ON - 350 grt 245 net*179.0bp x 31.0 x 6.0 ft.
H.C.S.C.2Cy. 17''-37''x48'' stroke, 107 nhp by builder.
Trials 24.12.1912 on the River Congo after shipment in pieces. Named after a township established by Lever Brothers Ltd., in the Belgian Congo.

**447  UNNAMED** Gal.Stl. Poling Canoe.
Delivered 1911. *30.0bp x 4.6 x 2.6 ft.
Owners - F. & A. Swanzy & Co. Ltd., London.

**448  DUC DE BRABANT** Steel Sternwheel Steamer.
Built 1912 Registered Liverpool.
Owners - La Societe Anonyme des Huileries du Congo Belge.
ON - 415 grt 290 net 182.0 x 31.0 x 7.0 ft.
H.C.S.C.2Cy. 17''-37''x60'' stroke by builder.
The hull was shipped to the Congo on 15.3.1912 and the engines on 2.7.1912.

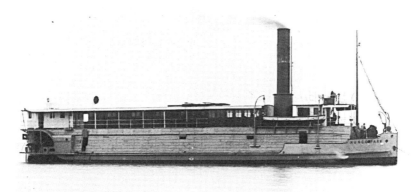

*MUNGO PARK boarded up for her voyage in 7.1912.*

**449  MUNGO PARK** Steel Quarterwheel Steamer.
Launched 30.5.1912 Registered London.
Owners - Niger Co. Ltd., London.
ON 132739 264 grt 177 net 134.2 x 26.0 x 5.7 ft.
H.C.S.C.2Cy. 17"-37"x42" stroke, 55 nhp by builder.
Trials 2.7.1912. Sailed from Preston for Nigeria on 7.7.1912.
Named after a young Scottish doctor and surgeon who discovered the River
Niger on 20th July, 1796 and wrote the following -'the long sought for, majestic
Niger, glittering to the morning sun, as broad as the Thames at Westminster,
and flowing slowly to the eastward.'

**450  FARO** Gal.Stl. Quarterwheel Steamer.
Built 1912 *85.0bp x 17.4 x 4.6 ft.
Owners - Niger Co. Ltd., London.
C.N.C.2Cy. 9"-18"x30" stroke, 75 ihp by builder.
Delivered to Nigeria in pieces. Named after the River Faro.

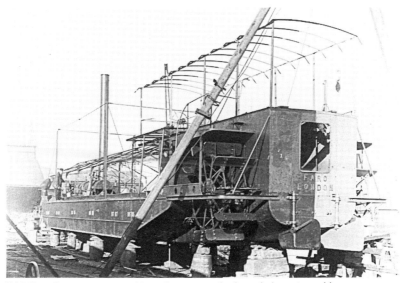

*FARO under construction. Note the quarterwheels and the twin rudders.*

451-2 **UNNAMED** Two Steel Dumb Barges.
Built 1912 45 tons d.w. 120 tons cap.*105.0bp x 18.6½ x 7.6 ft.
Owners - La Societe Anonyme des Huileries du Congo Belge.


453 **UNNAMED** Steel Dumb Barge.
Shipped 8.8.1912 40 tons cap.*65.0bp x 14.6 x 6.0 ft.
Owners - La Societe Anonyme des Huileries du Congo Belge.

*ULLSGARTH.* *World Ship Photo Library*

454 **ULLSGARTH** Single Screw Steel Steam Tug.
Launched 13.7.1912 Registered Liverpool.
Owners - Rea Transport Co. Ltd., Liverpool.
ON 131450 45 grt - net 61.0 x 15.6 x 7.5 ft.
C.S.C.2Cy. 12½"-28"x18" stroke, 39 nhp by builder.
Trials 12.8.1912.


455 **UNNAMED** Steel Cargo Lighter.
Built 1912 60 grt


456 **BARAO DE URUSSUHY** Steel Side Paddle Steamer.
Launched 31.8.1912 Registered Theresina, Brazil.
Owners - Companhia de Navegacao a Vapor do Rio Parnahyba.
ON - 193 grt 122 net*120.0bp x 24.0 x 5.9 ft.
2xC.S.C.2Cy. 14"-28"x42" stroke, 170 ihp by builder.
Trials 1.11.1912. Sailed from Preston 13.11.1912 via Madeira & St. Vincent arriving Brazil 13.1.1913.

*BARAO DE URUSSUHY.*

**457 CHRISTINO CRUZ** Twin Screw Steel Tunnel Steamer.
Launched 26.10.1912 Registered Theresina, Brazil.
Owners - Companhia de Navegacao a Vapor do Rio Parnahyba.
ON - 178 grt 121 net*115.0bp x 23.0 x 5.9 ft.
2xC.S.C.2Cy. 9''-20''x14'' stroke, 175 ihp by builder.
Sailed from Preston 4.2.1913 via Madeira and St. Vincent arriving Brazil 17.8.1913.

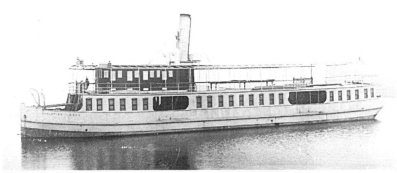

*CHRISTINO CRUZ.*

**458 BERWIND** Single Screw Steel Steam Tug.
Launched 28.9.1912 Registered Vera Cruz, Mexico,
Owners - Vera Cruz Coal Company, Mexico.
ON - 136 grt 20 net 84.5 x 20.1 x 10.0 ft.
C.S.C.2Cy. 16''-34''x24'' stroke, 76 nhp by builder.
Trials 27.12.1912. Sailed from Preston 5.1.1913.
Invoice Price £5,957.13.0d.

**459 DUFFO** Twin Screw Gal.Stl. Steam Launch.
Launched 9.11.1912 *66.0bp x 14.0 x 5.9 ft.
Owners - Volta Transport Co. Ltd., London.
2xC.N.C.2Cy. 8''-15''x9'' stroke by builder.
Trials 20.11.1912. Delivered to Liverpool 21.11.1912.
Built for use on the River Volta & Lake Volta, West Africa.

460 **KAMPE** Steel Sternwheel Steamer.
Built 1913 Registered London.
Owners - Niger Co. Ltd., London.
ON 165522 215 grt 97 net 117.0 x 24.3 x 4.7 ft.
C.S.C.2Cy. 13"-28"x42" stroke, 230 ihp by builder.
Built in 9 ft sections and shipped to Nigeria where trials took place on the River
Niger on 5.6.1913. Invoice Price £6,713.

461 **KEBBI** Steel Sternwheel Steamer.
Built 1913 Registered London.
Owners - Niger Co. Ltd., London.
ON 165508 215 grt 97 net 117.0 x 24.3 x 4.7 ft.
C.S.C.2Cy. 13"-28"x42" stroke, 230 ihp by builder.
Built in 9 ft sections and shipped to Nigeria where trials took place on the River
Niger. Invoice Price £6,713.

462 **ELLESMERE** Single Screw Steel Steam Canal Tug.
Launched 26.2.1913 *61.0 x 8.0 x 4.10 ft.
Owners - Bridgewater Colliery and Ellesmere Estate.
C.S.C.2Cy. 7"-15"x9" stroke by builder.
Trials took place on the canal 10.3.1913.

463-5 **UNNAMED** Three Dumb Gal.Stl. Lighters.
Built 1913 60 grt *78.0 x 14.0 x 6.6 ft.
Owners - Niger Co. Ltd., London.

466 **SIR JOHN KIRK** Steel Quarterwheel Steamer.
Launched 22.4.1913 Registered London.
Owners - Niger Co. Ltd., London.
ON 135240 622 grt 472 net 200.0 x 38.1 x 7.6 ft.
2xV.C.S.C.2Cy. 12½"-30"x24" stroke, 70 nhp by builder.
Trials 7.7.1913. Sailed from Preston for Nigeria on 13.7.1913.
Named after a Director of the Niger Company 1900 to 1917.

*CAIRNGARTH lying alongside the yard.*                    *Courtesy K.E. Ingham*

467 **CAIRNGARTH** Single Screw Steel Steam Tug.
Launched 5.7.1913 Registered Liverpool.
Owners - Rea Transport Co. Ltd., Liverpool.
ON 135499 133 grt - net 85.2 x 21.1 x 9.5 ft.
C.S.C.2Cy. 16"-34"x24" stroke, 78 nhp by builder.
Trials 17.9.1913.

468 **PIDDOCK** Steel Dumb Barge.
Launched 16.1.1914 Registered Liverpool.
Owners - Rea Transport Co. Ltd., Liverpool.
ON 135545 167 grt 164 net 100.0 x 21.0 x 9.6 ft.

469 **PICKEREL** Steel Dumb Barge.
Launched 13.12.1913 Registered Liverpool.
Owners - Rea Transport Co. Ltd., Liverpool.
ON 135532 167 grt 164 net 100.0 x 21.0 x 9.6 ft.

470 **PRAWN** Steel Dumb Barge.
Launched 12.1.1914 Registered Liverpool.
Owners - Rea Transport Co. Ltd., Liverpool.
ON 135547 167 grt 164 net 100.0 x 21.0 x 9.6 ft.

471 **GRIBBLE** Steel Dumb Barge.
Launched 2.10.1913 Registered Liverpool.
Owners - Rea Transport Co. Ltd., Liverpool.
ON 135505 167 grt 164 net 100.0 x 21.0 x 9.6 ft.

472 **LING** Steel Dumb Barge.
Launched 13.11.1913 Registered Liverpool.
Owners - Rea Transport Co. Ltd., Liverpool.
ON 135518 167 grt 164 net 100.0 x 21.0 x 9.6 ft.

473 **MACKEREL** Steel Dumb Barge.
Built 1913 Registered Liverpool.
Owners - Rea Transport Co. Ltd., Liverpool.
ON 135520 167 grt 164 net 100.0 x 21.0 x 9.6 ft.

474 **CALBUCO** Single Screw Steel Steam Tug.
Launched 2.8.1913 Registered Liverpool.
Owners - Pacific Steam Navigation Co. Ltd., Liverpool.
ON 135486 55 grt 27 net 62.2 x 15.1 x 7.4 ft.
C.S.C.2Cy. 9"-18"x12" stroke, 14 nhp by builder.
Trials 11.8.1913. Cost £2,700.

475 **HINDIA** Gal.Stl. Sternwheel Steamer.
Built 1913. Delivered in pieces to Liverpool 18.10.1913 by rail.
Owners - Jones, Burton & Co. Ltd., Liverpool, Agents.
ON - *75.0bp x 18.0 x 4.0 ft.
C.N.C.2Cy. 10½"-19"x24" stroke by builder.

476-8 **LIGHTER NO.23-25** Three Steel Dumb Lighters.
Delivered 1913 *50.0bp x 10.0 x 5.0 ft.
Owners - Niger Co. Ltd., London.

479 **13 G.W.R.** Steel Dumb Coal Barge.
Launched 25.2.1914 Registered Liverpool.
Owners - Rea Transport Co. Ltd., Liverpool.
ON 135559 59 net 70.0 x 14.3 x 7.0 ft.

480 **14 G.W.R.** Steel Dumb Coal Barge.
Launched 10.3.1914 Registered Liverpool.
Owners - Rea Transport Co. Ltd., Liverpool.
ON 135558 59 net 70.0 x 14.3 x 7.0 ft.

481 **15 G.W.R.** Steel Dumb Coal Barge.
Launched 10.3.1914 Registered Liverpool.
Owners - Rea Transport Co. Ltd., Liverpool.
ON 135557 59 net 70.0 x 14.3 x 7.0 ft.

482 **WAMBA** Gal.Stl. Sternwheel Steamer.
Built 1914 *60.0bp x 15.6 x 4.0 ft.
Owners - La Societe Anonyme des Huileries du Congo Belge.
C.N.C.2Cy. 9''-16''x30'' stroke by builder.
Shipped in pieces. Trials on the River Congo 6.6.1919.

483 **MAYO** Gal.Stl. Sternwheel Steamer.
Built 1914, shipped in pieces to Nigeria January 1914.
Owners - Niger Co. Ltd., London.
ON - 70 grt 32 net *85.0bp x 17.4 x 4.6 feet.
C.N.C.2Cy. 9''-18''x30'' stroke, 75 ihp by builder.
Later named MAYO UA (165521).

484 **DONGA** Gal.Stl. Sternwheel Steamer.
Built 1914, shipped in pieces to Nigeria in March 1914.
Owners - Niger Co. Ltd., London.
ON - 70 grt 32 net *85.0bp x 17.4 x 4.6 ft.
C.N.C.2Cy. 9''-18''x30'' stroke, 75 ihp by builder.

485-6 **LIGHTER NO.26-27** Two Gal.Stl. Dumb Lighters.
Delivered 1914 *60.0bp x 11.0 x 5.6 ft.
Owners - Niger Co. Ltd., London.

487 **CUERVO** Single Screw Steel Steam Tug.
Launched 28.3.1914 Registered Liverpool.
Owners - Pacific Steam Navigation Co. Ltd., Liverpool.
ON 135570 25 grt 11 net 45.3 x 11.6 x 6.1 ft.
C.S.C.2Cy. 8''-18''x12'' stroke, 13 nhp by builder.
Trials 20.4.1914.

488 **UNNAMED** Steel Dumb Lighter.
Built 1914 *60.0bp x 16.0 x 7.0 ft.
Owners - Arauco Company. Delivered Liverpool by rail 2.4.1914.

489 **MOLUA** Gal.Stl. Sternwheel Steamer.
Built 1914 *60.0bp x 15.6 x 4.0 ft.
Owners - La Societe Anonyme des Huileries du Congo Belge.
C.N.C.2Cy. 9''-16''x30'' stroke by builder.
Shipped to the Congo where trials took place 6.6.1919.

490 **ASHFIELD** Single Screw Steel Cargo Steamer.
Launched 25.7.1914 Registered Liverpool.
Owners - Zillah Shipping & Carrying Co. Ltd., Liverpool.
ON 137401 436 grt 167 net 142.5 x 26.0 x 11.5 ft.
T.E.S.C.3Cy. 14''-22''-38''x24'' stroke, 70 rhp by builder.
Trials 5.10.1914.

491-2 **UNNAMED** Two Gal.Stl. Poling Canoes.
Built 1914 *56.0 x 8.6 x 2.6 ft.
Owners - Crown Agents for the Colonies, Northern Nigeria.
Shipped to Nigeria June 1914.

493-4 **UNNAMED** Two Gal.Stl. Poling Canoes.
Built 1914 *54.2 x 7.8 x 2.6 ft.
Owners - Crown Agents for the Colonies, Northern Nigeria.
Shipped to Nigeria.

495-6 **UNNAMED** Two Gal.Stl. Poling Canoes.
Built 1914 *52.6 x 6.10 x 2.6 ft.
Owners - Crown Agents for the Colonies, Northern Nigeria.
Shipped to Nigeria.

*ASHFIELD.*

**497-8  NO.14-15** Two Gal.Stl. Poling Canoes.
Built 1914 *55.0bp x 7.6 x 2.3 ft.
Owners - J. Holt & Co. Ltd., Liverpool.
Shipped to Nigeria July 1914.

**499-504  UNNAMED** Six Swim Ended Steel Dumb Barges.
Built 1914 *103.0 x 26.0 x 6.0 ft.
Owners - Crown Agents for the Colonies, Uganda.
Cost £795 each. Shipped June 1914 in pieces.

**505  BATOE RADJA** Gal.Stl. Sternwheel Steamer.
Built 1914 and delivered to Liverpool in pieces by rail.
Owners - Jones, Burton & Co. Ltd., Liverpool, Agents.
ON - *75.0bp x 16.0 x 4.0 ft.
C.N.C.2Cy. 10½"-19"x24" stroke by builder.

**506  ENGENNI** Twin Screw Steel Steam Launch.
Launched 24.9.1914 *66.0bp x 14.0 x 5.6 ft.
Owners - J. Holt & Co. Ltd., Liverpool.
2xC.N.C.2Cy. 8"-15"x9" stroke by builder. Trials 8.10.1914.

*ENGENNI.*

507 **KLINGI** Gal.Stl. Sternwheel Steamer.
Built 1914 and delivered to Liverpool in pieces by rail.
Owners - Jones, Burton & Co. Ltd., Liverpool, Agents.
ON - *75.0bp x 18.0 x 4.0 ft.
C.N.C.2Cy. 10½"-19"x24" stroke by builder.

SILVERFIELD.                                    World Ship Photo Library

508 **SILVERFIELD** Single Screw Steel Cargo Steamer.
Launched 2.2.1915 Registered Liverpool.
Owners - Zillah Shipping & Carrying Co. Ltd., Liverpool.
ON 137436 436 grt 165 net 142.5 x 26.0 x 11.5 ft.
T.E.S.C.3Cy. 14"-22"-38"x24" stroke, 88 rhp by builder.
Trials 1.4.1915.

509 **A.54** Single Screw Gal.Stl. Steam Launch.
Launched 23.10.1914
Owners - The War Office, London.
ON - 39 grt 5 net *64.0bp x 13.0 x 5.9 ft.
C.S.C.2Cy. 9"-20"x14" stroke by builder.
Trials 22.12.1914 & 6.1.1915. Requisitioned on the stocks whilst building for the
African Transport Co., as the PIONEER.

510 **ABO** Single Screw Gal.Stl. Steam Launch.
Launched 22.10.1914
Owners - J. Holt & Co. Ltd., Liverpool.
ON - 39 grt 5 net *64.0bp x 13.0 x 5.9 ft.
C.S.C.2Cy. 8½"-20"x14" stroke by builder.
Trials 15.12.1914. Named after a township on the River Niger.

511 **NEDERLAND** Gal.Stl. Sternwheel Steamer.
Built 1914 and delivered to Liverpool in pieces by rail.
Owners - Jones, Burton & Co. Ltd., Liverpool, Agents.
ON - *75.0bp x 18.0 x 4.0 ft.
C.N.C.2Cy. 10½"-19"x24" stroke by builder.

512-513 no record.

514  **DANEGARTH** Single Screw Steel Steam Tug.
Launched 18.3.1915 Registered Bristol.
Owners - Rea Transport Co. Ltd., Liverpool.
ON 134708 139 grt - net 85.0 x 21.2 x 9.6 ft.
C.S.C.2Cy. 16"-34"x24" stroke, 80 rhp by builder.
Trials 15 & 21.5.1915.

515  **GRAYGARTH** Single Screw Steel Steam Tug.
Launched 28.6.1915 Registered Southampton.
Owners - Rea Transport Co. Ltd., Liverpool.
ON 135691 139 grt - net 85.0 x 21.2 x 9.6 ft.
C.S.C.2Cy. 16"-34"x24" stroke, 80 rhp by builder.
Trials 10.9.1915.

*ABO, see opposite.*

516  **AXE** Steel Schooner Rigged Coal Barge.
Launched 9.10.1915 Registered Bristol.
Owners - Rea Transport Co. Ltd., Liverpool.
ON 134713 342 grt 297 net 125.2 x 24.0 x 11.9 ft.
Later name AIREDALE.

517  **A.101** Single Screw Steel Steam Tug.
Launched 24.1.1916, trials 10.3.1916.
Owners - The War Office, Inland Waterway Transport Department.
ON - 51 grt 9 net 65.0 x 15.0 x 7.5 ft.
C.S.C.2Cy. 9"-18"x15" stroke, 200 ihp by builder.
Originally built for the L. & Y. Railway Company for work as a tug at Fleetwood.
Requisitioned by the War Office for Estuary work. Later names HS.10 and
LANDY (ON.141948).

518  **LIMESFIELD** Single Screw Steel Cargo Steamer.
Launched 4.3.1916 Registered Liverpool.
Owners - Zillah Shipping & Carrying Co. Ltd., Liverpool.
ON 137523 427 grt 160 net 142.2 x 26.0 x 11.5 ft.
T.E.S.C.3Cy. 14"-22"-38"x24" stroke, 88 rhp by builder.
Trials 28.10.1916. Sunk by submarine off the Isle of Man 7.2.1918.

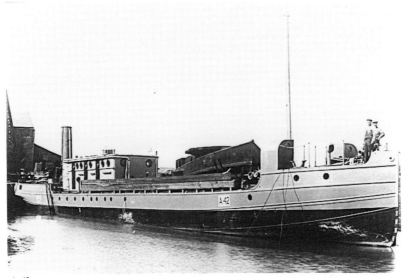

*A.42*

519 **A.42** Twin Screw Steel Telegraph Repair S.S.
Launched 1.4.1915, trials 18.4.1915.
Owners - The War Office, London.
ON - 135 grt 107 net*124.0 x 16.2 x 7.6 ft.
2xC.S.C.2Cy. 9"-18"x15" stroke by builder.

520 **TANA** Single Screw Steel Steam Launch.
Launched 7.9.1917 *45.0bp x 9.0 x 2.9 ft.
Owners - Crown Agents for the Colonies, Kenya.
C.S.C.2Cy. 5¾"-12"x7" stroke by builder.
Trials 31.10.1917. Delivered to Liverpool by rail 13.12.1917.
Named after the River Tana in Kenya which is the only river navigable in this
territory but not for all its length.

521 **A.44** Twin Screw Steel Steam Tug.
Launched 30.6.1915, trials 16.7.1915.
Owners - The War Office, London.
ON - 56 grt - net *68.6bp x 15.0 x 7.0 ft.
2xC.S.C.2Cy. 8"-18"x12" stroke, 160 ihp by builder.

522 **A.45** Twin Screw Steel Steam Tug.
Launched 15.7.1915, trials 13.8.1915.
Owners - The War Office, London.
ON - 56 grt - net *68.6bp x 15.0 x 7.0 ft.
2xC.S.C.2Cy. 8"-18"x12" stroke, 160 ihp by builder.

523 **A.46** Twin Screw Steel Steam Tug.
Launched 28.7.1915, trials 23.9.1915.
Owners - The War Office, London.
ON - 56 grt - net *68.6bp x 15.0 x 7.0 ft.
2xC.S.C.2Cy. 8"-18"x12" stroke, 160 ihp by builder.

524   **A.47** Twin Screw Steel Steam Tug.
Launched 26.8.1915, trials 8.10.1915.
Owners - The War Office, London.
ON - 56 grt - net *68.6bp x 15.0 x 7.0 ft.
2xC.S.C.2Cy. 8"-18"x12" stroke, 160 ihp by builder.

*A.48*

525   **A.48** Twin Screw Steel Steam Tug.
Launched 10.9.1915, trials 26.10.1915.
Owners - The War Office, London.
ON - 56 grt - net *68.6bp x 15.0 x 7.0 ft.
2xC.S.C.2Cy. 8"-18"x12" stroke, 160 ihp by builder.

526   **A.49** Twin Screw Steel Steam Tug.
Launched 23.9.1915, trials 11.11.1915.
Owners - The War Office, London.
ON - 56 grt - net *68.6bp x 15.0 x 7.0 ft.
2xC.S.C.2Cy. 8"-18"x12" stroke, 160 ihp by builder.
Two of the above six vessels were renamed BAYSWATER and KILBURN.

527   **A.459** Steel Dumb Barge.
Launched 3.7.1916 *126.0bp x 16.3½ x 7.6 ft.
Owners - The War Office, Inland Waterway Transport Department.

528   **A.460** Steel Dumb Barge.
Launched 15.7.1916 *126.0bp x 16.3½ x 7.6 ft.
Owners - The War Office, Inland Waterway Transport Department.

529   **A.461** Steel Dumb Barge.
Launched 31.8.1916 *126.0bp x 16.3½ x 7.6 ft.
Owners - The War Office, Inland Waterway Transport Department.

530   **A.462** Steel Dumb Barge.
Launched 31.8.1916 *126.0bp x 16.3½ x 7.6 ft.
Owners - The War Office, Inland Waterway Transport Department.

*A.S.104*

531 **A.S.104** Twin Screw Steel Steam Tug.
Launched 3.4.1916, trials 27.5.1916.
Owners - The War Office, Inland Waterway Transport Department.
ON - 69 grt - net *75.0bp x 15.0 x 7.0 ft.
2xC.S.C.2Cy. 8"-18"x12" stroke by builder.

532 **A.S.105** Twin Screw Steel Steam Tug.
Launched 20.4.1916, trials 13.6.1916.
Owners - The War Office, Inland Waterway Transport Department.
ON - 69 grt - net *75.0bp x 15.0 x 7.0 ft.
2xC.S.C.2Cy. 8"-18"x12" stroke by builder.

533 **A.S.106** Twin Screw Steel Steam Tug.
Launched 18.5.1916, trials 11.7.1916.
Owners - The War Office, Inland Waterway Transport Department.
ON - 69 grt - net *75.0bp x 15.0 x 7.0 ft.
2xC.S.C.2Cy. 8"-18"x12" stroke by builder.
Later name CRAIG (ON.145143). Sank 10.4.1925 at Sierra Leone.

534 **A.S.107** Twin Screw Steel Steam Tug.
Launched 19.5.1916, trials 2.8.1916.
Owners - The War Office, Inland Waterway Transport Department.
ON - 69 grt - net *75.0bp x 15.0 x 7.0 ft.
2xC.S.C.2Cy. 8"-18"x12" stroke by builder.
Later name ORON (ON.143632). Sold 1920 to The Nigerian Transport Co. Ltd.,
Liverpool & registered at Liverpool.

535 **A.S.142** Twin Screw Steel Steam Tug.
Launched 22.2.1917, trials 4.4.1917.
Owners - The War Office, Inland Waterway Transport Department.
ON - 69 grt - net *75.0bp x 15.0 x 7.0 ft.
2xC.S.C.2Cy. 8"-18"x12" stroke by builder.
Later names SPALDING (ON.146475), SAINT BREANDUN, NAOMH BREANDUN
and KALISCO.

536 **A.S.143** Twin Screw Steel Steam Tug.
Launched 22.2.1917, trials 22.4.1917.
Owners - The War Office, Inland Waterway Transport Department.
ON - 69 grt - net *75.0bp x 15.0 x 7.0 ft.
2xC.S.C.2Cy. 8"-18"x12" stroke by builder.
Later name TABE (ON.147262).

537 Yard number cancelled and not used.

538  **HS.15** Twin Screw Steel Steam Tug.
Launched 25.11.1916, trials 8.1.1917.
Owners - The War Office, Inland Waterway Transport Department.
ON - 144 grt 29 net 85.5 x 22.1 x 8.9 ft.
2xC.S.C.2Cy. 10½"-24"x18" stroke, 400 bhp by builder.
Later name M.S.C. MANCHESTER (ON.147416).

539  **HS.16** Twin Screw Steel Steam Tug.
Launched 30.11.1916, trials 28.2.1917.
Owners - The War Office, Inland Waterway Transport Department.
ON - 144 grt 29 net 85.5 x 22.1 x 8.9 ft.
2xC.S.C.2Cy. 10½"-24"x18" stroke, 400 bhp by builder.
Later names M.S.C. SALFORD (ON.147418) and SALGARTH.

540  **HS.17** Twin Screw Steel Steam Tug.
Launched 30.12.1916, trials 24.3.1917.
Owners - The War Office, Inland Waterway Transport Department.
ON - 144 grt 29 net 85.5 x 22.1 x 8.9 ft.
2xC.S.C.2Cy. 10½"-24"x18" stroke, 400 bhp by builder.
Later names M.S.C. RUNCORN (ON.147417) and RUNGARTH.

*HS.18*

541  **HS.18** Twin Screw Steel Steam Tug.
Launched 19.5.1917, trials 4.7.1917.
Owners - The War Office, Inland Waterway Transport Department.
ON - 144 grt 29 net 85.5 x 22.1 x 8.9 ft.
2xC.S.C.2Cy. 10½"-24"x18" stroke, 400 bhp by builder.
Later names M.S.C. ELLESMERE PORT (ON.147415) and ELLESGARTH.

542-7  **A.C.1019-1024** Six Dumb Steel Ammunition Barges.
Delivered between 12.10.1916 and 16.3.1917.
Owners - The War Office, Inland Waterway Transport Department.
Holds lined with pinewood.*124.0bp x 16.4 x 7.9 ft.

*S.40, boarded up for her voyage to Basra.*

548  **S.40** Steel Quarterwheel River Steamer.
Launched 21.4.1917, trials 3.7.1917.
Owners - The War Office, Inland Waterway Transport Department.
ON - 299 grt 128 net*150.0bp x 33.0 x 6.0 ft.
2xC.S.C.2Cy. 13"-28"x54" stroke by builder.
Sailed from Preston 21.7.1917 and arrived Basra 21.10.1917.

549  **S.41** Steel Quarterwheel River Steamer.
Built 1917, dismantled and sent to Basra in pieces.
Owners - The War Office, Inland Waterway Transport Department.
ON - 299 grt 128 net*150.0bp x 33.0 x 6.0 ft.
2xC.S.C.2Cy. 13"-28"x54" stroke by builder.

550  **S.42** Steel Quarterwheel River Steamer.
Built 1917, dismantled and sent to Basra in pieces.
Owners - The War Office, Inland Waterway Transport Department.
ON - 299 grt 128 net*150.0bp x 33.0 x 6.0 ft.
2xC.S.C.2Cy. 13"-28"x54" stroke by builder.

551  **S.43** Steel Quarterwheel River Steamer.
Built 1917, dismantled and sent to Basra in pieces.
Owners - The War Office, Inland Waterway Transport Department.
ON 299 grt 128 net*150.0bp x 33.0 x 6.0 ft.
2xC.S.C.2Cy. 13"-28"x54" stroke by builder.

552  **S.61** Steel Quarterwheel River Steamer.
Built 1917, dismantled and sent to Basra in pieces.
Owners - The War Office, Inland Waterway Transport Department.
ON - 299 grt 128 net*150.0bp x 33.0 x 6.0 ft.
2xC.S.C.2Cy. 13"-28"x54" stroke by builder.

The above five vessels, Yard Nos. 548 to 552 inclusive, were built for use as Hospital Ships on the River Tigris. One of them was acquired by the Irrawady Flotilla Co. Ltd., Rangoon in 1929 and renamed CANMORESK.

553-8  **A.C.1086-1091** Six Steel Dumb Ammunition Barges.
Delivered between 31.7.1917 and 10.9.1917.
Owners - The War Office, Inland Waterway Transport Department.
Holds lined with pinewood.*124.0bp x 16.4 x 7.9 ft.


559  **A.S.145** Single Screw Steel Steam Tug.
Launched 15.12.1917, trials 30.1.1918.
Owners - The War Office, Inland Waterway Transport Department.
ON - 60 grt - net *75.0bp x 15.0 x 7.6 ft.
C.S.C.2Cy. 10½"-24"x18" stroke, 25 nhp by builder.


560  **A.S.146** Single Screw Steel Steam Tug.
Launched 18.12.1917, trials 12.2.1918.
Owners - The War Office, Inland Waterway Transport Department.
ON - 60 grt - net *75.0bp x 15.0 x 7.6 ft.
C.S.C.2Cy. 10½"-24"x18" stroke, 25 nhp by builder.


561  **A.S.147** Single Screw Steel Steam Tug.
Launched 26.1.1918, trials 2.3.1918.
Owners - The War Office, Inland Waterway Transport Department.
ON - 60 grt - net *75.0bp x 15.0 x 7.6 ft.
C.S.C.2Cy. 10½"-24"x18" stroke, 25 nhp by builder.


562  **A.S.148** Single Screw Steel Steam Tug.
Launched 31.1.1918, trials 26.3.1918.
Owners - The War Office, Inland Waterway Transport Department.
ON - 60 grt - net *75.0bp x 15.0 x 7.6 ft.
C.S.C.2Cy. 10½"-24"x18" stroke, 25 nhp by builder.


563  **A.S.149** Single Screw Steel Steam Tug.
Launched 16.2.1918, trials 24.4.1918.
Owners - The War Office, Inland Waterway Transport Department.
ON - 60 grt - net *75.0bp x 15.0 x 7.6 ft.
C.S.C.2Cy. 10½"-24"x18" stroke, 25 nhp by builder.


564  **A.S.150** Single Screw Steel Steam Tug.
Launched 12.3.1918, trials 30.4.1918.
Owners - The War Office, Inland Waterway Transport Department.
ON - 60 grt - net *75.0bp x 15.0 x 7.6 ft.
C.S.C.2Cy. 10½"-24"x18" stroke, 25 nhp by builder.


Three of the above six vessels were renamed BRIDGENESS, PATSY and
STAMFORD.


565  **HS.80** Single Screw Steel Steam Tug.
Launched 18.6.1919, trials 6.2.1920.
Owners - The War Office, Inland Waterway Transport Department.
ON - 123 grt - net *85.0bp x 21.0 x 11.0 ft.
C.S.C.2Cy. 15"-33"x24" stroke, 43 nhp by builder.
Later named FERROLANO in Spanish Navy.


566  **HS.81** Single Screw Steel Steam Tug.
Launched 26.8.1919, trials 20.2.1920.
Owners - The War Office, Inland Waterway Transport Department.
ON - 123 grt - net *85.0bp x 21.0 x 11.0 ft.
C.S.C.2Cy. 15"-33"x24" stroke, 43 nhp by builder.
Later named CASTAGENERO in Spanish Navy.

*HS.82*

567  **HS.82** Single Screw Steel Steam Tug.
Launched 9.10.1919, trials 8.3.1920.
Owners - The War Office, Inland Waterway Transport Department.
ON - 123 grt - net *85.0bp x 21.0 x 11.0 ft.
C.S.C.2Cy. 15"-33"x24" stroke, 43 nhp by builder.
Later named GADITANO in Spanish Navy.

568  **HS.83** Single Screw Steel Steam Tug.
Launched 9.6.1920.
Owners - The War Office, Inland Waterway Transport Department.
ON - 123 grt - net *85.0bp x 21.0 x 11.0 ft.
C.S.C.2Cy. 15"-33"x24" stroke, 43 nhp by builder.
Later names AVYLOS and VERNICOS VARVARA.

569  **E.T.7** Twin Screw Steel Steam Tunnel Tug.
Launched 28.5.1918, trials 6.7.1918.
Owners - The Admiralty, London.
ON - 224 grt 88 net*130.0bp x 26.0 x 7.0 ft.
2xC.S.C.2Cy. 11"-23"x15" stroke by builder.
Sailed from Preston 18.7.1918 and arrived Alexandria 8.9.1918.
Distance steamed 3276 n.m. Actual steaming time 17.6 days.
Later named MISR in Egypt.

*E.T.8 boarded up for her delivery voyage. Note the gun aft.*

570  **E.T.8** Twin Screw Steel Steam Tunnel Tug.
Launched 30.6.1918, trials 23.9.1918.
Owners - The Admiralty, London.
ON - 224 grt 88 net*130.0bp x 26.0 x 7.0 ft.
2xC.S.C.2Cy. 11"-23"x15" stroke by builder.
Delivered to Plymouth.

*E.T.10 as SWORD DANCE during Baltic Operations in 1919.*
*Imperial War Museum, negative no. SP2323.*

571  **E.T.10** Twin Screw Steel Steam Tunnel Tug.
Launched 28.7.1918, trials 29.1.1919.
Owners - The Admiralty, London.
ON - 224 grt 88 net*130.0bp x 26.0 x 7.0 ft.
2xC.S.C.2Cy. 11"-23"x15" stroke by builder.
Converted to a Minesweeper by builder and named SWORD DANCE.

572  **E.T.11** Twin Screw Steel Steam Tunnel Tug.
Launched 21.10.1918, trials 10.4.1919.
Owners - The Admiralty, London.
ON - 224 grt 88 net*130.0bp x 26.0 x 7.0 ft.
2xC.S.C.2Cy. 11"-23"x15" stroke by builder.
Converted to a Minesweeper by builder and named STEP DANCE.

*E.T.11, renamed STEP DANCE, boarded up for her delivery voyage.*

573  **T.98** Twin Screw Steel Steam Tunnel Tug.
Launched 4.3.1919, trials 15.4.1919.
Owners - The Admiralty, London.
ON - 224 grt 88 net*130.0bp x 26.0 x 7.0 ft.
2xC.S.C.2Cy. 11"-23"x15" stroke by builder.
Converted to a Minesweeper by builder and named FANDANGO.

*T.99 as MORRIS DANCE in the Dvina River 24.6.1919, towing two Seaplane lighters.*
*Imperial War Museum, negative no. SP2401*

574  **T.99** Twin Screw Steel Steam Tunnel Tug.
Launched 31.3.1919, trials 11.4.1919.
Owners - The Admiralty, London.
ON - 224 grt 88 net*130.0bp x 26.0 x 7.0 ft.
2xC.S.C.2Cy. 11"-23"x15" stroke by builder.
Converted to a Minesweeper by builder and named MORRIS DANCE.
Later named ELVIRA when sold to Mexican interests in 1920.

*ST. FAGAN.*                                          *Wright & Logan Ltd.*

575  **ST. FAGAN** Single Screw Steel Rescue Steam Tug.
Launched 21.9.1918. Registered London.
Owners - The Admiralty, London.
ON 143309 420 grt 12 net 135.2 x 29.1 x 13.6 ft.
T.E.S.C.3Cy. 18¼"-28½"-48¼"x28" stroke, 1200 ihp by builder.

576　**ST. FAITH** Single Screw Steel Rescue Steam Tug.
Launched 19.12.1918. Registered London.
Owners - The Admiralty, London.
ON 143397 414 grt 11 net 135.3 x 29.1 x 13.6 ft.
T.E.S.C.3Cy. 18¼"-28½"-48¼"x28" stroke, 1200 ihp by builder.
Later names HAIDA MONARCH, LE BEAU, UNIT SHIPPER, KILLARNEY and
S.D.BROOKS.


577　**ST. HILARY** Single Screw Steel Rescue Steam Tug.
Launched 28.7.1919 Registered London.
Owners - The Admiralty, London.
ON 143778 414 grt 11 net 135.3 x 29.1 x 13.6 ft.
T.E.S.C.3Cy. 18¼"-28½"-48¼"x28" stroke, 1200 ihp by builder.


578　**GLENAGEARY** Single Screw Steel Cargo Steamer.
Launched 21.2.1920 Registered Dublin.
Owners - Alliance and Dublin Consumers Gas Company.
ON 140469 446 grt 170 net 142.0 x 25.8 x 11.5 ft.
T.E.S.C.3Cy. 14"-22"-38"x24" stroke, 480 ihp by builder.
Trials 20.5.1920.

*BRIARFIELD.*　　　　　　　　　　　　　　*World Ship Photo Library*


579　**BRIARFIELD** Single Screw Steel Cargo Steamer.
Launched 20.5.1920 Registered Liverpool.
Owners - Zillah Shipping & Carrying Co. Ltd., Liverpool.
ON 143663 446 grt 172 net 142.2 x 26.0 x 11.5 ft.
T.E.S.C.3Cy. 14"-22"-38"x24" stroke, 480 ihp by builder.
Trials 13.9.1920.

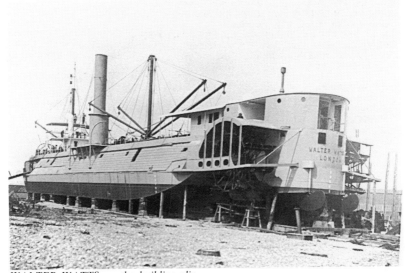

*WALTER WATTS on the building slip.*

580  **WALTER WATTS** Steel Quarterwheel River Steamer.
Launched 26.7.1922 Registered London.
Owners - Niger Co. Ltd., London.
ON 146603 753 grt 466 net 216.8 x 38.0 x 7.9 ft
2xV.C.S.C.2Cy. 12½''-30''x24'' stroke, 700 ihp by Cammell Laird & Co. Ltd.,
Birkenhead.
Trials 11.8.1922, sailed from Preston 18.8.1922 and arrived at Lagos 15.9.1922.
Named after the Agent General of the Niger Co. Ltd., who served from 1900 to
1914.

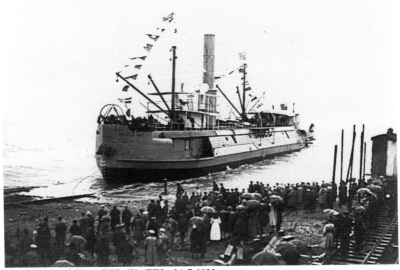

*The launch of WALTER WATTS, 26.7.1922.*

581 **DAVID McINTOSH** Twin Screw Steel River Steamer.
Launched 24.12.1919 Registered London.
Owners - Niger Co. Ltd., London.
ON 144648 449 grt 249 net 154.1 x 29.1 x 9.9 ft.
2xC.S.C.2cy. 12½"-28"x18" stroke, 500 ihp by builder.
Trials 24.7.1920. Named after the Agent General of the Royal Niger Co. Chartered
& Ltd., from 1886 until he died in 1888.

582 **INSULINDE** Gal.Stl. Sternwheel Steamer.
Shipped in pieces 1920 *75.0bp x 18.0 x 4.0 ft.
Owners - Jones, Burton & Co. Ltd., Liverpool, Agents.
C.N.C.2Cy. 10½"-19"x24" stroke by builder.

583 **PAGER-ALAM** Gal.Stl. Sternwheel Steamer.
Shipped in pieces 1920 *75.0bp x 18.0 x 4.0. ft.
Owners - Jones, Burton & Co. Ltd., Liverpool, Agents.
C.N.C.2Cy. 10½"-19"x24" stroke by builder.

584 **ELLEN** Gal.Stl. Sternwheel Steamer.
Built 1920 *70.0bp x 16.0 x 4.0 ft.
Owners - Jones, Burton & Co. Ltd., Liverpool, Agents.
C.N.C.2Cy. 10½"-19"x24" stroke by builder.
Shipped 26.11.1920 in 135 pieces and cases & one case machinery.

585-6 **BARGE NO.38-39** Two Gal.Stl. Dumb Barges.
Built 1920 *80.0bp x 15.0 x 6.6 ft.
Owners - Niger Co. Ltd., London.
Left 24.7.1920 for delivery in the hold of T.S. DAVID McINTOSH.

*NUPE at Preston in 7.1921.*

587 **NUPE** Twin Screw Steel River Steamer.
Launched 9.4.1921 Registered London.
Owners - Niger Co. Ltd., London.
ON 145261 297 grt 193 net 136.0 x 24.1 x 8.8 ft.
2xC.S.C.2Cy. 9"-22"x15" stroke, 32 nhp by builder.
Trials 10.7.1921, sailed from Preston 26.7.1921 and arrived at Lagos 25.8.1921 a
distance of 4120 nautical miles. Named after the territory of Nupe, an ancient
Kingdom in Nigeria.

588 **UDI** Twin Screw Steel River Steamer.
Launched 14.3.1922 Registered London.
Owners - Niger Co. Ltd., London.
ON 146624 289 grt 188 net 136.0 x 24.1 x 8.8 ft.
2xC.S.C.2Cy. 9"-22"x15" stroke, 300 ihp by builder.
Trials 7.9.1922, sailed from Preston 10.9.1922 via Las Palmas.
Named after a coal mining township in Southern Nigeria.

589 **JAMES FENTON** Single Screw Gal.Stl. Steam Launch.
Launched 27.11.1920 *45.0bp x 10.0 x 5.0 ft.
Owners - African Oil Nuts Co. Ltd., London.
C.S.C.2Cy. 7"-15"x9" stroke by builder.
Hull built by MacLaren Brothers, Dumbarton & erected at Lytham.
Trials 4.5.1921, sailed to Liverpool 1.6.1921 for shipment.

*BEECHFIELD.*                    *World Ship Photo Library*

590 **BEECHFIELD** Single Screw Steel Cargo Steamer.
Launched 17.11.1921 Registered Liverpool.
Owners - Zillah Shipping & Carrying Co. Ltd., Liverpool.
ON 145912 449 grt 175 net 142.0 x 25.9 x 11.4 ft.
T.E.S.C.3Cy. 14"-22"-38"x24" stroke, 71 rhp by builder.
Trials 30.1.1922. Invoice price £32,000.

591 no record

592 **JEKRIMAN** Single Screw Gal.Stl. Steam Launch.
Trials 27.7.1921 *45.0bp x 10.0 x 5.0 ft.
Owners - Miller Brothers Ltd., Liverpool.
C.S.C.2Cy. 7"-15"x9" stroke by builder.
Hull built by MacLaren Brothers, Dumbarton & erected at Lytham.
Sailed to Liverpool 28.7.1921 for shipment.

593 **LAUNCH NO.9** Single Screw Gal.Stl. Steam Launch.
Trials 21.12.1921 *45.0bp x 10.0 x 5.0 ft.
Owners - Niger Co. Ltd., London.
C.S.C.2Cy. 7"-15"x9" stroke by builder.
Hull built by MacLaren Brothers, Dumbarton & erected at Lytham.
Sailed via the River Douglas and the canal from Tarleton to Liverpool for
shipment. The Niger Company commissioned this vessel as a present for a
Niger Chief.

594 **VOLTAMAN** Twin Screw Steel Steamer.
Launched 23.4.1921 Registered London.
Owners - African & Eastern Trade Corporation Ltd., London.
ON 146091 605 grt 395 net 180.0 x 32.1 x 10.7 ft.
2xT.E.S.C.3Cy. 11"-17¼"-29"x22" stroke, 84 rhp by builder.
Trials 15.9.1921. Named after the River & Lake Volta on the Gold Coast, where
the company operated a ferry service.

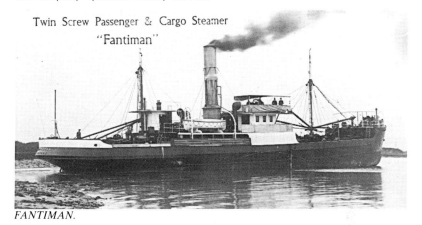

Twin Screw Passenger & Cargo Steamer
"Fantiman"

*FANTIMAN.*

595 **FANTIMAN** Twin Screw Steel Steamer.
Launched 5.1.1924 Registered London.
Owners - African & Eastern Trade Corporation Ltd., London.
ON 147598 647 grt 402 net 180.0 x 32.1 x 10.7 ft.
2xT.E.S.C.3Cy. 11"-17¼"-29"x22" stroke, 84 rhp by builder.
Trials 19.3.1924. Named after the Fanti Tribe who lived on the Gold Coast. Both
594 & 595 were cargo passenger vessels.

596 **POLITA** Twin Screw Steel Motor Barge.
Launched 14.10.1920 Registered Chester.
Owners - J. Summers & Sons Ltd., Shotton, Flints.
ON 145691 109 grt 45 net 99.3 x 16.4 x 7.3 ft
Two 2Cy.2S.C.S.A. Oil Engines 10⅝"x11" stroke, 50 bhp by J. och C. G.
Bolinders Mekaniska Verksted, Stockholm, Sweden.

597 **DORITA** Twin Screw Steel Motor Barge.
Launched 12.10.1920 Registered Chester.
Owners - J. Summers & Sons Ltd., Shotton, Flints.
ON 145690 109 grt 45 net 99.3 x 16.4 x 7.3 ft
Two 2Cy.2S.C.S.A. Oil Engines 10⅝"x11" stroke, 50 bhp by J. och C. G.
Bolinders Mekaniska Verksted, Stockholm, Sweden.

598 **CARMENITA** Twin Screw Steel Motor Barge.
Launched 29.10.1920 Registered Chester.
Owners - J. Summers & Sons Ltd., Shotton, Flints.
ON 145695 109 grt 45 net 99.3 x 16.4 x 7.3 ft.
Two 2Cy.2S.C.S.A. Oil Engines 10⅝"x11" stroke, 50 bhp by J. och C. G.
Bolinders Mekaniska Verksted, Stockholm, Sweden.

599 **ALITA** Twin Screw Steel Motor Barge.
Launched 12.11.1920 Registered Chester.
Owners - J. Summers & Sons Ltd., Shotton, Flints.
ON 145697 109 grt 45 net 99.3 x 16.4 x 7.3 ft
Two 2Cy.2S.C.S.A. Oil Engines 10⅝"x11" stroke, 50 bhp by J. och C. G.
Bolinders Mekaniska Verksted, Stockholm, Sweden.

**600 GLENCULLEN** Single Screw Steel Cargo Steamer.
Launched 5.8.1921 Registered Dublin.
Owners - Alliance and Dublin Consumers Gas Company.
ON 144974 448 grt 176 net 142.7 x 26.0 x 11.5 ft.
T.E.S.C.3Cy. 14''-22''-38''x24'' stroke, 71 rhp by builder.
Trials 18.10.1921.

**601 OFFIN** Single Screw Steel Steam Launch.
Launched 24.3.1921 *60.0bp x 14.0 x 6.9 ft.
Owners - F. & A. Swanzy Ltd., London.
C.S.C.2Cy. 9''-18''x15'' stroke by builder.
Trials 17.10.1921. Cost £5,141.

**602 BURTON** Gal.Stl. Sternwheel Steamer.
Launched 29.11.1921, trials 7.12.1921.
Owners - J. Holt & Co. Ltd., Liverpool.
ON - 84 grt 53 net *85.0bp x 17.4 x 4.6 ft.
C.N.C.2Cy. 9''-18''x30'' stroke by builder.
Invoice Price £6,741.13.4d. Left Lytham on 10.12.1921 for Liverpool in tow of
YEWGARTH for shipment. Named after Sir Richard Francis Burton, consul and
explorer and one time companion of J. H. Speke. He died in 1890 at Trieste.

**603 GRANGE** Gal.Stl. Sternwheel Steamer.
Launched 11.2.1922, trials 27.2.1922.
Owners - J. Holt & Co. Ltd., Liverpool.
ON 84 grt 53 net *85.0bp x 17.4 x 4.6 ft.
C.N.C.2Cy. 9''-18''x30'' stroke by builder.
Invoice Price £6,741.13.4d. Left Lytham on 6.3.1922 for
Liverpool in tow of OVERGARTH for shipment.

**604 LUDDINGTON** Gal.Stl. Sternwheel Steamer.
Launched 14.2.1922, trials 6.3.1922.
Owners - J. Holt & Co. Ltd., Liverpool.
ON - 84 grt 53 net *85.0bp x 17.4 x 4.6 ft.
C.N.C.2Cy. 9''-18''x30'' stroke by builder.
Invoice Price £6,741.13.4d. Left Lytham 14.3.1922 in tow for shipment from
Liverpool.

*GORSEFIELD.*          *World Ship Photo Library*

**605 GORSEFIELD** Single Screw Steel Cargo Steamer.
Launched 21.10.1922 Registered Liverpool.
Owners - Zillah Shipping & Carrying Co. Ltd., Liverpool.
ON 147177 628 grt 250 net 175.0 x 28.2 x 11.2 ft.
T.E.S.C.3Cy. 14''-22''-38''x24'' stroke, 71 rhp by builder.
Trials 20.12.1922. Invoice Price £35,000.

606  **ESPERANCA** Steel Dumb Lighter.
Launched 6.10.1922 Cost £832.
Owners - Booth Steamship Co. Ltd., Liverpool.
ON - 42 grt - net *60.0bp x 15.0 x 5.6 ft.

607-612  **UNNAMED** Six Gal.Stl. Poling Canoes.
Built 1922 *55.0bp x 8.3 x 2.6 ft.
Owners - J. Holt & Co. Ltd., Liverpool.
Total Cost of the six £2,958.7.5½d. Invoice Price £675 each.
Delivered to Liverpool by rail, 2 on 11.9. & 4 on 30.11.1922.

*CARBO.*

613  **CARBO** Single Screw Steel Cargo Steamer.
Launched 18.1.1923 Registered Liverpool.
Owners - Joseph Crosfield & Sons Ltd., Warrington.
ON 147198 155 grt 80 net 93.3 x 22.1 x 8.3 ft.
C.S.C.2Cy. 10½''-24''x18'' stroke, 23 nhp by builder.
Trials 16.2.1923. Cost £4,893.

614  **UNNAMED** Gal.Stl. Poling Canoe.
Built 1922 *55.0bp x 8.3 x 2.6 ft.
Owners - T. Welsh & Co. Ltd., Liverpool.
Delivered to Liverpool by rail on 27.12.1922.

615-620  **SURF BOATS 1-6** Six Gal.Stl. Surf Boats.
Built 1922 23 cwt d.w. *21.8bp x 6.10 x 3.0 ft.
Owners - African & Eastern Trade Corporation Ltd., London.
Delivered to Liverpool by rail on 5 & 6.10.1922.

621  **UNNAMED** Steel Dumb Barge.
Launched 19.12.1922 *87.3bp x 16.4 x 7.9 ft.
Owners - African & Eastern Trade Corporation Ltd., London.
Left Lytham for Liverpool in tow 1.1.1923.

622 **UNNAMED** Steel Dumb Barge.
Launched 4.5.1923 *87.3bp x 16.4 x 7.9 ft.
Owners - African & Eastern Trade Corporation Ltd., London.
Left Lytham for Liverpool in tow 8.5.1923.

623 **G.C.H.1** Steel Bascule Type Dumb Tipping Barge.
Launched 5.4.1923 *130.0bp x 29.0 x 7.6 ft.
Owners - Crown Agents for the Colonies, Gold Coast.
Trials 15.4.1923. Cost £3,875.

624 **G.C.H.2** Steel Bascule Type Dumb Tipping Barge.
Launched 18.5.1923 *130.0bp x 29.0 x 7.6 ft.
Owners - Crown Agents for the Colonies, Gold Coast.
Cost £3,875. Both 623 and 624 left Lytham on 28.6.1923 for Takoradi on the Gold
Coast, West Africa, in tow of S.T. HUDSON.

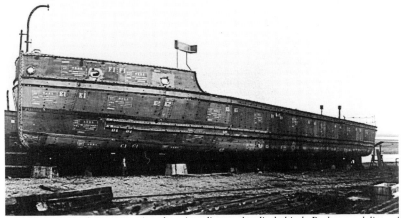

*G.C.H. 3 or 4 under construction; her sister lies on the slip behind. Both were delivered
in "kit" form and the various sections are marked O.H.M.S. Chief Harbour Engineer,
Takoradi Harbour, Seccondee.*

625 **G.C.H.3** Steel Bascule Type Dumb Tipping Barge.
Built 1923 *130.0bp x 29.0 x 7.6 ft.
Owners - Crown Agents for the Colonies, Gold Coast.
Delivered 19.5.1923 to Takoradi, West Africa.

626 **G.C.H.4** Steel Bascule Type Dumb Tipping Barge.
Built 1923 *130.0bp x 29.0 x 7.6 ft.
Owners - Crown Agents for the Colonies, Gold Coast.
Delivered 1.1.1924 to Takoradi, West Africa.
The above 4 Dumb Tipping Barges were specifically built to be used in the
construction of two breakwaters at Takoradi Harbour on the Gold Coast. G.C.H.
probably meant 'Gold Coast Hopper'.

627 **UNNAMED** Steel Dumb Barge.
Launched 23.2.1924 *87.3bp x 16.4 x 7.9 ft.
Owners - J. Holt & Co. Ltd., Liverpool.
Towed to Liverpool 23.2.1924, immediately after launch.

628 **UNNAMED** Steel Dumb Barge.
Launched 4.6.1924 *87.3bp x 16.4 x 7.9 ft.
Owners - J. Holt & Co. Ltd., Liverpool.
Towed to Liverpool 4.6.1924, immediately after launch.

629-632   **M.L.** Four Gal.Stl. Dumb Barges.
Built 1923 *36.0bp x 9.6 x 3.9 ft.
Owners - Bromport S. S. Co. Ltd., Liverpool.
All four barges were referred to as M.L. and were towed to Liverpool via the
River Douglas and the Leeds & Liverpool Canal, the first two on 2.4.1923 and the
second two on 17.7.1923.

633-4   **UNNAMED** Two Gal.Stl. Dumb Barges.
Launched 30.4. & 1.5.1923. *45.0bp x 10.0 x 5.0 ft.
Owners - Bromport S. S. Co. Ltd., Liverpool.
Both left Lytham in tow on 8.5.1923 for Liverpool.

635   **KWANGO** Gal.Stl. Sternwheel Steamer.
Built 1923, shipped to the Belgian Congo in pieces 28.12.1923.
Owners - La Societe Anonyme des Huileries du Congo Belge.
ON - 150 grt 70 net*125.0bp x 24.0 x 5.4 ft.
C.H.J.C.2Cy. 13''-28''x42'' stroke by builder.
Named after a tributary of the River Congo.

636   **SANKURU** Gal.Stl. Sternwheel Steamer.
Built 1923, shipped to the Belgian Congo in pieces 28.12.1923.
Owners - La Societe Anonyme des Huileries du Congo Belge.
ON - 150 grt 70 net*125.0bp x 24.0 x 5.4 ft.
C.H.J.C.2Cy. 13''-28''x42'' stroke by builder.
Named after a tributary of the River Congo. Both of the above vessels were of
the Semi Tanker type and cost £18,091 the pair.

*ADA.*

637   **ADA** Single Screw Steel Steam Tug.
Launched 6.2.1924, trials 22.2.1924.
Owners - J. Holt & Co. Ltd., Liverpool.
ON - 45 grt 17 net *64.0bp x 15.0 x 7.3 ft.
C.S.C.2Cy. 10½''-24''x18'' stroke by builder.

638-643   **UNNAMED** Six Mild Steel Dumb Barges.
Built 1923-1924 *85.0bp x 20.0 x 7.6 ft.
Owners - J. Birch & Co. Ltd., London.
Designed to carry 200 tons on a 6½ ft. draft. Delivered on 15.9., 16.10., &
12.11.1923 & on 2.2., 31.3., & 3.5.1924.

HEATHERFIELD.                                    *World Ship Photo Library*

644   **HEATHERFIELD** Single Screw Steel Cargo Steamer.
Launched 22.4.1924 Registered Liverpool.
Owners - Zillah Shipping & Carrying Co. Ltd., Liverpool.
ON 147261 447 grt 174 net 142.4 x 26.0 x 11.5 ft.
T.E.S.C.3Cy. 14"-22"-38"x24" stroke, 71 rhp by builder.

645   **TESSA** Twin Screw Steel Ferry Steamer.
Launched 18.7.1924 Registered London.
Owners - London, Midland & Scottish Railway Co. Ltd., London.
ON 147730 371 grt 175 net 135.1 x 30.0 x 10.5 ft.
2xC.S.C.2Cy. 11"-24"x18" stroke, 46 rhp (400 ihp) by builder.
Trials 26.9.1924. Extreme breadth 38 ft. Served on the River Thames as a
passenger and vehicle ferry.

*TESSA, a builders' photograph taken in Preston Docks.*

98

*One of the two barges Yard Numbers 646-7. To be shipped to Mombasa in "kit" form, the hull is temporarily bolted together and the weights of the various sections are stencilled on them.*

**646-7** **UNNAMED** Two Steel Dumb Swim Ended Barges.
Built 1924 *102.6bp x 26.0 x 6.0 ft.
Owners - Crown Agents for the Colonies, Uganda.
Delivered to Lake Kioga, Uganda in pieces on 18.8. & 4.9.1924.


**648** **GRANT** Steel Sternwheel Steam Tug.
Built 1924, shipped 24.2.1925 to Lake Kioga, Uganda in pieces.
Owners - Crown Agents for the Colonies, Uganda.
ON - 240 grt 160 net*134.0bp x 26.0 x 5.4 ft.
H.C.S.C.2Cy. 17''-37''x48'' stroke by builder.


**649** **UNNAMED** Steel Dumb Barge.
Launched 3.7.1924 *65.0bp x 15.0 x 6.0 ft.
Owners - African & Eastern Trade Corporation Ltd., London.
Towed to Liverpool on 5.11.1924.


**650-3** **UNNAMED** Four Mild Steel Dumb Barges.
Built 1924 *85.0bp x 20.0 x 7.6 ft.
Owners - J. Birch & Co. Ltd., London.
Designed to carry 200 tons on a 6½ ft. draft. Delivered on 20.8., 17.9., 15.10., and 11.11.1924.

*TANO.*

**654 TANO** Single Screw Steel Steam Tug.
Launched 7.7.1924, trials 19.7.1924.
Owners - African & Eastern Trade Corporation Ltd., London.
ON 180695 55 grt 25 net *63.7bp x 16.5 x 6.9 ft.
C.S.C.2Cy. 10½"-24"x18" stroke, 200 ihp by builder.
Destroyed at Calabar, Nigeria in 1952.

**655 UNNAMED** Mild Steel Dumb Barge.
Launched 27.10.1924 *65.0bp x 15.0 x 6.0 ft.
Owners - African & Eastern Trade Corporation Ltd., London.
Towed to Liverpool on 5.11.1924.

**656 JOYCE** Single Screw Steel Steam Tug.
Launched 24.11.1924 Registered Liverpool.
Owners - J. Holt & Co. Ltd., Liverpool.
ON - 48 grt 18 net *67.4bp x 16.0 x 7.3 ft.
C.S.C.2Cy. 10½"-24"x18" stroke by builder.
Trials 8.12.1924.

**657 UNNAMED** Mild Steel Dumb Barge.
Launched 5.9.1924 *87.3bp x 16.4 x 7.9 ft.
Owners - J. Holt & Co. Ltd., Liverpool.

**658 UNNAMED** Mild Steel Dumb Barge.
Launched 14.3.1925 *87.3bp x 16.4 x 7.9 ft.
Owners - J. Holt & Co. Ltd., Liverpool.

**659 AGNELEY** Mild Steel Dumb Barge.
Launched 8.12.1924 *60.0bp x 16.0 x 6.0 ft.
Owners - African & Eastern Trade Corporation Ltd., London.
A crane was fitted forward on this dumb barge.

660-1 **UNNAMED** Two Steel Dumb Barges.
Launched 9.12.1924 and delivered to Sekondi, Gold Coast.
Owners - African & Eastern Trade Corporation Ltd., London.
ON - 52 grt 48 net *65.0bp x 16.0 x 6.0 ft.

662 **BENI** Single Screw Gal.Stl. Steam Launch.
Launched 12.2.1925.
Owners - African & Eastern Trade Corporation Ltd., London.
ON - 28 grt 13 net *45.0bp x 11.6 x 5.0 ft.
C.S.C.2Cy. 7"-15"x9" stroke by builder.

663 **ARS** Gal.Stl. Sternwheel Steamer.
Delivered 1.1.1925 to Liverpool in pieces.
Owners - Niger Co. Ltd., London.
ON - 16 grt 9 net *50.0bp x 12.0 x 3.0 ft.
C.N.C.2Cy. 8"-14"x20" stroke by builder.

664 **JUS** Gal.Stl. Sternwheel Steamer.
Delivered 15.1.1925 to Liverpool in pieces.
Owners - Niger Co. Ltd., London.
ON - 16 grt 9 net *50.0bp x 12.0 x 3.0 ft.
C.N.C.2Cy. 8"-14"x20" stroke by builder.

665 **PAX** Gal.Stl. Sternwheel Steamer.
Delivered 29.1.1925 to Liverpool in pieces.
Owners - Niger Co. Ltd., London.
ON - 16 grt 9 net *50.0bp x 12.0 x 3.0 ft.
C.N.C.2Cy. 8"-14"x20" stroke by builder.

All the above three vessels were transported to Liverpool from Lytham by road
for shipment to Nigeria in pieces.

666-671 **N1-N6** Six Gal.Stl. Poling Canoes.
All delivered to Liverpool by rail on 17.1.1925.
Owners - Niger Co. Ltd., London.
ON - 12.5 grt *50.0bp x 9.0 x 3.0 ft.

672-3 **BARGE 44-45** Two Steel Dumb Mooring Barges.
Launched 14.3.1925 & 26.3.1925.
Owners - Niger Co. Ltd., London.
ON - 31 grt 29 net *60.0bp x 11.0 x 5.6 ft.

*ELMFIELD, see next page.*                    *World Ship Photo Library*

674  **ELMFIELD** Single Screw Steel Cargo Steamer.
Launched 8.7.1925 Registered Liverpool.
Owners - Zillah Shipping & Carrying Co. Ltd., Liverpool.
ON 147331 450 grt 175 net 142.5 x 25.9 x 11.5 ft.
C.S.C.2Cy. 17"-38"x24" stroke, 58 rhp by builder.
Trials 3.10.1925.

675-7  **LIGHTER NO.46-48** Three Steel Dumb Lighters.
Launched 11.5.1925, 21.5.1925 & 4.6.1925.
Owners - Niger Co. Ltd., Liverpool.
ON 102 grt 99 net *88.0bp x 16.0 x 8.0 ft.

678  **BONDO** Gal.Stl. Sternwheel Steamer.
Built 1925, shipped in packages to the Congo on 7.8.1925.
Owners - La Societe Anonyme des Huileries du Congo Belge.
ON - 54 grt 26 net *70.0bp x 17.0 x 4.0 ft.
C.N.C.2Cy. 9"-16"x30" stroke by builder.

679  **MOMA** Gal.Stl. Sternwheel Steamer.
Built 1925, shipped in packages to the Congo on 4.9.1925.
Owners - La Societe Anonyme des Huileries du Congo Belge.
ON - 54 grt 26 net *70.0bp x 17.0 x 4.0 ft.
C.N.C.2Cy. 9"-16"x30" stroke by builder.
Named after a township in Zaire.

680  **GANDA** Gal.Stl. Sternwheel Steamer.
Built 1926, shipped in packages to the Congo on 22.2.1926.
Owners - La Societe Anonyme des Huileries du Congo Belge.
ON 54 grt 26 net *70.0bp x 17.0 x 4.0 ft.
C.N.C.2Cy. 9"-16"x30" stroke by builder.

681  **BELO** Gal.Stl. Sternwheel Steamer.
Built 1926, shipped in packages to the Congo on 15.3.1926.
Owners - La Societe Anonyme des Huileries du Congo Belge.
ON - 54 grt 26 net *70.0bp x 17.0 x 4.0 ft.
C.N.C.2Cy. 9"-16"x30" stroke by builder.

682  **KUTU** Gal.Stl. Sternwheel Steamer.
Built 1926, shipped in packages to the Congo in July 1926.
Owners - La Societe Anonyme des Huileries du Congo Belge.
ON - 54 grt 26 net *70.0bp x 17.0 x 4.0 ft.
C.N.C.2Cy. 9"-16"x30" stroke by builder.
Named after a township in Zaire.

683  **UNNAMED** Gal.Stl. Sailing & Poling Barge.
Built 1925 *55.0 x 12.6 x 4.10 ft.
Owners - no record. Fitted with a square sail as Humber Keel.

684  **KAPANGA** Gal.Stl. Sternwheel Steamer.
Built 1925 and shipped in packages to the Congo.
Owners - La Societe Anonyme des Huileries du Congo Belge.
ON - 116 grt 58 net *96.0bp x 24.0 x 4.6 ft.
C.N.C.2Cy. 12"-21"x36" stroke by builder.

685-6  **UNNAMED** Two Steel Dumb Lighters.
Launched 7.9.1925 and 14.9.1925.
Owners - African & Eastern Trade Corporation Ltd., London.
ON - 58 grt 53 net *66.0bp x 16.0 x 6.6 ft.
Shipped to Sekondi, Gold Coast, West Africa.

687 **COTONOU** Single Screw Gal.Stl. Motor Barge.
Launched 3.10.1925, trials 15.11.1925. (Tunnel Type).
Owners - African & Eastern Trade Corporation Ltd., London.
ON 181723 45 grt 23 net *70.0bp x 17.0 x 4.4 ft.
Gleniffer 4Cyl. paraffin engine, 50 bhp.
Renamed UNICORN in March 1926. Cotonou is a town in W. Africa.

688-9 **UNNAMED** Two Steel Dumb Lighters.
Launched 21.10.1925 and 2.12.1925.
Owners - African & Eastern Trade Corporation Ltd., London.
ON - 58 grt 53 net *66.0bp x 16.0 x 6.6 ft.
Shipped to Sekondi, Gold Coast, West Africa.

690 **LUGARD** Steel Sternwheel Steamer.
Built 1925, trials 9.3.1926 on Lake Albert, Uganda.
Owners - Crown Agents for the Colonies, Uganda.
ON - 245 grt 165 net*145.0bp x 29.0 x 4.6 ft.
H.C.S.C.2Cy.15''-32½''x45'' stroke by builder.
Shipped in 274 packages to Uganda where she was assembled.
Trials took place on 9.3.1926 on Lake Albert. Named after Captain Sir F. D.
Lugard, a British Officer, who as Lord Lugard, was a heroic figure in Britain's
Colonial history.

*IJAW in the Liggard Brook.*

691 **IJAW** Single Screw Steel Steam Tug.
Launched 16.11.1925, trials 12.12.1925.
Owners - African & Eastern Trade Corporation Ltd., London.
ON 168268 78 grt 23 net *72.0bp x 17.0 x 8.0 ft.
C.S.C.2Cy. 10½''-24''x18'' stroke, 400 ihp by builder.
Named after a tribe in the Niger Delta. Sank Calabar 1960.

692-3 **LIGHTER A.1-A.2** Two Steel Dumb Lighters.
Launched 16.12.1925 and 17.12.1925.
Owners - Niger Co. Ltd., London.
ON - 31 grt 29 net *60.0bp x 11.0 x 5.6 ft.

694-5 **UNNAMED** Two Gal.Stl. Poling Canoes.
Built 1925 *50.0bp x 9.0 x 3.0 ft.
Owners - African & Eastern Trade Corporation Ltd., London.
Delivered to Liverpool by rail on 5.1.1926 for shipment.

696 **UNNAMED** Steel Dumb Lighter.
Launched 3.2.1926
Owners - African & Eastern Trade Corporation Ltd., London.
ON - 86 grt 79 net *80.0bp x 16.0 x 8.0 ft.

697 **ABO** Gal.Stl. Sternwheel Steamer.
Built 1925 *50.0bp x 12.0 x 3.0 ft.
Owners - African & Eastern Trade Corporation Ltd., London.
C.N.C.2Cy. 8"-14"x20" stroke by builder.
Paddle Wheel 7'6" dia over floats. Floats 6'8" x 11" x 1½",
Delivered to Liverpool by road in pieces for shipment 7.1.1926.

698-9 **BARGE NO.52-53** Two Steel Dumb Barges.
Launched 17.3.1926 and 7.6.1926
Owners - J. Holt & Co. (Liverpool) Ltd., Liverpool.
ON - 62 grt 57 net *75.0bp x 16.4 x 6.0 ft.

700-2 **BARGE NO.54-56** Three Steel Dumb Barges.
Launched 27.7.1926, 23.8.1926 and 9.9.1926.
Owners - J. Holt & Co. (Liverpool) Ltd., Liverpool.
ON - 62 grt 57 net *75.0bp x 16.4 x 6.0 ft.

703-5 **BARGE NO.57-59** Three Steel Dumb Barges.
Launched 12.4.1926 and 19.10.1926.
Owners - J. Holt & Co. (Liverpool) Ltd., Liverpool.
ON - 62 grt 57 net *75.0bp x 16.4 x 6.0 ft.

706 **UNNAMED** Steel Dumb Lighter.
Launched 28.4.1926 *60.0bp x 11.0 x 5.6 ft.
Owners - Niger Co. Ltd., London.
Delivered to Grand Bassam, Ivory Coast, West Africa.

707-8 **BARGE NO.59-60** Two Steel Dumb Open Hatch Barges.
Launched 9.6.1926 and 14.6.1926.
Owners - African & Eastern Trade Corporation Ltd., London.
ON - 58 grt 53 net *66.0bp x 16.0 x 6.6 ft.
These barges were specially built to carry manganese ore.

709-710 **BARGE NO.61-62** Two Steel Dumb Open Hatch Barges.
Launched 17.2.1927 and 19.2.1927.
Owners - African & Eastern Trade Corporation Ltd., London.
ON - 58 grt 53 net *66.0bp x 16.0 x 6.6 ft.
These barges were specially built to carry manganese ore.

711-3 **N.16-18** Three Gal.Stl. Poling Canoes.
Built 1926, delivered to Liverpool by rail on 14 & 27.10.1926.
Owners - Niger Co. Ltd., London.
ON - 12½ grt *50.0bp x 9.0 x 3.0 ft.

714-6 **UNNAMED** Three Steel Dumb Barges.
Launched 18.3.1927 (2) and 19.3.1927 (1).
Owners - Niger Co. Ltd., London.
ON - 30½ grt 29 net *55.0bp x 12.0 x 5.6 ft.

717 **FARO II** Gal.Stl. Quarterwheel Steamer.
Built 1927 Registered London.
Owners - Niger Co. Ltd., London.
ON 165518 105 grt 47 net 87.0 x 19.1 x 4.5 ft.
C.N.C.2Cy. 9"-18"x30" stroke, 75 ihp by builder.
The engines were removed from FARO (Yard No. 450) in Nigeria and sent to
Lytham for overhaul and installation in this ship.

718-20 **NO.60-62** Three Gal.Stl. Poling Canoes.
Built 1926, delivered to Liverpool by rail on 2,3 & 4.12.1926.
Owners - J. Holt & Co. Ltd., Liverpool.
ON - 14 grt 13½ net*52.0bp x 9.11 x 2.9 ft.

721 **BENUE** Gal.Stl. Quarterwheel Steamer.
Launched 12.7.1927 Registered London.
Owners - Niger Co. Ltd., London.
ON 165519 105 grt 47 net 87.0 x 19.1 x 4.5 ft.
C.N.C.2Cy. 9"-18"x30" stroke, 75 ihp by builder.

722-4 **UNNAMED** Three Steel Dumb Barges.
Launched 22.4, 4.6, & 25.6.1927.*48.0bp x 10.0 x 4.0 ft.
Owners - Niger Co. Ltd., London.

*BLUE CIRCLE at Preston.*

725 **BLUE CIRCLE** Single Screw Steel Steam Tug.
Launched 12.9.1927. Registered London.
Owners - Associated Portland Cement Manufacturers Ltd., London.
ON 149924 111 grt - net 77.7 x 21.6 x 10.6 ft.
T.E.S.C.3Cy. 14"-22"-36"x24" stroke, 66 rhp by builder.

726-7 **BARGE NO.63-64** Two Steel Dumb Open Hatch Barges.
Launched 27.5.1927 and 31.5.1927.
Owners - African & Eastern Trade Corporation Ltd., London.
ON - 58 grt 53 net *66.0bp x 16.0 x 6.6 ft.
These barges were specially built to carry manganese ore.

728  **LION** Single Screw Gal.Stl. Motor Barge.
Launched 30.7.1927 (Tunnel Type).
Owners - African & Eastern Trade Corporation Ltd., London.
ON 181722 45 grt 23 net *70.0 x 17.0 x 4.4 ft.
Gleniffer 4Cy. Paraffin Engine, 50 bhp.
Later name LION U A.

729  **APPLEBY** Gal.Stl. Sternwheel Steam Tug.
Launched 2.7.1927, trials 13.8.1927.
Owners - J. Holt & Co. Ltd., Liverpool.
ON - *75.0bp x 18.6 x 5.0 ft.
C.H.J.C.2Cy. 13"-28"x42" stroke by builder.

730-1  **BARGE NO.63-64** Two Gal.Stl. Dumb Barges.
Launched 2.9.1927 and 14.10.1927.
Owners - J. Holt & Co. Ltd., Liverpool.
ON - 126 grt 120 net*120.0bp x 18.6 x 6.6 ft.

732  **N'DONI** Single Screw Steel Steam Tug.
Launched 9.12.1927, trials 23.12.1927.
Owners - Niger Co. Ltd., London.
ON - 55 grt - net *70.0bp x 17.0 x 7.0 ft.
C.S.C.2Cy. 10½"-24"x18" stroke by builder.

733-4  **BARGE NO.58-59** Two Steel Dumb Barges.
Launched 11.10.1927 & 10.11.1927.
Owners - Niger Co. Ltd., London.
ON - 70½ grt 69 net *80.0bp x 15.0 x 6.6 ft.
These barges were fitted with Roller Hatch Covers.

735  **IRIS** Single Screw Gal.Stl. Steam Tug.
Launched 10.1.1928
Owners - Crown Agents for the Colonies, Nigeria.
ON - 38 grt 12 net *66.0bp x 12.6 x 5.4 ft.
C.S.C.2Cy. 8"-16"x12" stroke by builder.

736-741  **UNNAMED** Six Gal.Stl. Poling Canoes.
Built 1928 *25.0bp x 3.0 x 1.9 ft.
Owners - E. Bates & Sons Ltd., Liverpool, Agents.
Cost £42 each to build. Invoice price £60 each.
Delivered to Liverpool by rail on 29 & 30.3.1928

742-3  **ANCHOR BOAT 12-13** Two Gal.Stl. Anchor Boats.
Launched August 1928 *24.0bp x 6.6 x 2.4 ft.
Owners - Niger Co. Ltd., London.

744-9  **H20-25** Six Gal.Stl. Poling Canoes.
Built 1928 *50.0bp x 8.0 x 2.6 ft.
Owners - Niger Co. Ltd., London.

750  **ANCHOR BOAT** Gal.Stl. Anchor Boat.
Built 1928 *24.0bp x 6.6 x 2.4 ft.
Owners - Niger Co. Ltd. London.

751  **M.L.** Steel Dumb Barge.
Built 1928 *50.0bp x 10.0 x 5.0 ft.
Owners - Niger Co. Ltd., London.

752  **UNNAMED** Steel Dumb Lighter.
Launched 15.6.1928
Owners - African & Eastern Trade Corporation Ltd., London.
ON - 66 grt 63 net *70.0bp x 16.0 x 7.0 ft.

*GEORGE LIVESEY leaving Preston. Note the temporary timber breakwater fitted forward for her voyage to the Thames.* World Ship Photo Library

**753 GEORGE LIVESEY** Single Screw Steel Steam Tug.
Launched 29.11.1928, Registered London.
Owners - South Metropolitan Gas Company, London.
ON 161212 110 grt - net *77.6 x 21.6 x 10.6 ft.
T.E.S.C.3Cy. 14"-22"-36"x24" stroke, 44 rhp by builder.
Trials 12.3.1929. Later name CARBEILE.

**754 BUZZ** Gal.Stl. Gig.
Built 1928 *20.0bp x 6.0 x 2.0 ft.
Owners - Niger Co. Ltd., London.
Fitted with outboard motor.

**755-6 UNNAMED** Two Gal.Stl. Poling Canoes.
Built 1928 *50.0bp x 9.0 x 3.0 ft.
Owners - African & Eastern Trade Corporation Ltd., London.
Delivered to Liverpool by rail on 9.8.1928.

**757-9 ANCHOR BOAT 14-16** Three Gal.Stl. Anchor Boats.
Built 1928 *20.0bp x 6.6 x 2.4 ft.
Owners - Niger Co. Ltd., London.
Delivered to Liverpool by rail August 1928.

**760-6 SURF BOATS 7-13** Seven Gal.Stl. Surf Boats.
Built 1928 23 cwt dw *21.8bp x 6.10 x 3.0 ft.
Owners - African & Eastern Trade Corporation Ltd., London.
Delivered to Liverpool by own wagon starting 1.10.1928.

**767-9 PASSACEIRO** Three Gal.Stl. Dumb Passenger Barges.
Launched 29.1.1929 *70.0bp x 13.0 x 6.6 ft.
Owners - Niger Co. Ltd., London.

*CLEVELEYS.*                                    *World Ship Photo Library*

770  **CLEVELEYS** Twin Screw Steel Steam Tug.
Launched 8.8.1929 Registered Fleetwood.
Owners - London, Midland & Scottish Railway Co. Ltd., London.
ON 148234 110 grt - net 80.2bp x 19.4 x 9.3 ft.
2xC.S.C.2Cy. 10½''-24''x18'' stroke, 320 bhp by builder.
Trials 4.10.1929. Cost £8,412. Invoice Price £10,200.

771  **OGULA** Single Screw Steel Motor Launch.
Launched 24.5.1929 Registered Liverpool.
Owners - Elder Dempster Lines Ltd., Liverpool.
ON 161101 11 grt 5 net 39.7 x 8.8 x 3.9 ft.
6Cy. Parsons Engine 48 bhp 950 rpm. Trials 28.5.1929.

*OGULA.*

772 **UNNAMED** Single Screw Steel Motor Barge.
Built 1929, delivered to Liverpool 15.5.1929.
Owners - Jones, Burton & Co. Ltd., Liverpool, Agents.
ON - 60 grt 37 net *75.0 x 15.6 x 7.0 ft.
Twin Cy. Heavy Oil Engine, 90 bhp by H. Widdop & Co. Ltd.
Designed to carry 100 tons on a 6 foot draft.

773-6 **H26-29** Four Gal.Stl. Poling Canoes.
Built 1929 *50.0 x 8.0 x 2.6 ft.
Owners - Niger Co. Ltd., London.
Delivered to Liverpool by road on 23.5.(2), 27 & 28.6.1929.
The Niger Co. Ltd., became part of the United Africa Co. Ltd., on 1st May, 1929.

777 **N'KISSI** Gal.Stl. Sternwheel Steamer.
Launched 26.7.1929 Registered London.
Owners - United Africa Co. Ltd., London.
ON 165511 48 grt 28 net 78.0 x 19.5 x 3.7 ft.
C.N.C.2Cy. 9"-16"x30" stroke, 50 ihp by builder.

778 **KADUNA** Gal.Stl. Sternwheel Steamer.
Launched 14.9.1929 Registered London.
Owners - United Africa Co. Ltd., London.
ON 165510 48 grt 28 net 78.0 x 19.5 x 3.7 ft.
C.N.C.2Cy. 9"-16"x30" stroke, 50 ihp by builder.
Named after a tributary of the River Niger, Nigeria.

779-781 **ANCHOR BOAT 17-19** Three Gal.Stl. Anchor Boats.
Built 1929 *20.0 x 6.6 x 2.4 ft.
Owners - Niger Co. Ltd., London.
Delivered to Liverpool by road June 1929.
The Niger Co. Ltd., became part of the United Africa Co. Ltd., on 1st May, 1929.

782-3 **ANCHOR BOAT 20-21** Two Gal. Stl. Anchor Boats.
Built 1929 *24.0 x 6.6 x 2.6 ft.
Owners - United Africa Co. Ltd., London.
Delivered to Liverpool by road 13.10.1929.

784 **DU 4** Steel Dumb Barge.
Launched 23.10.1929 Registered Liverpool.
Owners - Nigerian Transport Co. Ltd. (Elder Dempster Lines).
ON 161121 57 net 71.0 x 16.0 x 6.4 ft.

785 **LUTSHIMA** Gal.Stl. Quarterwheel Steamer.
Built 1930 (Semi Tanker).
Owners - La Societe Anonyme des Huileries du Congo Belge.
ON - 371 grt 136 net*156.0bp x 31.0 x 6.3 ft.
2xC.H.J.C.2Cy. 13"-28"x42" stroke by builder.
Cost £10,970.12.5d. Shipped in cases from Preston on 24.5.1930 per S.S.
E.HAYWARD. Named after a tributary of the Congo.

786 **OKO** Steel Motor Lighter.
Launched 5.11.1929 Registered Liverpool.
Owners - West African Lighterage & Transport Co. Ltd., Liverpool.
ON 161127 29 grt 14 net 46.6 x 14.1 x 5.0 ft.
Gardner Type 3J5 Oil Engine, 54 bhp. Invoice Price £1,900.
Trials 21.11.1929. Towed to Liverpool by tug OVERGARTH.

787 **SCAWBY** Gal.Stl. Sternwheel Steam Tug.
Launched 4.4.1930, trials 30.4.1930.
Owners - J. Holt & Co. Ltd., Liverpool.
ON - Cost £4,245 *75.0 x 18.6 x 5.0 ft.
C.H.J.C.2Cy. 13"-28"x42" stroke by builder.
Towed to Liverpool by Rea tug on 3.5.1930.

788-9 **LIGHTER No.65-66** Two Gal.Stl. Dumb Lighters.
Launched 30.1.& 27.2.1930 *120.0 x 18.6 x 6.6 ft.
Owners - J. Holt & Co. Ltd., Liverpool.
Towed to Liverpool by Rea tug on 3.3.1930 & 22.4.1930.

790-1 **LIGHTER NO.67-68** Two Gal.Stl. Dumb Lighters.
Launched 2.6.1930 *120.0 x 18.6 x 6.6 ft.
Owners - J. Holt & Co. Ltd., Liverpool.
Towed to Liverpool by Rea tug on 3.6. & 8.7.1930.

792 **TIGER** Single Screw Steel Steam Launch.
Launched 11.2.1930, trials 29.2.1930.
Owners - United Africa Co. Ltd... London.
ON - *64.0bp x 13.0 x 6.0 ft.
C.S.C.2Cy. 9"-18"x15" stroke by builder. Shipped to Lagos.

793 **LUKULU** Gal.Stl. Quarterwheel Steamer.
Built 1930 (Semi Tanker).
Owners - La Societe Anonyme des Huileries du Congo Belge.
ON - 371 grt 136 net*156.0bp x 31.0 x 6.3 ft.
2xC.H.J.C.2Cy. 13"-28"x42" stroke by builder.
Shipped in cases from Lytham by rail on 1.12.1930.

794-9 **H30-35** Six Gal.Stl. Poling Canoes.
Built 1930 *50.0 x 8.0 x 2.6 ft.
Owners - United Africa Co. Ltd., London.
Delivered to Liverpool by road on 30.5.(2), 13.6.(1), 24.7.(2), and 12.9.1930(1).

800-1 **BARGE NO.66-67** Two Steel Dumb Barges.
Launched 1.8.1930 *88.0 x 16.0 x 8.0 ft.
Owners - United Africa Co. Ltd., London.

802-4 **ANCHOR BOAT 25-27** Three Steel Anchor Boats.
Built 1930 *20.0 x 6.6 x 2.6 ft.
Owners - United Africa Co. Ltd., London.
Delivered to Liverpool.

805-7 **ANCHOR BOAT 22-24** Three Steel Anchor Boats.
Built 1930 *24.0 x 6.6 x 2.6 ft.
Owners - United Africa Co. Ltd., London.
Delivered to Liverpool on 12.9.1930.

808-9 **UNNAMED** Two Steel Ferry Pontoons.
Built 1930 *18.0 x 8.10½ x 3.5½ ft.
Owners - United Africa Co. Ltd., London.
Delivered to Liverpool by road on 23.7.1930 for shipment to
Port Opobo, Nigeria.

810 **ITACUA** Twin Screw Steel Steam Tug.
Launched 17.1.1931 Registered Buenos Aires, Argentina.
Owners - The Argentine Navigation Co. Ltd., Buenos Aires.
ON - 75 grt - net 72.0 x 18.0 x 6.2 ft
2xT.E.S.C.3Cy. 7"-11"-18"x12" stroke, 41 nhp by builder.
Trials took place on 19 & 20.3.1931. She was built for towing services on the
River Uruguay, Argentina. Towed to Liverpool by Rea tug on 29.4.1931, lifted
aboard by floating crane and shipped to Argentina as deck cargo. Weight in
slings 82½ tons.

811 **UNNAMED** Steel Dumb Barge.
Built 1931 *55.0 x 14.0 x 5.6 ft.
Owners - United Africa Co. Ltd., London.

*ITABERA and ITACURA prior to departure in 4.1931.*

812 **ITABERA** Twin Screw Steel Steam Tug.
Launched 17.3.1931 Registered Buenos Aires, Argentina.
Owners - The Argentine Navigation Co. Ltd., Buenos Aires.
ON - 75 grt - net 72.0 x 18.0 x 6.2 ft
2xT.E.S.C.3Cy. 7"-11"-18"x12" stroke, 41 nhp by builder.
Trials took place on 21 & 22.4.1931. She was built for towing services on the
River Uruguay, Argentina. Towed to Liverpool by Rea tug on 29.4.1931, lifted
aboard by floating crane and shipped to Argentina as deck cargo. Weight in
slings 81½ tons.

813 **MALEMBA** Steel Motor Barge.
Built 1931, trials 4.2.1931.
Owners - United Africa Co. Ltd., London.
ON - 37 grt 19 net *60.0 x 15.0 x 5.6 ft.
Widdop 2Cyl. diesel engine, 60 bhp at 400 rpm.

*BETA.*

**814** **BETA** Twin Screw Steel Motor Patrol Boat.
Built 1931, trials 28.7.1931.
Owners - Lancashire & Western Sea Fisheries Joint Committee.
ON - 23 grt 10 net *50.0 x 11.6 x 6.6 ft.
2 sets semi diesel 4J5 72 bhp at 400 rpm by Gardner and Sons Ltd., Manchester.
Later named SEA PREFECT (ON182810).

**815** **NORMANBY** Gal.Stl. Sternwheel Tug.
Launched 23.4.1932, trials 7.5.1932.
Owners - J. Holt & Co. Ltd., Liverpool.
ON - 74 grt 29 net *75.0bp x 18.5 x 5.0 ft.
C.H.J.C.2Cy. 13''-28''x42'' stroke by builder.
Cost £3,944. Towed to Liverpool 11.5.1932 by tug CAIRNGARTH.

**816-9** **BARGE NO.75-78** Four Steel Dumb Barges.
Built 1932 *120.0 x 18.6 x 6.6 ft.
Owners - J. Holt & Co. Ltd., Liverpool.
Towed to Liverpool on 4.4.,18.4.,17.6., & 5.7.1932.

**820-1** **UNNAMED** Two Steel Dumb Lighters.
Built 1932 *120.0 x 20.0 x 6.6 ft.
Owners - United Africa Co. Ltd., London.

**822** **IMP** Gal.Stl. Motor Gig.
Built 1932 *20.0bp x 6.0 x 2.0 ft.
Owners - United Africa Co. Ltd., London.
Fitted with an outboard motor.

**823-4** **ANCHOR BOAT 28-29** Two Steel Anchor Boats.
Built 1932 *20.0 x 6.6 x 2.6 ft.
Owners - United Africa Co. Ltd., London.

**825-6** **LIGHTER NO.78-79** Two Steel Dumb Lighters.
Built 1932 *130.0 x 24.0 x 7.0 ft.
Owners - United Africa Co. Ltd., London.

827   **RIBAGO** Part Gal.Stl. Sternwheel Steamer.
Built 1933 Registered London.
Owners - United Africa Co. Ltd., London.
ON 165520 253 grt 111 net 141.6bp x 26.0 x 6.6 ft.
H.C.S.C.2Cy. 17''-37''x48'' stroke, 450 ihp by builder.
Cost £8,349. The boiler used was taken from s/w TARAPA and rebuilt at Lytham.
The bow section was delivered to Liverpool by rail on 14.7.1933 and the stern
section by road on 23.10.1933. The vessel was insured for £10,327.10.0.d.

828-9   **ANCHOR BOAT 30-31** Two Steel Anchor Boats.
Built 1933 *20.0 x 6.6 x 2.6 ft.
Owners - United Africa Co. Ltd., London.

830   **ANCHOR BOAT 32** Steel Anchor Boat.
Built 1933 *24.0 x 6.6 x 2.6 ft.
Owners - United Africa Co. Ltd., London.

831-2   **LIGHTER NO.80-81** Two Steel Dumb Lighters.
Built 1933 *130.0 x 25.0 x 7.6 ft.
Owners - United Africa Co. Ltd., London.
These lighters were fitted with heavy sliding hatch covers.

833   **NARAGUTA** Part Gal.Stl. Sternwheel Steamer.
Built 1934 Registered London.
Owners - United Africa Co. Ltd., London.
ON 165509 306 grt 155 net 153.5 x 26.0 x 5.8 ft
H.C.S.C.2Cy. 17''-37''x48'' stroke, 450 ihp by builder,
Cost £9,694. The boiler was a Babcock & Wilcock water tube boiler in twelve
sections. Trials took place on 2.5.1934 and the vessel was delivered to Liverpool
in pieces by road starting on 10.5.1934. Insured for £12,094.

834   **UNNAMED** Steel Ferry Pontoon.
Built 1934 *47.8 x 13.3 x 2.10 ft.
Owners - United Africa Co. Ltd., London.
Delivered to Liverpool for shipment to Senchi.

835   **NORTHOP** Twin Screw Steel Diesel Motor Tug.
Launched 28.8.1934 Registered Liverpool.
Owners - Elder Dempster Lines Ltd., Liverpool.
ON 162412 70 grt 19 net 72.1bp x 17.6 x 5.8 ft.
2S.C.S.A.4Cy. 11½''x13½'' stroke diesel engines, 200 ihp by H. Widdop & Co.
Ltd., Keighley, Yorks.
Cost £5,373, invoice Price £5,700. Trials 24.9.1934, sailed from Liverpool for
Lagos on 29.9.1934 and arrived 23.10.1934.

Diesel Motor Tug
"Northop"

*A builders' retouched photograph of NORTHOP.*

113

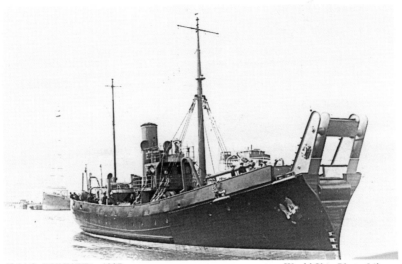

H.M.S. DUNNET in 1937.                              World Ship Photo Library

836  **DUNNET** Single Screw Steel Boom Working Vessel.
Launched 5.8.1936, trials 27.4.1937.
Owners - The Admiralty, London.
ON 167827 338 grt 136 net 124.5bp x 26.7 x 13.2 ft.
T.E.S.C.3cy. 10½"-17¼"-29"x22" stroke, 350 ihp by builder.
Later named KINGSMOOR as a salvage vessel.

837  **W.10** Steel Dumb Barge.
Built 1935, delivered to Liverpool 7.10.1935.
Owners - West African Lighterage & Transport Co. Ltd., Liverpool.
ON 164271 13 net 40.0 x 12.0 x 4.6 ft.

838  **C.B.T.7** Steel Dumb Tank Barge.
Launched 27.11.1935 *60.0bp x 12.0 x 5.6 ft.
Owners - United Africa Co. Ltd., London.
Towed to Liverpool on 14.1.1936.

839  **AKUSE** Steel Motor Launch.
Launched 21.2.1936 *45.0 x 10.0 x 3.0 ft.
Owners - United Africa Co. Ltd., London.
4L2 Oil Engine, 38 bhp at 1000 rpm by G. Gardner & Sons Ltd.,
Manchester. Lifted into the water 21.2.1936.

840  **BRACKENFIELD** Single Screw Steel Cargo Steamer.
Launched 14.4.1937 Registered Liverpool.
Owners - Zillah Shipping & Carrying Co. Ltd., Liverpool.
ON 164347 657 grt 268 net 171.0 x 28.8 x 11.2 ft.
T.E.S.C.3Cy. 12¾"-21"-36"x24" stroke, 68 rhp by builder.
Cost £21,417. Invoice Price £20,000.

BRACKENFIELD                                    *World Ship Photo Library*

841  **BROOMFIELD** Single Screw Steel Cargo Steamer.
Launched 18.11.1937 Registered Liverpool.
Owners - Zillah Shipping & Carrying Co. Ltd., Liverpool.
ON 166230 657 grt 268 net 171.0 x 28.8 x 11.2 ft.
T.E.S.C.3Cy. 12¾″-21″-36″x24″ stroke, 68 rhp by builder.
Cost £21,417. Invoice Price £20,000. Later named S.E.COOPER.

BROOMFIELD                                       *World Ship Photo Library*

115

842-3 **UNNAMED** Two Gal.Stl. Lifeboats
Built 1936 *24.0 x 7.6 x 2.9 ft:
Owners - United Africa Co. Ltd., London.
Delivered on 7.4.1936 for M.S. EKETIAN.

844-5 **ANCHOR BOAT 33-34** Two Steel Anchor Boats.
Built 1937 *24.0 x 6.6 x 2.6 ft.
Owners - United Africa Co. Ltd., London.

*JOHN MILLER at Preston, with the old grain elevator in the background.*
*World Ship Photo Library*

846 **JOHN MILLER** Single Screw Steel Steam Tug.
Launched 13.1.1937 Registered Cardiff.
Owners - Millers & Corys (Cape Verde Islands) Ltd.
ON 162119 40 grt - net 63.11 x 15.1 x 6.1 ft.
C.S.C.2Cy. 9"-20"x15" stroke, 16 hp by builder.
Trials 26.2.1937. Sailed from Preston on 6.3.1937 for St. Vincent arriving in early
April. For the voyage she stowed 10 ton 4 cwt of coal in her bunkers, 6 cwt on
the stokehold platform and 2 ton in bags on the engine casing top. The coal
consumed on the voyage was 35¾ tons.

847-8 **LIGHTER NO.82-83** Two Steel Dumb Lighters.
Built 1937 *130.0 x 25.0 x 7.6 ft.
Owners - United Africa Co. Ltd., London.
These lighters were fitted with heavy sliding hatch covers.
Delivered to Liverpool on 10.2. & 24.3.1937.

849 **ROWANFIELD** Single Screw Steel Cargo Steamer.
Launched 2.6.1938 Registered Liverpool.
Owners - Zillah Shipping & Carrying Co. Ltd., Liverpool.
ON 166248 495 grt 205 net 142.5 x 27.2 x 11.4 net.
T.E.S.C.3cy. 12¾"-21"-36"x24" stroke, 72 rhp by builder.
Cost £19,008. Invoice Price £18,350.
Later names ANTONIO MIGUEL and ROWAN.

850 **AID** Galvanised Steel Gig.
Built 1936 *20.0bp x 6.0 x 2.0 ft.
Owners - United Africa Co. Ltd., London.
Fitted with an outboard motor. Delivered 24.11.1936.

851 **NORTHWICH** Twin Screw Steel Diesel Motor Tug.
Launched 9.6.1937 Registered Liverpool.
Owners - West African Lighterage & Transport Co. Ltd., Liverpool.
ON 164330 71 grt 16 net 72.3 x 17.6 x 5.9 ft.
2S.C.S.A.4Cy. 11½"x13½" stroke diesel engines, 93 nhp by H.
Widdop & Co. Ltd., Keighley, Yorks. Left Liverpool 17.7.1937, arrived Freetown,
Sierra Leone on 2.8.1937. Cost £5,864.

*ROWANFIELD.*                                        *World Ship Photo Library*

852 **NEMBE** Twin Screw Steel Diesel Motor Tug.
Launched 6.8.1937 Registered Liverpool.
Owners - West African Lighterage & Transport Co. Ltd., Liverpool.
ON 164338 71 grt 16 net 72.3 x 17.6 x 5.9 ft
2S.C.S.A.4Cy. 11½"x13½" stroke diesel engines, 93 nhp by H.
Widdop & Co. Ltd., Keighley, Yorks. Left Liverpool 9.9.1937, arrived Lagos,
Nigeria 4.10.1937. Average speed 7¾ kts. Cost £5,864.

853-4 **LIGHTER No.84-85** Two Steel Dumb Lighters.
Built 1937 *130.0 x 25.0 x 7.6 ft.
Owners - United Africa Co. Ltd., London.
These lighters were fitted with heavy sliding hatch covers.
Delivered to Liverpool in December 1937 and 15.1.1938.

855 **LIGHTER NO.90** Steel Dumb Lighter.
Built 1938 *130.0 x 25.0 x 7.6 ft.
Owners - United Africa Co. Ltd., London.
Fitted with heavy sliding hatch covers.
Delivered to Liverpool in October 1938.

856-8 **LIGHTER NO.117-119** Three Steel Dumb Lighters.
Built 1938 *130.0 x 25.0 x 7.6 ft.
Owners - United Africa Co. Ltd., London.
These lighters were fitted with heavy sliding hatch covers.
Delivered to Liverpool in November and December 1938.

859 **HOHOE** Steel Motor Barge.
Built 1938 Registered London.
Owners - United Africa Co. Ltd., London.
ON - 37 grt 19 net 60.0bp x 15.0 x 5.6 ft.
Widdop 2Cyl. diesel engine, 60 bhp at 400 rpm.

*COLONEL RATSEY at Preston prior to departure.*　　　　　*World Ship Photo Library*

860 **COLONEL RATSEY** Gal.Stl. Quarterwheel Cargo Steamer.
Launched 3.5.1939 Registered London.
Owners - United Africa Co. Ltd., London.
ON 167278 758 grt 414 net 172.5 x 35.1 x 8.0 ft.
2xC.S.C.2Cy. 17"-37"x48" stroke, 93 hp by builder.
Trials 27.6.1939. Built to push and pull six loaded barges. Sailed from Preston
3.7.1939 in convoy to Burutu, Nigeria via Las Palmas, arriving on 31.7.1939. For
the voyage she stowed 80 tons of coal in her bunkers and on the stokehold floor,
100 tons in the tween deck and 75½ tons in No.2 hold. She loaded 63 tons of
water ballast, 9 tons of drinking water and 6 tons of stores and carried a crew of
nine with personal effects. Her deadweight was 338½ tons drawing 5'10½" of
water. She was named in honour of Colonel H. E. Ratsey, a director of the United
Africa Co., Ltd., which he joined in 1893, serving for 47 years.

861 **UNNAMED** Steel Ferry Pontoon.
Built 1939 *72.0 x 20.0 x 3.0 ft.
Owners - United Africa Co. Ltd., London.
Delivered to Liverpool on 23.5.1939 for shipment to Hwamakope.

862 **FRESHWATER** Single Screw Steel Steam Water Boat.
Launched 23.3.1940 Registered London.
Owners - The Admiralty, London. (Royal Fleet Auxiliary).
ON 149287 264 grt 101 net 121.2 x 24.7 x 11.7 ft.
T.E.S.C.3Cy. 11"-18"-30"x21" stroke, 59 hp by builder.
Cost £24,162. Capable of carrying 205 tons of fresh water.
Trials 8.8.1940. Left Fleetwood for Chatham on 11.9.1940. Later named PORTO
GRANDE.

118

*The launch of FRESHWATER, 23.3.1940.*

**863 FRESHET** Single Screw Steel Steam Water Boat.
Launched 6.7.1940 Registered London.
Owners - The Admiralty, London. (Royal Fleet Auxiliary).
ON 168228 264 grt 101 net 121.2 x 24.7 x 11.7 ft.
T.E.S.C.3Cy. 11"-18"-30"x21" stroke, 59 hp by builder.
Cost £24,162. Capable of carrying 205 tons of fresh water. Completed 10.12.1940.
Left Fleetwood for Greenock 17.12.1940.

*FRESHET.*                                            *World Ship Photo Library*

**864 MAPLEFIELD** Single Screw Steel Cargo Steamer.
Launched 28.1.1941. Registered Liverpool.
Owners - Zillah Shipping & Carrying Co. Ltd., Liverpool.
ON 166322 495 grt 205 net 142.5 x 27.2 x 11.4 ft.
T.E.S.C.3Cy. 12¾"-21"-36"x24" stroke, 68 rhp by builder.
Delivered to owners 12.6.1941.

*LARCHFIELD.*                              *World Ship Photo Library*

865   **LARCHFIELD** Single Screw Steel Cargo Steamer.
Launched 11.6.1941 Registered Liverpool.
Owners - Zillah Shipping & Carrying Co. Ltd., Liverpool.
ON 168803 493 grt 215 net 142.5 x 27.2 x 11.4 ft.
T.E.S.C.3Cy. 12¾"-21"-36"x24" stroke, 68 rhp by builder.
Delivered to owners 15.10.1941.

866-7   **UNNAMED** Two Steel Ferry Pontoons.
Built 1941 *72.0 x 20.0 x 3.0 ft.
Owners - United Africa Co. Ltd., London.
Delivered to Liverpool by road on 7 & 8.7.1941 (866) and on 21 & 22.7.1941 (867)
for shipment to Senchi and Yeji.

868   **FRESHBROOK** Single Screw Steel Steam Water Boat.
Launched 5.11.1941 Registered London.
Owners - The Admiralty, London. (Royal Fleet Auxiliary).
ON 168273 278 grt 99 net 121.2 x 24.7 x 11.7 ft.
T.E.S.C.3Cy. 11"-18"-30"x21" stroke, 59 hp by builder.
Cost £29,333. Trials 11.4.1942.

869   **FRESHENER** Single Screw Steel Steam Water Boat.
Launched 16.3.1942 Registered London.
Owners - The Admiralty, London. (Royal Fleet Auxiliary).
ON 168298 278 grt 99 net 121.2 x 24.7 x 11.7 ft.
T.E.S.C.3Cy. 11"-18"-30"x21" stroke, 59 hp by builder.
Cost £29,333. Trials 17.7.1942.

870   **FRESHLAKE** Single Screw Steel Steam Water Boat.
Launched 15.7.1942 Registered London.
Owners - The Admiralty, London. (Royal Fleet Auxiliary)
ON 168333 278 grt 99 net 121.2 x 24.7 x 11.7 ft.
T.E.S.C.3Cy. 11"-18"-30"x21" stroke, 59 hp by builder.
Cost £29,333. Trials 10.11.1942.

871 **FRESHMERE** Single Screw Steel Steam Water Boat.
Launched 23.11.1942 Registered London.
Owners - The Admiralty, London. (Royal Fleet Auxiliary).
ON 168407 283 grt 93 net 121.2 x 24.7 x 11.7 ft.
T.E.S.C.3Cy. 11″-18″-30″x21″ stroke, 59 hp by builder.
Trials 18.3.1943.

*FRESHPOOL.* *World Ship Photo Library*

872 **FRESHPOOL** Single Screw Steel Steam Water Boat.
Launched 11.3.1943 Registered London.
Owners - The Admiralty, London. (Royal Fleet Auxiliary).
ON 168463 283 grt 93 net 121.2 x 24.7 x 11.7 ft.
T.E.S.C.3Cy. 11″-18″-30″x21″ stroke, 59 hp by builder.
Trials 20.6.1943.

873 **FRESHWELL** Single Screw Steel Steam Water Boat.
Launched 2.7.1943 Registered London.
Owners - The Admiralty, London. (Royal Fleet Auxiliary).
ON 169624 283 grt 93 net 121.2 x 24.7 x 11.7 ft.
T.E.S.C.3Cy. 11″-18″-30″x21″ stroke, 59 hp by builder.
Trials 26.10.1943.

*FRESHWELL.* *Wright and Logan Ltd.*

*FRESHBURN.*                                    *World Ship Photo Library*

874  **FRESHBURN** Single Screw Steel Steam Water Boat.
Launched 29.10.1943 Registered London.
Owners - The Admiralty, London. (Royal Fleet Auxiliary).
ON 169811 283 grt 93 net 121.2 x 24.7 x 11.7 ft.
T.E.S.C.3Cy. 11"-18"-30"x21" stroke, 59 hp by builder.
Trials 22.3.1944.

875  **FRESHFORD** Single Screw Steel Steam Water Boat.
Launched 23.3.1944 Registered London.
Owners - The Admiralty, London. (Royal Fleet Auxiliary).
ON 169906 283 grt 93 net 121.2 x 24.7 x 11.7 ft.
T.E.S.C.3Cy. 11"-18"-30"x21" stroke, 59 hp by builder.

*FRESHFORD.*                                    *Wright and Logan Ltd.*

*FRESHTARN.*

876  **FRESHTARN** Single Screw Steel Steam Water Boat.
Launched 22.8.1944 Registered London.
Owners - The Admiralty, London. (Royal Fleet Auxiliary).
ON 169994 283 grt 93 net 121.2 x 24.7 x 11.7 ft.
T.E.S.C.3Cy. 11"-18"-30"x21" stroke, 59 hp by builder.

877  **BOMBARDON TANKS** Steel Mulberry Harbour Sections.
Built January and February 1944.
Owners - The Admiralty, London.
These sections were built to provide a floating breakwater,
200 ft long and 25 ft high, mostly submerged, at the artificial harbour constructed
at Arromanches, Normandy in support of the Allied assault on the Continent of
Europe on the 6.6.1944. They were lost at sea in a storm whilst being towed to
Normandy. Bombardon was the code name for them.

878  **FRESHPOND** Single Screw Steel Steam Water Boat.
Launched 28.8.1945 Registered London.
Owners - The Admiralty, London. (Royal Fleet Auxiliary).
ON 180790 283 grt 93 net 121.2 x 24.7 x 11.7 ft.
T.E.S.C.3Cy. 11"-18"-30"x21" stroke, 59 hp by builder.

*FRESHPOND.*

**879-884   L.C.M.7147-7152** Six Twin Screw Steel Landing Craft.
Built 1945 *57.10 x 16.0 x 3.8½ ft.
Owners - The Admiralty, London.
Displacement 63 tons loaded with 35 ton tank, 28 tons light.
Two 250 bhp Hudson Crusader Petrol Engines. Speed 10 kts.
These vessels were Mark 7 Landing Craft Mechanised and were fitted with twin rudders.

**885   FRESHSPRAY** Single Screw Steel Steam Water Boat.
Launched 5.3.1946 Registered London.
Owners - The Admiralty, London. (Royal Fleet Auxiliary).
ON 180895 283 grt 93 net 121.2 x 24.7 x 11.7 ft.
T.E.S.C.3Cy. 11"-18"-30"x21" stroke, 59 hp by builder.
Left Fleetwood 9.8.1946 for Falmouth arriving 11.8.1946. Sailed 14.8.1946 for Malta arriving 26.8.1946. Steamed a distance of 2345 nautical miles in 12 days 6 minutes using 46 tons of coal.

*FRESHSPRING at Bristol soon after her arrival in 1980.*          B. Phillips

**886   FRESHSPRING** Single Screw Steel Steam Water Boat.
Launched 15.8.1946 Registered London.
Owners - The Admiralty, London. (Royal Fleet Auxiliary).
ON 181554 289 grt 100 net 121.2 x 24.7 x 11.7 ft.
T.E.S.C.3Cy. 11"-18"-30"x21" stroke, 59 hp by builder.

**887   UNNAMED** Steel Ferry Pontoon.
Built 1945 *45.0 x 15.0 x 2.6 ft.
Owners - United Africa Co. Ltd., London.
Delivered to Liverpool 20.9.1945 for shipment.

**888   UNNAMED** Steel Ferry Pontoon.
Built 1945 *72.0 x 20.0 x 3.0 ft.
Owners - United Africa Co. Ltd., London.
Delivered to Liverpool Jan.1946 for shipment to River Volta.

HAZELFIELD.　　　　　　　　　　　　　　World Ship Photo Library

889　**HAZELFIELD** Single Screw Steel Cargo Steamer.
Launched 18.8.1947 Registered Liverpool.
Owners - Zillah Shipping & Carrying Co. Ltd., Liverpool.
ON 182412 692 grt 324 net 178.4 x 28.9 x 11.4 ft.
T.E.S.C.3Cy. 13¼"-22½"-38"x24" stroke, 450 bhp by builder.
The keel was laid on 23.8.1946. She made her maiden voyage from Preston to
Belfast with a cargo of coal in April 1948 and was the first oil fired vessel to be
built for her owners. Later named SPRAYVILLE, FOULI and AGIOS GERASSIMOS

890-2　**UNNAMED** Three Steel Light Beacon Boats.
Launched 20.1. & 21.4.1949 *55.0 x 22.0 x 11.0 ft.
Owners - Mersey Docks & Harbour Board, Liverpool.
They were all towed to their respective stations, Formby, Crosby and Fairway on
the River Mersey approach channel.

893-8　**UNNAMED** Six Steel Dumb Towing Barges.
Built 1950 *135.0bp x 28.6 x 8.0 ft.
Owners - United Africa Co. Ltd., London.
Built for service on the Niger and Benue Rivers, Nigeria.

899　**OKORODUDU** Steel Quarterwheel Steamer.
Built 1951 Registered London.
Owners - United Africa Co. Ltd., London.
ON 184729 355 grt 205 net 150.0 x 34.1 x 5.7 ft
2xT.E.S.C.3Cy. 9½"-16"-25"x14" stroke, 415 bhp by Lobnitz. Shipped in pieces
from Liverpool to Burutu, Nigeria where she was reerected in 1952.

900　**CHADDA** Steel Quarterwheel Steamer.
Built 1951 Registered London.
Owners - United Africa Co. Ltd., London.
ON 186054 357 grt 206 net 150.1 x 34.1 x 5.8 ft.
2xT.E.S.C.3Cy. 9½"-16"-25"x14" stroke, 415 bhp by Lobnitz.
Shipped in pieces from Liverpool to Burutu, Nigeria in the Spring of 1952 where
she was reerected the following year. Named after the River Chadda, later
known as the Benue.

901  **JOHN VERNON** Steel Dumb River Lighter.
Launched 7.10.1952 Registered Liverpool.
Owners - Spillers Ltd., London.
ON 185448 - 126 net 94.0 x 18.6 x 8.6 ft.
Built to carry 200 tons of cargo on a 6½ ft draft.

902  **RICHARD VERNON** Steel Dumb River Lighter.
Launched 14.4.1953 Registered Liverpool.
Owners - Spillers Ltd., London.
ON 185466 - 129 net 94.0 x 18.6 x 8.6 ft.
Built to carry 200 tons of cargo on a 6½ ft draft.
Left Lytham for Liverpool on 28.4.1953.

*The Windermere ferry DRAKE.*

903  **DRAKE** Steel Steam Chain Ferry.
Built 1954, trials on Lake Windermere 13.7.1954.
Owners - County Councils of Westmorland and Lancashire.
ON - 70 grt - net *95.0oa (65.0bp) x 30.0 x 3.6 ft.
S2Cy. 6"x7" stroke IVB, HS177, 110 lb psi, by builder.
Hull transported to British Railways' slipway at Lakeside in seven sections on 10-23.6.1954, where she was assembled. Fitting out was completed in the afternoon of the 12.7.1954. Towed up Lake Windermere to the ferry site on 13.7.1954, coupled up, tried out and handed over. Invoice price £22,500.

**APPENDIX I - Vessels known to have been built at Lytham prior to the founding of the Lytham Shipbuilding and Engineering Company Ltd.**

**GRACE** Wood Brigantine.
Built 1818. Registered Preston.
Owners in 1855 - Seth Walmsley, Corn Merchant, Preston & James Butler, Master Mariner, Lytham.
ON 17264 98 tons reg. 66.2 x 18.3 x 9.4 ft.

**NANNY & BETTY** Wood Schooner.
Built 1821. Registered Fleetwood.
Owners in 1853 - J.Fisher & Co., Fleetwood.
ON 17229 55 tons reg.

**HARRIET** Wood Schooner.
Built 1824. Registered Belfast.
Owners in 1875 - William Hamilton, Larne.
ON - 35 tons reg.

**UNION** Wood Schooner.
Built 1826. Registered Preston.
Owners in 1875 - J.Thomas, Aberthaw, Glams.
ON - 39 tons reg.

**MOLLY & ANN** Wood Smack.
Built 1827. Registered Whitehaven.
Owners in 1875 - Richard Sumner, Whitehaven.
ON 17270 52 tons reg.

**TOM** Wood Schooner.
Built 1828. Registered Preston.
Owners in 1835 - Cookson & Co., Preston.
ON - 96 tons reg.

**SISTERS** Wood Sloop.
Built 1829. Registered Greenock.
Owners in 1875 - R.S.McMorland, Greenock.
ON 15918 42 tons reg.

**BRITANNIA** Wood Schooner.
Built 1837. Registered Carnarvon.
Owners in 1875 - Griffith Jones, Chester.
ON - 58 tons reg.

**FLEETWOOD** Wood Flat.
Built 1837. Registered Fleetwood.
Owners in 1875 - J.Chadwick, Runcorn.
ON - 38 tons reg.

**HESKETH** Wood Schooner.
Built 1837. Registered Preston.
Owners in 1875 - Blackpool, Lytham & Southport Steam Packet Co. Ltd., Preston.
ON 19831 41 tons reg.

**BRAZEN NOSE** Wood Smack.
Built 1839. Registered Fleetwood.
Owners in 1875 - Peter Leadbetter, Fleetwood.
ON 17237 28 tons reg.

**SIR ROBERT PEEL** Wood Wherry.
Built 1840. Registered Preston.
Owners in 1875 - John Hull, Tarleton.
ON - 37 tons reg.

**BUONY** Wood Flat.
Built 1841. Registered Preston.
Owners in 1875 - Anthony Cartmell, Parbold.
ON 24144 38 tons reg.

**PRINCE OF WALES** Wood Flat.
Built 1842. Registered Fleetwood.
Owners in 1858 - John James & William Henry Smith, Preston.
ON 24263 40 tons reg. 69.2 x 15.3 x 5.4 ft.

**OCEAN CHILD** Wood Ketch.
Built 1846. Registered Gloucester.
Owners in 1875 - C.Camm, Arlingham, Glos.
ON 26714 43 tons reg.

**AGNES** Wood Schooner.
Built 1856 by James Bannister. Registered Drogheda.
Owners in 1856 - Joseph & Edward Pyke, Preston & Dennis Drum, Master
Mariner, Drogheda.
ON 19837 86 grt 73 net 73.0 x 19.7 x 9.7 ft.

**CONFIDENCE** Wood Schooner.
Built 1856. Registered Preston.
Owners in 1856 - Thomas & James Latham, Master Mariners, Lytham & Tarleton
& others.
ON 14921 51 tons reg. 69.7 x 16.9 x 7.1 ft.

**JANE & ELLEN** Wood Schooner.
Built 1857. Registered Fleetwood.
Owners in 1863 - Ward & Company, Fleetwood.
ON 19295 60 tons reg. 63.0 x 18.4 x 8.0 ft.

**OCEAN QUEEN** Wood Schooner.
Built 1860. Registered Preston.
Owners in 1863 - Iddon & Company, Preston.
ON - 73 tons reg. 70.0 x 18.0 x 8.5 ft.
Builder - McMurdie, Lytham.

**APPENDIX II - Vessels built at Preston by Smith of Ashton Quay.**

**MARY AGNES** Wood Schooner.
Built 1859. Registered Preston.
Owners in 1875 - J. Ashcroft & Company, Barrow.
ON 26852 83 grt 74 net 82.0 x 19.0 x 9.2 ft.
Built for the coasting trade.

**THOMAS BLYTHE** Iron Barque.
Built 1859. Registered Liverpool.
Owners in 1874 - D.W. Bain & Company, Portreath, Cornwall.
ON 27648 387 tons o.m. 135.0 x 25.0 x 17.0 ft.
Built for the Indian trade.

**PHILLIS** Wood Schooner.
Built 1860. Registered Preston.
Owners in 1863 - Yates & Company, Preston.
ON 28902 69 tons o.m. 72.0 x 18.0 x 8.5 ft.
Built for the coasting trade.

**ANN POTTS** Wood Schooner.
Built 1862. Registered Fleetwood.
Owners in 1863 - Fair & Company, Fleetwood.
ON - 85 tons o.m. 78.0 x 18.8 x 9.5 ft.
Built for the coasting trade.

**ANN SHEPHERD** Wood Schooner.
Built 1862. Registered Fleetwood.
Owners in 1863 - Fair & Company, Fleetwood.
ON 42548 85 tons o.m. 78.0 x 18.8 x 9.5 ft.
Built for the coasting trade.

**GUILD MAYOR** Wood Schooner.
Built 1862. Registered Preston.
Owners in 1863 - Yates & Company, Preston.
ON 28906 90 tons o.m. 89.6 x 22.6 x 10.2 ft.
Built for the coasting trade.

**EDITH** Wood Schooner.
Built 1866. Registered Preston.
Owners in 1874 - D. Cooper, Valparaiso.
ON 52886 135 tons o.m. 99.0 x 23.2 x 11.0 ft.
Later named MERCEDES LUISA.

**APPENDIX III - Vessels built at Preston by Richard Smith and Company of Ashton Quay.**

**LILY OF THE WEST** Wood Yacht.
Built 1869. Registered -
Owners in 1872 - G.M. Neilson, Ardrossan.
ON - 17 tons o.m.

**PRINCESS** Wood Yacht.
Built 1869. Registered -
Owners in 1872 - Lord MacDonald, Cowes.
ON - 19 tons o.m. 50.0 x 9.3 ft.

**SHEITAN** Wood Schooner.
Built 1869. Registered Preston.
Owners in 1874 - P. Ball & Company, Mevagissey, Cornwall.
ON 62763 140 grt - net 99.3 x 23.0 x 10.8 ft.

**LAWSONS** Wood Schooner.
Built 1870. Registered Fleetwood.
Owners in 1874 - Wignall & Company, Fleetwood.
ON 63933 134 grt 120 net 100.3 x 22.8 x 10.8 ft.

**PEARL** Single Screw Wood Steam Yacht.
Built 1871. Registered -
Owners in 1875 - W.H. Marwood., Whitby, Yorks.
ON - 22 tons o.m. 52.0 x 10.0 ft.
C.10"x10" stroke by builder.

**AVON** Wood Yacht.
Built 1872. Registered -
Owners in 1878 - E. Greaves.
ON - 25 tons o.m.

**GLENELG** Single Screw Comp. Steam Yacht.
Built 1872. Registered Glasgow.
Owners in 1875 - Mrs. Ann Hector, Montrose, Scotland.
ON 71741 24 grt 8 net 56.2 x 11.7 x 6.1 ft.
C.2Cy.10"-10"x10" stroke, 10 hp by builder.

**MAYBIRD** Single Screw Wood Steam Yacht.
Built 1872. Registered Exeter.
Owners in 1872 - T.W. Clagett, Leicester.
ON 69566 35 grt 23 net 62.7 x 14.5 x 6.5 ft.
C.2Cy.9¾"-17"x15" stroke by Willoughby, Plymouth.

**CRESCENT** Wood Paddle Steam Yacht.
Built 1873. Registered Dublin.
Owners in 1873 - G.E.R. Dalton, Kingstown, Co. Dublin.
ON 67768 16 grt 10 net 47.4 x 10.4 x 5.6 ft.
Osc.2Cy.9″-16″x16″ stroke, 16 hp by builder.

**FLORENCE** Single Screw Iron Steamer.
Built 1873. Registered Preston.
Owners in 1874 - Lord Kilcoursin, Wheathampstead, Herts.
ON 69710 24 grt 14 net 71.3 x 11.1 x 4.85 ft.
I.D.A.2Cy.12″-12″x10″ stroke by builder.
Later named KONG-HUN.

**LELLA** Single Screw Wood Steam Yacht.
Built 1874. Registered Liverpool.
Owners in 1874 - H.O. George, Chester.
ON 69359 25 grt 12 net 60.8 x 11.5 x 6.7 ft.
C.10″x10″ stroke, 12 hp by builder.

**ROB ROY** Single Screw Wood Steam Yacht.
Built 1874. Registered -
Owners in 1879 - W.C. Williamson, Glasgow.
ON - 15 tons o.m. 47.0 x 8.6 ft.
C.10″x10″ stroke by builder.

**VULCAN** Twin Screw Iron Steamer.
Built 1877. Registered Preston.
Owners in 1877 - James Seed & others, Preston.
ON 73475 79 grt 50 net 84.3 x 17.8 x 7.6 ft.
2 I.C.D.A. 40 hp by Cornelius Parish, Preston.

**RESOLUTE** Iron Steamer.
Built 1877. Registered Harwich.
Owners in 1878 - The Great Eastern Railway Company, London.
ON 78978 33 grt 22 net 66.1 x 12.1 x 6.2 ft.
36 nhp by builder.

**CORMORANT** Single Screw Comp. Steam Yacht.
Built 1878. Registered Scarborough.
Owners in 1878 - Henry H. Forster, Scarborough.
ON 77348 39 grt 27 net 62.0 x 12.6 x 7.6 ft.
C.2Cy.9″-18″x12″ stroke, 17 hp by builder.

**BELTURBET** Iron Steamer.
Built 1880. Registered Preston.
Owners in 1880 - Richard Smith, Shipbuilder, Preston.
ON 81232 41 grt 23 net 72.0 x 12.5 x 5.1 ft. 15 hp by builder.
Later owned by John G.V. Porter & Company, Fermanagh.

**IBIS** Single Screw Iron Steam Tug.
Built 1880. Registered London.
Owners in 1880 - The P. & O. S. N. Company, London.
ON 85098 31 grt 5 net 63.0 x 12.6 x 6.5 ft.
C.2Cy.14″-25″x16″ stroke, 35 hp by Thames Ironworks.

**SPHINX** Single Screw Iron Steam Tug.
Built 1880. Registered London.
Owners in 1880 - The P. & O. S. N. Company, London.
ON 85099 31 grt 5 net 63.0 x 12.6 x 6.5 ft.
C.2Cy.14″-25″x16″ stroke, 35 hp by Thames Ironworks.

**SUNBURY** Twin Screw Iron Steam Tug.
Built 1880. Registered London.
Owners in 1902 - Clements Knowling & Co. Ltd., Brentford.
ON 115812 32 grt 8 net 60.5 x 13.5 x 5.5 ft.
2xC.2Cy.12½″-12½″x18″ stroke by builder.

**JACKAL** Twin Screw Iron Steamer.
Built 1881. Registered Preston.
Owners in 1881 - John F. Hitchins, Falmouth.
ON 81234 115 grt 78 net 89.2 x 19.0 x 7.5 ft.
2 I.C.D.A. 30 hp by builder.

**MABEL** Single Screw Iron Steam Tug.
Built 1881. Registered Brettesnoes.
Owners in 1885 - J. Jensen.
ON - 114 grt 61 net 85.7 x 16.5 x 9.0 ft.
C.I.2Cy.17"-32"x20" stroke, 50 hp by builder.
Later named NORLAENNINGEN.

69 **DUDDON** Single Screw Iron Steamer.
Built 1882. Registered Whitehaven..
Owners in 1883 - G. Nelson & Sons, Whitehaven.
ON 84632 326 grt 144 net 144.7 x 23.1 x 10.6 ft.
C.2Cy.17"-34"x24" stroke, 45 nhp by builder.
Later named HANSEAT 2, RELIS, VIRURAND, RELLI, and HIIULA.

**RIBBLE** Single Screw Iron Steamer.
Built 1883. Registered Whitehaven.
Owners in 1883 - G. Nelson & Sons, Whitehaven.
ON 84634 215 grt 100 net 119.8 x 21.2 x 8.6 ft.
C.I.2Cy.15"-28"x22" stroke, 50 hp by J. Stevenson & Company, Preston. Fitted
with three masts.

72 **SOLWAY QUEEN** Single Screw Iron Steamer.
Built 1883. Registered Whitehaven.
Owners in 1883 - The Solway Steamship Co. Ltd., Whitehaven.
ON 84635 304 grt 128 net 145.0 x 23.1 x 10.2 ft.
C.I.2Cy.17"-34"x24" stroke, 70 hp by builder.
Fitted with three masts.

78 **SOLWAY KING** Single Screw Iron Steamer.
Built 1883. Registered Whitehaven.
Owners in 1883 - The Solway Steamship Co. Ltd., Whitehaven.
ON 84637 309 grt 140 net 145.0 x 23.1 x 10.2 ft.
C.I.2Cy.17"-34"x24" stroke, 60 hp by builder.
Fitted with three masts. Later named RILDA.

**ALIANZA** Single Screw Iron Steam Tug.
Built 1884. Registered Preston.
Owners in 1884 - Cory Brothers & Company.
ON 89609 26 grt 2 net 52.4 x 12.7 x 6.3 ft.
C.2Cy.11"-20"x15" stroke, 17 hp by builder.

**RICHMOND** Single Screw Iron Steamer.
Built 1885. Registered London.
Owners in 1885 - Thomas Andrew Walker, London. (He was the main contractor
for the construction of Preston Dock which he started in 1884).
ON 95417 33 grt 22 net 60.0 x 13.2 x 5.4 ft.
C.2Cy.11"-20"x15" stroke, 35 hp by builder.

**ETHEL** Single Screw Wood Steam Yacht.
Built 1886. Registered -
Owners in 1886 - G. Anderton, Preston.
ON - 10 tons o.m. 33.0 x 9.0 ft.
C.2Cy.5"-5"x6" stroke by builder.

**KINGFISHER** Single Screw Steel Steam Yacht.
Built 1887. Registered -
Owners in 1887 - E.R. Belilios, Hong Kong.
ON - 66 g - n 102.0 x 13.5 ft. after lengthening in 1890.
C.3Cy.9"-14"-24½"x18" stroke by builder.

**Amongst others known to have been built by the Company were several steam
tugs for the Bridgewater Canal.**

# INDEX I
## Owners or agents showing yard number of vessel, vessels built at Lytham by Richard Smith & Company and by Lytham Shipbuilding & Engineering Co. (Ltd.)

| | |
|---|---|
| Admiralty, London | 569, 570, 571, 572, 573, 574, 575, 576, 577, 836, 862, 863, 868, 869, 870, 871, 872, 873, 874, 875, 876, 877, 878, 879, 880, 881, 882, 883, 884, 885, 886. |
| African & Eastern Trade Corporation Ltd., London. | 594, 595, 615, 616, 617, 618, 619, 620, 621, 622, 649, 654, 655, 659, 660, 661, 662, 685, 686, 687, 688, 689, 691, 694, 695, 696, 697, 707, 708, 709, 710, 726, 727, 728, 752, 755, 756, 760, 761, 762, 763, 764, 765, 766. |
| African Oil Nuts Co. Ltd., London. | 589. |
| Alliance & Dublin Consumers Gas Company, Dublin. | 578, 600. |
| Alty, Henry, Brickmaker, Hesketh Bank, Preston. | 272. |
| Arauco Company. | 366, 488. |
| Associated Portland Cement Manufacturers Ltd., London. | 725. |
| Bates, E. & Sons Ltd., Liverpool | 736, 737, 738, 739, 740, 741. |
| Beira Boating Co. Ltd., London. | 318. |
| Birch, J. & Co. Ltd., London. | 638, 639, 640, 641, 642, 643, 650, 651, 652, 653. |
| Bombay Port Trust, Bombay. | 285. |
| Booth S.S. Co. Ltd., Liverpool. | 262, 273, 606. |
| Boyne Valley Launch Company, Drogheda. | 320. |
| Bridgewater Colliery & Ellesmere Estate. | 462. |
| Bromport S.S. Co. Ltd. | 629, 630, 631, 632, 633, 634. |
| Brown, Hugo & Co. Ltd., Liverpool. | 314 |
| Brunner Mond & Co. Ltd., Northwich, Cheshire. | WATERWITCH (1894). |
| Caernarvon Port Trust. | 304. |
| Cecil S.S. Co. Ltd., Runcorn. | 149 |
| Constantine, Manchester. | 353. |
| Cook, J. W. & Co. Ltd., London. | 264. |
| Cork Harbour Commissioners. | LILY (1896). |
| County Councils of Westmorland & Lancashire. | 903. |
| Crosfield, Joseph & Sons Ltd., Soapworks, Warrington. | 613. |

| | |
|---|---|
| Crown Agents for the Colonies - | |
| Gold Coast. | 623, 624, 625, 626. |
| Northern Nigeria. | 491, 492, 493, 494, 495, 496, 735. |
| Uganda. | 394, 395, 499, 500, 501, 502, 503, 504, 520, 646, 647, 648, 690. |
| Edmondson, Thomas, Lytham. | 174, TOILER (1894). |
| Egyptian Delta Light Railways Ltd. | 274. |
| Elder Dempster Lines Ltd. | 771, 835. |
| Fylde Steam Fishing Co. Ltd., Fleetwood. | 346. |
| Gill, C. & Co. Ltd., London. | 345. |
| Grain Elevating & Automatic Weighing Co. Ltd., Liverpool. | NEW BOYNE (1896). |
| Hepburn, G. & Son, Liverpool. | 319. |
| Holt, J. & Co. Ltd. | 326, 381, 404, 497, 498, 506, 510, 602, 603, 604, 607, 608, 609, 610, 611, 612, 627, 628, 637, 656, 657, 658, 698, 699, 700, 701, 702, 703, 704, 705, 718, 719, 720, 729, 730, 731, 787, 788, 789, 790, 791, 815, 816, 817, 818, 819. |
| Hutton & Co. Ltd., Liverpool. | 293, 294. |
| Jones, Burton & Co. Ltd., Liverpool. | 323, 354, 355, 356, 357, 358, 359, 371, 372, 373, 374, 375, 376, 377, 378, 379, 380, 406, 407, 441, 444, 475, 505, 507, 511, 582, 583, 584, 772. |
| Japp & Kirby, Liverpool. | 327. |
| Kaiser Steam Tug Co. Ltd., London. | 234, 311. |
| King, R. & W., Bristol. | 414. |
| Knight Errant Tug Co. Ltd., Liverpool. | 337. |
| Lancashire & Western Sea Fisheries Joint Committee. | 814. |
| La Societe Anonyme des Huileries du Congo Belge. | 445, 446, 448, 451, 452, 453, 482, 489, 635, 636, 678, 679, 680, 681, 682, 684, 785, 793. |
| Leone, J. | 409. |
| Lever Brothers Ltd., Port Sunlight. | OLD HOME (1898), 141, 184, 185, |
| London, Midland & Scottish Railway Co. Ltd., London. | 645, 770. |
| Manchester Corporation. | 238. |
| Marquis of Zetland. | 316. |
| McNeill Scott, Liverpool. | 419. |
| Mersey Docks & Harbour Board. | 362, 890, 891, 892. |
| Mersey Mission to Seamen. | 313. |
| Mersey Pilots. | 321. |
| Miller Brothers Ltd., Liverpool. | 401, 402, 403, 405, 433, 592. |
| Millers & Corys (Cape Verde Islands), Ltd. | 846. |

| | |
|---|---|
| Monk, David & William and William Preston, Preston. | 315. |
| Monks, Hall & Co. Ltd., Warrington. | HELVETIA (1892), PROGRESS (1893). |
| Morrison, J. S., London. | 300. |
| Niger Co. Ltd., London. | 299, 328, 329, 330, 332, 339, 340, 352, 367, 368, 382, 389, 390, 391, 396, 397, 398, 399, 400, 410, 411, 412, 413, 415, 416, 417, 427, 428, 429, 434, 435, 436, 437, 438, 439, 440, 449, 450, 460, 461, 463, 464, 465, 466, 476, 477, 478, 483, 484, 485, 486, 580, 581, 585, 586, 587, 588, 593, 663, 664, 665, 666, 667, 668, 669, 670, 671, 672, 673, 675, 676, 677, 692, 693, 706, 711, 712, 713, 714, 715, 716, 717, 721, 722, 723, 724, 732, 733, 734, 742, 743, 744, 745, 746, 747, 748, 749, 750, 751, 754, 757, 758, 759, 767, 768, 769, 773, 774, 775, 776, 779, 780, 781 |
| Nigerian Transport Co. Ltd. | 784. |
| North Staffordshire Railway Company. | 338. |
| Pacific Steam Navigation Co. Ltd., Liverpool. | 290, 350, 387, 474, 487. |
| Preston, Lytham & Southport S.S. Co. Ltd., Preston. | PRINCE GEORGE (1892). |
| Rea Transport Co. Ltd., Liverpool London. | 206, 291, 307, 324, 331, 333, 334, 335, 336, 342, 343, 349, 365, 369, 392, 420, 454, 467, 468, 469, 470, 471, 472, 473, 479, 480, 481, 514, 515, 516. |
| Rodas, F. M., Bilbao, Spain. | 148. |
| Rogers & Sons, Wolverhampton. | 351. |
| Smith, J. & A., Birkenhead. | 308. |
| Soundy & Son, London. | SECRET (1892). |
| South Metropolitan Gas Company, London. | 753. |
| Spillers Ltd., London. | 901, 902. |
| S.S. FULWOOD Ltd., Preston. | 277. |
| Summers, J. & Sons Ltd. | 596, 597, 598, 599. |
| Swanzy, F. & A. & Co. Ltd. London. | 322, 325, 393, 418, 431, 432, 447, 601. |
| United Africa Co. Ltd., London. | 777, 778, 782, 783, 792, 794, 795, 796, 797, 798, 799, 800, 801, 802, 803, 804, 805, 806, 807, 808, 809, 811, 813, 820, 821, 822, 823, 824, 825, 826, 827, 828, 829, 830, 831, 832, 833, 834, 838, 839, 842, 843, 844, 845, 847, 848, 850, 853, 854, 855, 856, 857, 858, 859, 860, 861, 866, 867, 887, 888, 893, 894, 895, 896, 897, 898, 899, 900. |
| United Alkali Co. Ltd., Liverpool. | DAVY (1891), FARADAY (1891), LEBLANC (1891). |
| Valle Azevedo & Co. Ltd., Liverpool. | 317. |
| Vera Cruz Coal Company, Mexico. | 458. |
| Volta Transport Co. Ltd., Liverpool. | 459. |

| | |
|---|---|
| War Office, London. | 509, 517, 519, 521, 522, 523, 524, 525, 526, 527, 528, 529, 530, 531, 532, 533, 534, 535, 536, 538, 539, 540, 541, 542, 543, 544, 545, 546, 547, 548, 549, 550, 551, 552, 553, 554, 555, 556, 557, 558, 559, 560, 561, 562, 563, 564, 565, 566, 567, 568. |
| Welsh, T. & Co. Ltd., Liverpool. | 614. |
| West African Lighterage & Transport Co. Ltd., Liverpool. | 786, 837, 851, 852. |
| Young, Alex. & Co. Ltd., Liverpool. | 370. |
| Zillah Shipping & Carrying Co. Ltd., Liverpool. | 490, 508, 518, 579, 590, 605, 644, 674, 840, 841, 849, 864, 865, 889. |
| Unknown Owners. | KINGFISHER (c.1894) 267, 268, 269, 270, 271, 275, 276, 278, 279, 280, 281, 282, 283, 284, 286, 287, 288, 289, 292, 295, 296, 297, 298, 301, 302, 303, 305, 306, 309, 310, 312, 383, 455, 683. |

**South American Owners and Agents.**

| | |
|---|---|
| A. A. Martins, Brazil. | 385, 386. |
| A. de Miranda Araujo, Manaos, Brazil. | 216. |
| A. R. Alves, Para, Brazil. | 422. |
| Amazon River Steam Navigation Co. (1911) Ltd., Brazil | 430, 443. |
| Antofagasta Railway Company, Valparaiso, Chile. | 341, 360. |
| Argentine Navigation Co. Ltd., Buenos Aires, Argentina. | 810, 812. |
| Brazilian Government, Pernambuco, Brazil. | 193. |
| Brito & Company, Brazil. | 384. |
| Companhia de Navegacao a Vapor do Rio Parnahyba, Theresina, Brazil. | 456, 457. |
| E. A. da Costa & Co., Brazil. | 347, 348, 363. |
| F. Castro & Company, Brazil. | 421. |
| Gunzburger & Co., Brazil. | 408. |
| H. da Costa, Santos, Brazil. | 426. |
| J. M. de Freitas, Brazil. | 388. |
| L. da Silva Gomes, Brazil. | 217. |
| Lilly, John & Sons, Peru. | 344, 361, 364. |
| Mello, Frotas & Co., Brazil. | 423. |
| Pinho, Certo & Co., Brazil. | 442. |
| Roffe, Reis & Co., Brazil. | 425. |
| Tancredo, Porto & Co., Brazil. | 424. |

# INDEX II
## Vessels built at Lytham by Richard Smith & Company and by Lytham Shipbuilding & Engineering Co. (Ltd.) showing year built, yard number and later names where known

| | | | |
|---|---|---|---|
| A.42 | 1915 | 519) | |
| A.44 | 1915 | 521) | |
| A.45 | 1915 | 522) | |
| A.46 | 1915 | 523) | BAYSWATER, KILBURN. |
| A.47 | 1915 | 524) | |
| A.48 | 1915 | 525) | |
| A.49 | 1915 | 526) | |
| A.54 | 1914 | 509 | PIONEER. |
| A.101 | 1916 | 517 | H.S.10, LANDY. |
| A.459 | 1916 | 527 | |
| A.460 | 1916 | 528 | |
| A.461 | 1916 | 529 | |
| A.462 | 1916 | 530 | |
| ABO | 1914 | 510 | |
| ABO | 1925 | 697 | |
| A.C.1019-A.C.1021 | 1916 | 542-544 | |
| A.C.1022-A.C.1024 | 1917 | 545-547 | |
| A.C.1086-A.C.1091 | 1917 | 553-558 | |
| ACRE | 1911 | 443 | |
| ADA | 1924 | 637 | |
| ADDAH | 1906 | 351 | |
| AGNELEY | 1924 | 659 | |
| AID | 1936 | 850 | |
| AKUSE | 1936 | 839 | |
| ALITA | 1920 | 599 | |
| ALSACE | 1901 | 294 | |
| ALTO ACRE | 1910 | 424 | |
| ALVES DE FREITAS | 1908 | 388 | |
| ANASTACIA | 1906 | 361 | URUBAMBA. |
| Anchor Boat | 1928 | 750 | |
| ANCHOR BOATS 12-13 | 1928 | 742,743 | |
| ANCHOR BOATS 14-16 | 1928 | 757-759 | |
| ANCHOR BOATS 17-21 | 1929 | 779-783 | |
| ANCHOR BOATS 22-27 | 1930 | 802-807 | |
| ANCHOR BOATS 28-29 | 1932 | 823,824 | |
| ANCHOR BOATS 30-32 | 1933 | 828-830 | |
| ANCHOR BOATS 33-34 | 1937 | 844,845 | |
| APPLEBY | 1927 | 729 | |
| AQUILA | 1907 | 387 | |
| ARGUS | 1906 | 362 | |
| ARIPUANA | 1910 | 422 | |
| ARS | 1925 | 663 | |
| A.S.104 | 1916 | 531 | |
| A.S.105 | 1916 | 532 | |
| A.S.106 | 1916 | 533 | CRAIG. |
| A.S.107 | 1916 | 534 | ORON. |
| A.S.142 | 1917 | 535 | SPALDING, SAINT BREANDUN, NAOMH BREANDUN, KALISCO. |
| A.S.143 | 1917 | 536 | TABE. |
| A.S.145 | 1917 | 559 | |
| A.S.146 | 1917 | 560) | |
| A.S.147 | 1918 | 561) | BRIDGENESS, PATSY, |
| A.S.148 | 1918 | 562) | STAMFORD. |
| A.S.149 | 1918 | 563) | |
| A.S.150 | 1918 | 564) | |
| ASHFIELD | 1914 | 490 | |
| AUGUSTE BLANQUI | 1903 | 314 | |
| AYSGARTH | 1900 | 291 | |
| AXE | 1915 | 516 | AIREDALE. |
| BAMUM | 1907 | 381 | |
| BARAO DE URUSSHY | 1912 | 456 | |
| BARGE F | 1898 | 262 | |
| BARGE G | 1899 | 273 | |

| | | | |
|---|---|---|---|
| Barges - Lagoon | 1909 | 402,403 | |
| Barge - Sailing | 1902 | 308 | MERRILL as a steamship. |
| Barge - Sailing | 1925 | 683 | |
| Barges - Swim Ended | 1914 | 499-504 | Crown Agents-Uganda. |
| Barges - Swim Ended | 1924 | 646,647 | Crown Agents-Uganda. |
| Barge | 1922 | 621 | African & Eastern. |
| Barge | 1923 | 622 | African & Eastern. |
| Barges | 1924 | 649,655 | African & Eastern. |
| Barges | 1924 | 660,661 | African & Eastern. |
| BARGE NOs. 59-60 | 1926 | 707,708 | African & Eastern. |
| BARGE NOs. 61-62 | 1927 | 709,710 | African & Eastern. |
| BARGE NOs. 63-64 | 1927 | 726,727 | African & Eastern. |
| Barges | 1923 | 638-640 | J. Birch & Co. Ltd. |
| Barges | 1924 | 641-643 | J. Birch & Co. Ltd. |
| Barges | 1924 | 650-653 | J. Birch & Co. Ltd. |
| BARGES ML | 1923 | 629-632 | Bromport S.S. Co. Ltd. |
| Barges | 1923 | 633,634 | Bromport S.S. Co. Ltd. |
| Barges | 1924 | 627,628 | J. Holt & Co. Ltd. |
| Barge | 1924 | 657 | J. Holt & Co. Ltd. |
| Barge | 1925 | 658 | J. Holt & Co. Ltd. |
| BARGE NOs. 52-59 | 1926 | 698-705 | J. Holt & Co. Ltd. |
| BARGE NOs. 63-64 | 1927 | 730,731 | J. Holt & Co. Ltd. |
| BARGE NOs. 75-78 | 1932 | 816-819 | J. Holt & Co. Ltd. |
| Barges | 1906 | 354-359 | Jones, Burton & Co. |
| Barges | 1907 | 371-380 | Jones, Burton & Co. |
| Barges | 1929 | 772 | Jones, Burton & Co. |
| Barges | 1912 | 451-453 | Lever Brothers Ltd. |
| Barges | 1904 | 329,330 | Niger Co. Ltd. |
| Barges | 1909 | 396,397 | Niger Co. Ltd. |
| BARGE NOs. 38-39 | 1920 | 585,586 | Niger Co. Ltd. |
| BARGE NOs. 44-45 | 1925 | 672,673 | Niger Co. Ltd. |
| Barges | 1927 | 714-716 | Niger Co. Ltd. |
| Barges | 1927 | 722-724 | Niger Co. Ltd. |
| BARGE NOs. 58-59 | 1927 | 733,734 | Niger Co. Ltd. |
| BARGE M.L. | 1928 | 751 | Niger Co. Ltd. |
| Barge | 1908 | 393 | F.& A. Swanzy & Co. Ltd. |
| Barge | 1910 | 418 | F.& A. Swanzy & Co. Ltd. |
| BARGE NOs 66-67 | 1930 | 800,801 | United Africa Co. Ltd. |
| Barges | 1931 | 811 | United Africa Co. Ltd. |
| Barges | 1950 | 893-898 | United Africa Co. Ltd. |
| Barges | 1899 | 267-271 | |
| Barge | 1901 | 303 | |
| Barge - Steam | 1907 | 383 | |
| BARRACOUTA | 1905 | 343 | |
| BATOE RADJA | 1914 | 505 | |
| BEECHFIELD | 1921 | 590 | |
| BELITI | 1911 | 444 | |
| BELO | 1926 | 681 | |
| BENI | 1911 | 430 | MARISE, FLAMENGO, RIO BRANCO. |
| BENI | 1925 | 662 | |
| BENUE | 1927 | 721 | |
| BERWIND | 1912 | 458 | |
| BETA | 1931 | 814 | SEA PREFECT. |
| BLUE CIRCLE | 1927 | 725 | |
| BOMBARDON TANKS | 1944 | 877 | |
| BONDO | 1925 | 678 | |
| BONITO | 1905 | 342 | |
| BRACKENFIELD | 1937 | 840 | |
| BRIARFIELD | 1920 | 579 | |
| BRIGG | 1909 | 404 | |
| BRITANNIA | 1910 | 419 | |
| BRITO | 1907 | 384 | |
| BROOMFIELD | 1937 | 841 | S. E. COOPER. |
| BURTON | 1921 | 602 | |
| BUZZ | 1928 | 754 | |
| | | | |
| CAIRNGARTH | 1913 | 467 | |
| CALBUCO | 1913 | 474 | |
| CARBO | 1923 | 613 | |
| CARMENTIA | 1920 | 598 | |
| CASSIO REIS | 1910 | 425 | PARANA, ZEANTUNES, PARA RIO. |
| C.B.T.7 | 1935 | 838 | |
| CECIL | 1890 | 149 | |

| | | | |
|---|---|---|---|
| CHADDA | 1951 | 900 | |
| CHICA | 1900 | 290 | |
| CHRISTINO CRUZ | 1912 | 457 | |
| CLAUDE | 1899 | 276 | M.S.C. CLAUDE. |
| CLEVELEYS | 1929 | 770 | |
| COLOMBO | 1903 | 317 | |
| COLONEL RATSEY | 1939 | 860 | |
| COTONOU | 1925 | 687 | UNICORN. |
| CUERVO | 1914 | 487 | |
| CUMBRIA | 1895 | 206 | HALLGARTH. |
| | | | |
| DANEGARTH | 1915 | 514 | |
| DAVID McINTOSH | 1920 | 581 | |
| DAVY | 1891 | | |
| DOM CARLOS | 1903 | 318 | |
| DONGA | 1914 | 484 | |
| DORITA | 1920 | 597 | |
| DOURO | 1896 | 217 | |
| DRAGON | 1906 | 352 | |
| DRAKE | 1954 | 903 | |
| DU 4 | 1929 | 784 | |
| DUC-DE-BRABANT | 1912 | 448 | |
| DUFFO | 1912 | 459 | |
| DUNNET H.M.S. | 1936 | 836 | KINGSMOOR. |
| | | | |
| EBO | 1901 | 299 | |
| EDDA | 1910 | 414 | |
| EDENGARTH | 1903 | 324 | |
| EDWARD C. WHEELER | 1903 | 321 | SURVEYOR NO.5., SNAPSHOT. |
| EGGA | 1903 | 328 | |
| ELLEN | 1920 | 584 | |
| ELLESMERE | 1913 | 462 | |
| ELMFIELD | 1925 | 674 | |
| ELSIE | 1903 | 325 | |
| ENGENNI | 1914 | 506 | |
| ESPERANCA | 1922 | 606 | |
| E.T.7 | 1918 | 569 | MISR. |
| E.T.8 | 1918 | 570 | |
| E.T.10 | 1918 | 571 | SWORD DANCE. |
| E.T.11 | 1918 | 572 | STEP DANCE. |
| ETHIOPE | 1909 | 401 | |
| | | | |
| FANTIMAN | 1924 | 595 | |
| FARADAY | 1891 | | |
| FARO | 1912 | 450 | |
| FARO II | 1927 | 717 | |
| FELLGARTH | 1902 | 307 | |
| FERNANDO DE NORONHA | 1894 | 193 | |
| Ferry Pontoons | 1930 | 808,809 | |
| Ferry Pontoon | 1934 | 834 | |
| Ferry Pontoon | 1939 | 861 | |
| Ferry Pontoons | 1941 | 866,867 | |
| Ferry Pontoons | 1945 | 887,888 | |
| FORWARD | 1909 | 405 | |
| FRANCIS | 1903 | 322 | |
| FREIRECASTRO | 1910 | 421 | |
| FRESHBROOK | 1941 | 868 | |
| FRESHBURN | 1943 | 874 | |
| FRESHENER | 1942 | 869 | |
| FRESHFORD | 1944 | 875 | |
| FRESHET | 1940 | 863 | |
| FRESHLAKE | 1942 | 870 | |
| FRESHMERE | 1942 | 871 | |
| FRESHPOND | 1945 | 878 | |
| FRESHPOOL | 1943 | 872 | |
| FRESHSPRAY | 1946 | 885 | |
| FRESHSPRING | 1946 | 886 | |
| FRESHTARN | 1944 | 876 | |
| FRESHWATER | 1940 | 862 | PORTO GRANDE. |
| FRESHWELL | 1943 | 873 | |
| FULWOOD | 1899 | 277 | |
| FYEDE | 1899 | 274 | |
| FYLDE | 1899 | 272 | |

| | | | |
|---|---|---|---|
| GANDA | 1926 | 680 | |
| G.C.H.1 | 1923 | 623 | |
| G.C.H.2 | 1923 | 624 | |
| G.C.H.3 | 1923 | 625 | |
| G.C.H.4 | 1923 | 626 | |
| GEORGE LIVESEY | 1928 | 753 | CARBEILE. |
| GLENAGEARY | 1920 | 578 | |
| GLENCULLEN | 1921 | 600 | |
| GOOD CHEER | 1902 | 313 | |
| GORSEFIELD | 1922 | 605 | |
| GRANGE | 1922 | 603 | |
| GRANT | 1924 | 648 | |
| GRAYGARTH | 1915 | 515 | |
| GRIBBLE | 1913 | 471 | |
| 13 G.W.R. | 1914 | 479 | |
| 14 G.W.R. | 1914 | 480 | |
| 15 G.W.R. | 1914 | 481 | |
| | | | |
| HAZELFIELD | 1947 | 889 | SPRAYVILLE, FOULI, AGIOS GERASSIMOS. |
| | | | |
| HEATHERFIELD | 1924 | 644 | |
| HELVETIA | 1892 | | |
| HINDIA | 1913 | 475 | |
| HOHOE | 1938 | 859 | |
| HORNET | 1905 | 339 | |
| HS.15 | 1916 | 538 | M.S.C.MANCHESTER. |
| HS.16 | 1916 | 539 | M.S.C.SALFORD, SALGARTH. |
| HS.17 | 1916 | 540 | M.S.C.RUNCORN, RUNGARTH. |
| HS.18 | 1917 | 541 | M.S.C.ELLESMERE PORT, ELLESGARTH. |
| HS.80 | 1919 | 565 | FERROLANO. |
| HS.81 | 1919 | 566 | CASTAGENERO. |
| HS.82 | 1919 | 567 | GADITANO. |
| HS.83 | 1920 | 568 | AVYLOS, VERNICOS VARVARA. |
| | | | |
| IJAW | 1925 | 691 | |
| IMP | 1932 | 822 | |
| INSULINDE | 1920 | 582 | |
| IRIS | 1928 | 735 | |
| ISELGARTH | 1904 | 331 | CARDIFFIAN. |
| ITABERA | 1931 | 812 | |
| ITACUA | 1931 | 810 | |
| | | | |
| JAMES FENTON | 1920 | 589 | |
| JEKRIMAN | 1921 | 592 | |
| JOHN MILLER | 1937 | 846 | |
| JOHN RICHARDS | 1897 | 238 | |
| JOHN VERNON | 1952 | 901 | |
| JOSE MARTINS | 1907 | 386 | |
| JOYCE | 1924 | 656 | |
| JUS | 1925 | 664 | |
| | | | |
| KADUNA | 1929 | 778 | |
| KAMPE | 1913 | 460 | |
| KAPANGA | 1925 | 684 | |
| KEBBI | 1913 | 461 | |
| KESTREL | 1897 | 234 | |
| KINGSWAY | 1906 | 346 | LA POINTE. |
| KITE | 1902 | 311 | |
| KLINGI | 1914 | 507 | |
| KNIGHT ERRANT | 1905 | 337 | MONTORIOL. |
| KUTU | 1926 | 682 | |
| KWANGO | 1923 | 635 | |
| KWILU | 1911 | 445 | |

| | | | |
|---|---|---|---|
| LAHAT | 1911 | 441 | |
| LAMATANG | 1902 | 305 | |
| LARCHFIELD | 1941 | 865 | |
| Launches | 1899 | 275 | |
| Launches | 1900 | 282-284,286-289 | |
| Launches | 1902 | 310,312 | |
| Launches | 1903 | 319 | |
| LAUNCH NO.9 | 1921 | 593 | |
| LCMs(7) 7147-7152 | 1945 | 879-884 | |
| LEBLANC | 1891 | | |
| LEDA | 1900 | 285 | |
| LETTEREWE | 1903 | 316 | |
| LEVERVILLE | 1912 | 446 | |
| Life Boats | 1936 | 842,843 | for M.S. EKETIAN. |
| LIFE BUOY | 1894 | 184 | |
| Light Beacon Boats | 1949 | 890-892 | |
| Lighters (sail) | 1901 | 295-298 | |
| Lighter | 1906 | 366 | |
| Lighter | 1912 | 455 | |
| Lighters | 1913 | 463-465 | |
| Lighter | 1914 | 488 | |
| Lighters | 1925 | 685,686,688,689 | |
| Lighter | 1926 | 696 | |
| Lighter | 1928 | 752 | |
| LIGHTER NOs. 65-68 | 1930 | 788-791 | J. Holt & Co. Ltd. |
| LIGHTER NOs. 5-7 | 1907 | 367,368,382 | Niger Co. Ltd. |
| Lighters | 1909 | 399,400 | Niger Co. Ltd. |
| Lighters | 1911 | 427,428 | Niger Co. Ltd. |
| LIGHTER NOs. 23-25 | 1913 | 476-478 | Niger Co. Ltd. |
| LIGHTER NOS. 26-27 | 1914 | 485,486 | Niger Co. Ltd. |
| LIGHTER NOs. 46-48 | 1925 | 675-677 | Niger Co. Ltd. |
| LIGHTERS A.1-A.2 | 1925 | 692,693 | Niger Co. Ltd. |
| Lighter | 1926 | 706 | Niger Co. Ltd. |
| Lighters | 1911 | 431,432 | F.& A. Swanzy & Co. Ltd. |
| Lighters | 1932 | 820,821 | United Africa Co. |
| LIGHTER NOs. 78-79 | 1932 | 825,826 | United Africa Co. |
| LIGHTER NOs. 80-81 | 1933 | 831,832 | United Africa Co. |
| LIGHTER NOs. 82-83 | 1937 | 847,848 | United Africa Co. |
| LIGHTER NOs. 84-85 | 1937 | 853,854 | United Africa Co. |
| LIGHTER NOs. 90 | 1938 | 855 | United Africa Co. |
| LIGHTER NOs. 117-119 | 1938 | 856-858 | United Africa Co. |
| LILY | 1896 | | |
| LIMESFIELD | 1916 | 518 | |
| LING | 1913 | 472 | |
| LION | 1927 | 728 | LION U.A. |
| LORRAINE | 1901 | 293 | |
| LOWGARTH | 1906 | 349 | |
| LUDDINGTON | 1922 | 604 | |
| LUGARD | 1925 | 690 | |
| LUKULU | 1930 | 793 | |
| LUNA | 1893 | 174 | |
| LUTSHIMA | 1930 | 785 | |
| LYNN | 1908 | 392 | |
| | | | |
| MACKEREL | 1913 | 473 | |
| MADRYN | 1905 | 327 | |
| MALEMBA | 1931 | 813 | |
| MAPLEFIELD | 1941 | 864 | |
| MAYO | 1914 | 483 | MAYO U.A. |
| MEJILLONES | 1905 | 341 | |
| MIRAFLORES | 1906 | 363 | |
| MOLUA | 1914 | 489 | |
| MOMA | 1925 | 679 | |
| MUCURIPE | 1910 | 423 | MIGUEL BITTAR, ALMERIM. |
| MUNGO PARK | 1912 | 449 | |
| MUNSHI | 1911 | 433 | |
| MYSTIC | 1899 | 264 | H.T.12., AVONCOCK. |

| | | | |
|---|---|---|---|
| NARAGUTA | 1908 | 390 | |
| NARAGUTA | 1934 | 833 | |
| NAUTILUS | 1904 | 336 | |
| N'DONI | 1927 | 732 | |
| NEDERLAND | 1914 | 511 | |
| NEMBE | 1937 | 852 | |
| NETHERGARTH | 1907 | 365 | PEAKE. |
| NEW BOYNE | 1896 | | |
| NIGRETIA | 1911 | 434 | |
| N'KISSI | 1929 | 777 | |
| NORMANBY | 1932 | 815 | |
| NORTHOP | 1934 | 835 | |
| NORTHWICH | 1937 | 851 | |
| NUPE | 1921 | 587 | |
| | | | |
| OCTOPUS | 1904 | 334 | |
| OFFIN | 1921 | 601 | |
| OGULA | 1929 | 771 | |
| OGUTA | 1910 | 413 | |
| OKO | 1929 | 786 | |
| OKORODUDU | 1951 | 899 | |
| OLD HOME | 1898 | | |
| OVERGARTH | 1907 | 369 | |
| | | | |
| PACIFICO | 1906 | 360 | |
| PAGER-ALAM | 1920 | 583 | |
| PASSACEIRO | 1929 | 767-769 | |
| PAX | 1925 | 665 | |
| PICKEREL | 1913 | 469 | |
| PIDDOCK | 1914 | 468 | |
| Pinnace - Steam | 1902 | 309 | |
| Poling Canoes | 1925 | 694,695 | African & Eastern. |
| Poling Canoes | 1928 | 755,756 | African & Eastern. |
| Poling Canoes | 1928 | 736-741 | E. Bates & Sons. |
| Poling Canoes | 1914 | 491-496 | Crown Agents-Nigeria. |
| POLING CANOE NO. 14 | 1914 | 497 | J. Holt & Co. Ltd. |
| POLING CANOE NO. 15 | 1914 | 498 | J. Holt & Co. Ltd. |
| Poling Canoes | 1922 | 607-612 | J. Holt & Co. Ltd. |
| Poling Canoes | 1926 | 718-720 | J. Holt & Co. Ltd. |
| Poling Canoes | 1909 | 410-412 | Niger Co. Ltd. |
| Poling Canoes | 1910 | 415,416 | Niger Co. Ltd. |
| POLING CANOES K.2-7 | 1911 | 435-440 | Niger Co. Ltd. |
| POLING CANOES N.1-6 | 1925 | 666-671 | Niger Co. Ltd. |
| POLING CANOES N.16-8 | 1926 | 711-713 | Niger Co. Ltd. |
| POLING CANOES H.20-5 | 1928 | 744-749 | Niger Co. Ltd. |
| POLING CANOES H.26-9 | 1929 | 773-776 | Niger Co. Ltd. |
| POLING CANOES H.30-5 | 1930 | 794-799 | United Africa Co. Ltd. |
| Poling Canoe | 1911 | 447 | F.& A.Swanzy & Co. Ltd. |
| Poling Canoe | 1922 | 614 | T. Welsh & Co. |
| POLITA | 1920 | 596 | |
| PORPOISE | 1904 | 335 | |
| PORTADOR | 1906 | 350 | |
| PRAWN | 1914 | 470 | |
| PRINCE GEORGE | 1892 | | |
| PROGRESS | 1893 | | WESTON MAID. |
| | | | |
| RAWAS | 1905 | 345 | |
| REPUBLICA | 1907 | 364 | |
| RIBAGO | 1933 | 827 | |
| RIBBLE QUEEN | 1903 | 315 | NEPTUN, NETTUNO, CETINJE. |
| RICHARD LANDER | 1911 | 429 | |
| RICHARD VERNON | 1953 | 902 | |
| RIO ARIPUANA | 1911 | 426 | |
| RIO GUAMA | 1905 | 347 | ALTAMIRA. |
| RIO MADEIRA | 1909 | 408 | MOREY, CAPITAO ASSIS. |
| RIOZINHO | 1911 | 442 | |
| RODAS | 1890 | 148 | M.PASTOR LANDERO. |
| ROSAMIRO | 1905 | 344 | |
| ROS-NA-RIGH | 1903 | 320 | |
| ROWANFIELD | 1938 | 849 | ROWAN, ANTONIO MIGUEL. |

| | | | |
|---|---|---|---|
| S.40 | 1917 | 548) | |
| S.41 | 1917 | 549) | |
| S.42 | 1917 | 550) | CANMORESK. |
| S.43 | 1917 | 551) | |
| S.61 | 1917 | 552) | |
| ST.FAGAN | 1918 | 575 | |
| ST.FAITH | 1919 | 576 | HAIDA MONARCH, UNIT SHIPPER, S.D.BROOKS, KILLARNEY, LE BEAU. |
| ST.HILARY | 1919 | 577 | |
| SAMUEL BAKER | 1909 | 394 | |
| SANDBECK | 1908 | 389 | |
| SANKURU | 1923 | 636 | |
| SANTO ANTONIO | 1895 | 216 | CARAMURA. |
| SCARBROUGH | 1904 | 332 | |
| SCAWBY | 1930 | 787 | |
| SCORPION | 1908 | 391 | TARTAR. |
| SECRET | 1892 | | |
| SEIONT | 1901 | 304 | |
| SILVERFIELD | 1915 | 508 | |
| SI THAN | 1901 | 301 | |
| SIN HONG BIE | 1902 | 306 | |
| SIN YOE SENG | 1903 | 323 | |
| SIR JOHN KIRK | 1913 | 466 | |
| SOCIAL | 1894 | 185 | |
| SOPHIA MARTINS | 1907 | 385 | RIO MURU, RIO ZINGU. |
| SOUDAN | 1901 | 292 | |
| SPEKE | 1909 | 395 | |
| STANEGARTH | 1910 | 420 | |
| Steamships | 1900 | 278-281 | |
| Sternwheelers | 1906 | 353 | |
| Sternwheelers | 1907 | 370 | |
| Sternwheelers | 1909 | 406,407 | |
| S'THOME | 1909 | 409 | |
| STURGEON | 1904 | 333 | |
| SUNLIGHT | 1889 | 141 | |
| SURF BOATS 1-6 | 1922 | 615-620 | |
| SURF BOATS 7-13 | 1928 | 760-766 | |
| T.98 | 1919 | 573 | FANDANGO. |
| T.99 | 1919 | 574 | MORRIS DANCE, ELVIRA. |
| TANA | 1917 | 520 | |
| TANO | 1924 | 654 | |
| TESSA | 1924 | 645 | |
| TIGER | 1930 | 792 | |
| TOILER | 1894 | | |
| TRADER | 1903 | 326 | |
| Tug | 1905 | 338 | |
| TUGWELL | 1910 | 417 | |
| UDI | 1922 | 588 | |
| ULLSGARTH | 1912 | 454 | |
| VAMPIRE | 1909 | 398 | |
| VICTORIA | 1901 | 302 | |
| VOLTAMAN | 1921 | 594 | |
| W.10 | 1935 | 837 | |
| WHELP | 1901 | 300 | |
| WALLIN | 1905 | 348 | |
| WALTER WATTS | 1922 | 580 | |
| WAMBA | 1914 | 482 | |
| WATERWITCH | 1894 | | |
| WASP | 1905 | 340 | |

# INDEX III — General

A.54 - Tug 21
Abbreviations 36
Admiralty 21, 24, 25, 31, 32
African & Eastern Trade Corporation Ltd 26, 28
African Transport Company 21
African Queen - film 30
AFRICAN QUEEN 30
Albert Edward Dock, Preston 9
Alliance & Dublin Consumers Gas Company 25
Allsup & Sons, William 9
ALTO ACRE 17
Ammunition Barges 21
Antofagasta Railway Company 16
Argentine Navigation Co. Ltd 18
ARIPUANA 17
Arromanches, Normandy 31
ASHFIELD 20
Ashton Quays, Preston 8, 9, 12
AYSGARTH 20

BARAO DE URUSSUHY 17
Basoko 27
Basongo 27
Basra 23
BEECHFIELD 32
Belem 17
Belgian Congo 26, 27, 28
Belgian Government 27
Bengal Marine, India 23
Bolton., John 8
Bombardon Tanks (floating breakwater) 31
Bombay Port Trust 16
Bracewell, Frederick 10
BRACKENFIELD 32
Brazilian Government 16
BRIARFIELD 25, 32
Bridgewater Canal Company 8
Brieryfield Road, Preston 13
British Army 21
British East Africa Railway, Uganda 30
British Government 27
British Railways 33
Bromborough Dock 26
Bromborough Port Estate Ltd. 26
Bromport Steamship Co. Ltd. 26
BROOMFIELD 32
Bumba 27
Burma 23

Canal Foundry, Preston 13
CANMORESK 23
CASSIO REIS 17
Cavalla River Company 26
Ceylon 16
Certificate of Naturalization 13
Chapel Walks, Preston 12
CHRISTINO CRUZ 17
Clifton, Thomas 8
Clifton, Mrs. 9
COLONEL RATSEY 24, 31
Coltar, Mrs. E. 24
Crichton, J. & Co. Ltd. 29
Croft Street, Preston 13
Crown Agents for the Colonies 28, 30

DRAKE 33
DUC DE BRABANT 27, 28
DUNNET, H.M.S. 31

Edmondson, Thomas 10
Egyptian Delta Light Railway Ltd. 16
ENTERPRISE 7
E.T.7 - Tug 24

FANDANGO 24
Fawcett, P.H., Lt.Col. 16
Films - African Queen 30
Fitzcarraido 18
Trader Horn 30
FREIRECASTRO 17
Fresh Class Water Carriers 31
FRESHSPRING, H.M.S. 31
FRESHWATER, H.M.S. 31
Friedenthal, Albert Louis 13
Friedenthal, Frederick Francis Joseph 12, 14
Friedenthal, Frederick John Joseph 13
Friedenthal, George Charles 13
Friedenthal, George Leonard 13
Friedenthal, John Alfred 14, 30
Friedenthal, Richard Ernest James 8, 13, 14, 25, 29, 30
Friedenthals Ltd. 13
Friedenthal's Patent Circle Propeller 12, 13

G.C.H.1 - 4 28
GLENAGEARY 25
GLENCULLEN 25
Gold Coast 26, 28
GORSEFIELD 32
GRACE 7
GRANT 20
Graving Dock, Preston 8

Hansen Shipping Co. Ltd. 29
Harris Museum & Art Gallery, Preston 7
HAZELFIELD 32, 33
H.C.B. (abbreviation for a company). 27
Hendricks, James W. 30
Herzog, Werner. 18
Holt, J. & Co. Ltd. 28
Hospital Ships 21, 22
H.T.12 - Tug 21

Indian State Government, H.M. 16
Ingende 27
Inland Water Transport Department 22, 23
Iquitos, Peru 16
Irrawaddy Flotilla Co. Ltd., Rangoon 23

Joint Liquidators 34
Jones Burton & Co. Ltd., Liverpool 16

King, R. & W. 26
KWANGO 26
KWILU 27

La Societe Anonyme des Huileries
   du Congo Belge 27
LADY ALICE 20
Lakes - Albert 30
      Kioga 19, 30
      Tanganyika 19
      Victoria 19
      Windermere 32, 33
Landing Craft Mechanised 32
LARCHFIELD 32
Leeds and Liverpool Canal 26
Lever Brothers Ltd. 9, 16, 20,
   25, 26, 27, 28
Lever, Elizabeth 9
Lever, James 9
Lever, William 9, 28
Leverville 27
LEVERVILLE 27
Liggard Brook 9, 11
LIVINGSTONE 30
Lodge Pool, Lytham 8
London International Boat Show 30
LUGARD 20
Lusanga 27
Lytham Creek 9
Lytham Dock 8
Lytham Pier 9
Lytham S.B. & E. Co. Ltd. 7, 8, 10,
   12, 14, 32

MacIver, W.B. & Company 26
Malaya 16
MALLARD 33
Manaos 16
MAPLEFIELD 32
Mersey Docks & Harbour Board 32
MISR 24
MOLUA 27
MORRIS DANCE, H.M.S. 24
MUCURIPE 17
MUNGO PARK 20
MYSTIC 21

NAVINHO 18
Niger Co. Ltd. 16, 20, 22, 23,
   26, 28
Normandy Invasion 31

Orme Shipping Co. Ltd. 10

Pacific Steam Navigation Co.
   Ltd. 16
Palm Oil 27
Passenger Dumb Barges 28
P. & O. Steam Navigation Com-
   pany 8
PIONEER 21
Port Sunlight 9, 26
Preston Corporation 8
Preston County Borough
   Council 33
Preston Dock 7, 8
Preston Marsh 8

Ratcliffe, P. & Company 26
Ratsey, Colonel H.E. 23
Rea Transport Co. Ltd. 16, 20
Ribble Cruising Club, Lytham 25
Ribble Engine Works 13
Ribble Navigation & Preston Dock
   Act 8
Ribble Navigation Company 8

RIO ARIPUANA 17
Rivers - Amazon 16, 17, 18
      Benue 23
      Clyde 18, 21
      Congo 20, 26, 28
      Douglas 26
      Euphrates 24
      Kwenge 27
      Kwilu 27
      Madeira 16
      Mersey 9, 26
      Negro 16
      Niger 16, 23
      Ribble 7, 8, 9, 28, 33, 34
      Tigris 22, 24
Romans 7
ROWANFIELD 32
Royal Fleet Auxiliary Service 31
Royal Niger Company Chartered &
   Limited 26
Rubber Boom 16, 18

ST FAGAN 25
ST. FAITH 25
ST. HILARY 25
SAMUEL BAKER 20, 30
SANKURU 26
Savonneries Lever Freres 28
Shipyard Channel - silting 33
Smith, John Abel 8
Smith, Richard & Company 8,
   9, 10, 12
Smith, Thomas 8
Soap Works, Port Sunlight 9
South America 16, 17, 18, 30
SPEKE 20
Spillers 32
Stanley, Henry Morton 20
STEP DANCE, H.M.S. 24
Stevenson & Co. Ltd. 13
Sunlight Soap 9
SUNLIGHT 9
Swanzy, F. & A. & Co. Ltd. 16, 20
SWORD DANCE, H.M.S. 24
Swim Ended Barges 20

Takoradi Harbour, West Africa 28
TANA 30
Trader Horn, film 30
TOILER 21

Uganda 19, 20, 28, 30
United Africa Co. Ltd. 26, 29, 32

Valparaiso 29
Victoria Quays, Preston 9

Walkden, John & Co. Ltd. 26
WAMBA 27
War Department 21, 22, 23, 24
Warton Brook 8
Watson, Herbert & Company 26
Werner Herzog Filmproduktion 18
Wet Dock, Preston 8
Williams, Hugh 7
Woodside 7

Zillah Shipping & Transport Co.
   Ltd. 25, 29, 32

# The Gap Year

## by Clare McMahon

First produced and performed at the
Lyric Theatre, Belfast,

GW00982839

## ‖SAMUEL FRENCH‖

**FOR AMATEUR PRODUCTION ENQUIRIES**

UNITED KINGDOM AND WORLD
EXCLUDING NORTH AMERICA
licensing@concordtheatricals.co.uk
020-7054-7298

Each title is subject to availability from Concord Theatricals,
depending upon country of performance.

*The Gap Year* was developed through Fishamble: The New Play Company's *A Play for Ireland* in association with the Lyric Theatre. *The Gap Year* was first produced at the Lyric Theatre, Belfast in association with Commedia of Errors on the 3rd of September 2022. The cast was as follows:

KATE MULGREW ...................................... Carol Moore

OONAGH MADDEN ..............................Marion O'Dwyer

ROISIN MCANESPIE................................. Libby Smyth

FR DONNELLY / PAT / PAUL / EDDIE ............. Frankie McCafferty

KIERAN / CAMPERVAN MAN / FIONNTAN / ETHAN .. Keith Singleton

CAOIMHE / JOSIE / SISTER THOMASINA / ALISON /

TOURIST / CATHERINE .............................. Meghan Tyler

Special appearance from Matthew Cavan

## THE COMPANY

| | |
|---|---|
| WRITER | CLARE MCMAHON |
| DIRECTOR | BENJAMIN GOULD |
| SET DESIGNER | STUART MARSHALL |
| LIGHTING DESIGNER | JAMES MCFETRIDGE |
| COSTUME DESIGNER | ENDA KENNY |
| SOUND DESIGNER | GARTH MCCONAGHIE |
| DRAMATURG | REBECCA MAIRS |
| CASTING DIRECTOR | CLARE GAULT CDG |
| CHOREOGRAPHER | FLEUR MELLOR |
| VOCAL COACH | BRENDAN GUNN |
| VIDEOGRAPHER | WILL McCONNELL |
| | |
| EXECUTIVE PRODUCER | JIMMY FAY |
| SENIOR PRODUCER | MORAG KEATING |
| HEAD OF PRODUCTION | ADRIAN MULLAN |
| PRODUCTION MANAGER | SIOBHÁN BARBOUR |
| SCENIC CONSTRUCTION MANAGER | COURTENAY DRAKOS |
| SCENIC CONSTRUCTION ASSISTANT | JACK McGARRIGLE |
| COMPANY STAGE MANAGER | AIMEE YATES |
| STAGE MANAGERS | STEPHEN DIX, LOUISE GRAHAM |
| DEPUTY STAGE MANAGER | KERRI MCGIMPSEY |
| ASSISTANT STAGE MANAGERS | JUDE BARRISCALE |
| COSTUME SUPERVISOR | GILLIAN LENNOX |
| MAKE-UP ARTIST/HAIR | CAROLINE REYNOLDS |
| DRESSER | NIAMH MOCKFORD |
| SENIOR PRODUCTION TECHNICIAN | IAN VENNARD |
| TECHNICIANS | LIAM HINCHCLIFFE, DECLAN PAXTON, CORENTIN WEST |
| CHIEF LX | JONATHAN DALEY |
| STAGE TECHNICIAN/FLYMAN TECHNICIAN | PATRICK FREEMAN |

# CAST

## CAROL MOORE

Carol was born in Glengormley and now lives in Bangor. Theatre includes: *Rough Girls, Lovers, Macbeth, Pentecost* (Lyric Theatre); One-woman play – *The Experience of Being – Baby Grand, Grand Opera House* (Irish tour); *Those You Pass on the Streets, Belfast by Moonlight, Two Roads West* (Kabosh touring (Ireland/South Africa/ Rwanda/Germany); *Across the Threshold* – Flowerfield Arts Centre (Big Telly); Television includes: *The Lovers* (Sky); *William of Orangedale* (Hat Trick); *Marcella* (ITV); *Mother's Day* (BBC); *The Lodge* (Disney Channel). Film includes: *Gone* (Future Screens); *Nowhere Special* (BBC); *Mercy* (Out of Orbit).
Writing includes: *Flying, The Experience of Being.*
Film directing includes: *Mind the Time* (Stage Beyond; *Pumpgirl* (Holywood Productions); *History Unfinished* (Carol Moore Production); *The Farther, The Dearer* (NESTA), *Gort na gCnámh* (About Face Productions). Awards: *History Unfinished* (BAFTA 60 secs NI Regional Winner); *Gort na gCnámh* (Best First Time Director – Celtic Film festival/Youth Prize; *Oberhausen* (Best short – joint prize Foyle Film Festival 3rd prize – Mo-Viola Festival).

## MARION O'DWYER

Marion O'Dwyer is from Dublin and is delighted to be back at the Lyric, where she last performed as Aunty Lizzy in *Philadelphia Here I Come!* Recent theatre includes: *The Beauty Queen of Leenane* (Theatre Royal, Waterford and Irish tour); *The Secrets of Primrose Square* (Online, Deeramber); *Drama at Innish, The Unmanageable Sisters* (Abbey Theatre); *The Red Shoes* (Gate Theatre).
Other theatre includes: *Cavalcaders, The Mai* (Decadent Theatre Co); *The Silver Tassie* (Druid, New York); *Be Infants in Evil, Poor Beast in the Rain, The Loves of Cass Maguire, Lovers Meeting, The Donahue Sisters* (Druid Theatre, Galway); *Wonderful Tennessee* (Abbey Theatre and Broadway); *Dancing at Lughnasa* (Abbey Theatre, Sydney Opera House); *Bookworms, Kevin's Bed, School for Scandal, The Rivals, The Plough and the Stars, The Crucible, All My Sons, The Silver Tassie, You Can't Take it With You, She Stoops to Conquer* (Abbey); *A Woman of No Importance, The Importance of Being Earnest, Stella by Starlight, A Tale of Two Cities, Pride and Prejudice* (Gate Theatre).
Television and film: *The Dry* (Element TV/Britbox); *Miss Scarlet and the Duke* (A + E Networks); *God's Creatures* (Sixty Six Pictures); *The Silence of Mercy* (Luma Features); *The Christmas Break* (Marxmas); *An Cailín Ciúin* (Tobar films); *Finding You* (Nook Lane); *End of Sentence* (Sentence Films); *Ballykissangel* (World Productions); *Poirot – Sad Cypress* (Granada); *Rebel Heart* (BBC); *An Old Fashioned Christmas* (Cameron Films); *Agnes Browne* (October Films).

## LIBBY SYMTH

Libby began her career in Dublin when she was a student at Trinity College. She took part in many theatrical productions as a student and was spotted by a producer from R.T.E who offered her the opportunity to front a magazine programme for television. Soon, however, the acting bug became too great and, when offered a season in the Lyric Theatre, she returned to Belfast. Since then she has appeared in over 40 productions in various theatres both north and south. In 1981, Libby appeared in the first ever six-part comedy series based and shot here in Northern Ireland along with Ian McIlhinney and Marie Jones. She also worked with BBC NI on a part-time basis fronting a children's education series, *One Potato, Two Potato*, which ran for 25 years. Recently, Libby has appeared in an award-winning, much acclaimed one-woman show about the life of Ruby Murray. Having already completed two sell-out tours of this play, she is hoping to take "Ruby" to England in 2022.

## KEITH SINGLETON

Keith studied Performing Arts at The Liberties College, Dublin and since graduating in 2003 his pursuits have seen him well travelled in a career characterised by variety. He has worked on a great number of shows on the island of Ireland and the highlights of his shows abroad include clowning on a stage made of bamboo in the valley of Kathmandu with The Smile Project and donning a monofin in Taiwan to play the role of a Merman in Big Telly Theatre Companies aqua theatre production *The Little Mermaid*.

Theatre credits include: *The Untold Truth Of Captain Hook* (Replay); *The Worst Café In The World* (BigTelly) and *Epic Borders* (Tinderbox). In addition to performing regularly on stage and appearing occasionally on television (BBC NI's *Soft Border Patrol*, Seasons 1 -3) Keith also loves visiting hospitals as a member of Aoife's Clown Doctors, is consistently recording as a Voice-Over Artist and has been part of The MAC's 2021-22 Hatch & Scratch programme. Keith has been resident in wonderful Belfast for just over a decade now and is only delighted to be making his debut in a Lyric and Commedia of Errors show.

## FRANKIE MCCAFFERTY

Frankie McCafferty has been an actor, writer and director in theatre, film, television and radio for more than thirty years. Most recently he appeared in the sellout production *The Lonesome West* at the Gaiety Theatre; *Derry Girls* (CH4); *Wine from Greenland* (RTE Radio Drama) and in the upcoming TV series *Blue Lights*. Previous roles at the Lyric include: *Observe the Sons of Ulster Marching Towards the Somme* (Irish Times Best Supporting Actor Award); *Conversations on a Homecoming, Fire Below, Molly Sweeney, The Crucible, Arms and the Man, Much Ado About Nothing, The Blind Fiddler, The Playboy of the Western World* and *Bah Humbug!* He has directed many of Grimes and McKee's Christmas shows at the Lyric and during the pandemic performed in an online production of *Translations*; a Lyric collaboration with Rage Theatre in Mumbai. He was a facilitator and director on Stage Beyond Theatre's lockdown project Mind the Time, creating memory films for actors with learning difficulties.

Other notable theatre roles include: *Vincent Woods' At the Black Pig's Dyke*, *Sharon's Grave* (IT Best Actor nomination); *The Seafarer, The Weir, The Thing About December* (Decadent Theatre); *Dealer's Choice, Endgame* (Prime Cut) and *The Plough and the Stars* (Abbey Theatre).

TV and film roles include: *Vikings, Philomena, In the Name of the Father, Fools of Fortune, Far and Away* and *Ballykissangel*. He wrote and performed a one-man play *Tintype* at the Kilkenny Arts Festival to critical acclaim and his epic history play *Godscursed* received a public reading as part of Prime Cut's Verge series.

He is from Donegal and trained at the Conservatoire National Superieur d'Art Dramatique in Paris on a scholarship to support young artists funded by the European Union.

### MEGHAN TYLER

Meghan Tyler is an award-winning actor and writer from Newry who trained at the Royal Conservatoire of Scotland. After winning an Olivier Award for *Pride and Prejudice\* \*sort of* in the West End, they have recently finished filming *Hope Street* for the BBC, and are delighted to be back at The Lyric for *The Gap Year.*

Selected theatre credits include: *Pride and Prejudice\* \*sort of* (Criterion Theatre); *A Streetcar Named Desire* (The Lyric Theatre); *Medicine* (Off The Middle, The Hope Theatre); *King Keich, The Persians*, and *The Weir Sisters* (Oran Mor in association with The Traverse Theatre); *The Merchant of Venice* (Shakespeare's Globe); *The Crucible* (Royal Lyceum Theatre); *A Midsummer Night's Dream*, and *Two Gentlemen of Verona* (Guildford Shakespeare Company); *Hamlet* (Citizen's Theatre); *Lovers*, and *Look Back in Anger* (Cumbernauld Theatre); and *Nothing To Be Done* (SETKANI/ENCOUNTER Festival, NEU/NOW Festival, Edinburgh Fringe Festival). Selected screen credits include: *Hope Street* (long story tv); *Ballywalter* (Empire Street Productions); *Almost Never*, and *Shetland* (BBC); *The Toll* (Western Edge Pictures); *Everything Will Be Okay* (BBC Northern Ireland); and *Scot Squad* (Comedy Unit, BBC). Selected writing credits include: *Crocodile Fever* (Traverse Theatre and Lyric Theatre); *Hotline* (Tron Theatre); *One With The Lockdown* (National Theatre of Scotland); *Medicine* (Off The Middle); *The Persians* (Oran Mor in association with the Traverse Theatre); and *Nothing To Be Done* (Edinburgh Festival, SETKANI/ENCOUNTER Festival, NEU/ NOW Festival), which was awarded the MARTA Award for Best Script, "representing artistic hope for the future".

As of 2019, Meghan has been awarded the Channel 4 Playwrights Bursary with the Traverse Theatre, a New Playwrights Award with Playwrights' Studio Scotland, and was one of the writers on the New Playwrights Programme at the Lyric Theatre in 2018.

## CREATIVE TEAM

### CLARE MCMAHON

Clare is a playwright and actor based in Belfast and is Co-Creative of Commedia of Errors. A graduate of the Lir Academy's MFA Playwriting she is currently under commission with Lyric Theatre, Kabosh Theatre, Commedia of Errors and is one of the Abbey Theatre's Centenary development awardees. *The Gap Year* is her Lyric Theatre mainstage debut. It was first developed through Fishamble's Play for Ireland 2018, the Lyric Theatre's New Playwrights Programme 2019, selected for New York's 1st Irish Origin Festival as part of their Vital Voices programme and produced for the Lyric's 'Listen at the Lyric' audio series 2020. She was a shortlisted writer for the Zodiak Kids Award with CBBC.

Previous plays include: *Shakespeare's Women, Women Troubles* (co-writer), and *I Am Maura*.

As an actor Clare trained at Royal Central School of Speech & Drama and has worked in theatres across the UK & Ireland including the West End's *The Cripple of Inishmaan, A Midsummer Nights Dream* (The Almeida) and Philip Pullman's *Twist of Gold* (Polka Theatre).

She has worked with most companies in Northern Ireland including The Lyric, The Mac, Tinderbox, Bruiser and Cahoots.

Television credits include playing Fanny in *The Woman in White* (BBC1) and Carlo in *Agatha - The Truth of Murder* (Netflix).

### BENJAMIN GOULD

Benjamin founded Commedia of Errors in 2014 and is Artistic Director of the Company. He holds a BA (Hons) Drama (1st Class) from Liverpool Hope University, and an MA Professional Acting from Alra, London. His productions have toured across Ireland, the UK, Italy and the USA. He won the 2019 John Fernald Award for Emerging Directors in UK and Ireland and is a multiple Arts Council Northern Ireland and British Council Award winner.

Recent credits as director/producer include: *The Gap Year* (Lyric Theatre) New Playwrights Programme (Lyric Theatre); *The Gap Year* (Listen at the Lyric); *Lily* (VR Film); *The Gap Year* (1st Irish Festival, New York); *I Am Maura* (Lyric Theatre and NI Tour); *That Scottish Play!* (Lyric Theatre and NI Tour); *Women Troubles* (CQAF); *Shakespeare's Women* (CQAF, Lyric Theatre and National Tour); *The Tain* (Milan, Italy and tour of Ireland) and *Romeo and Juliet* (Hen & Chickens, London). As Assistant/Associate Director: *Three Sisters* (SITI Company, Singapore International Arts Festival); *Molly Sweeney* (Goodman Theatre Chicago); *Sweeney Todd* (NI Opera / Lyric Theatre); *A Midsummer Night's Dream* (Terra Nova)

### STUART MARSHALL

Stuart previously designed *That Scottish Play!* and Clare McMahon's *I Am Maura*, both of which were performed in the Lyric's Naughton Studio.

His many other designs for the Lyric include: *The Crucible, Dancing*

at Lughnasa, Of Mice and Men, Little Shop of Horrors, A Night in November, Our Country's Good, A Whistle in the Dark, Charlotte's Web, The Hypochondriac, The Absence of Women, Translations, Death of a Salesman, Light Shining in Buckinghamshire, Brendan at the Chelsea, Peter Pan, The Ladykillers, Sadie, The Heresy of Love and Educating Rita.
Designs for other companies include: The 25th Annual Putnam County Spelling Bee and Cabaret (Bruiser); American Buffalo and Blackbird (Prime Cut); Callings and Green and Blue (Kabosh); Vernon God Little and Top Girls (Brian Friel Theatre); The Diary of Anne Frank and Chicago (Bardic Theatre) and Carthaginians (Millennium Forum Derry).

### ENDA KENNY
Enda is an award winning costume designer based in Belfast.
He also works as a Prop Costume Maker, Textile Artist, Leather worker and Milliner for Theatre, TV and film. He has created work for many UK based theatres including ENO, NI Opera, ROH Covent Garden, National Theatre London, Saddlers wells and the Lyceum Theatre London to name a few. He has created work for Tokyo Ballet, Opera du Montpellier, Opera NI and teatro Nacional de Sao Carlos Lisbon. Previously costume design theatre credits include: Sylvan (Tinderbox 2021); One Good Turn (Abbey 2021); Father the Father (Prime cut 2021); A Streetcar Named Desire (Lyric Belfast 2019 – Winner of Best costume design at the Irish times theatre awards 2020); Lovers (Lyric Belfast 2018); Red (Prime cut/Lyric Belfast 2017); Educating Rita (Lyric 2016) and Scorch (Prime cut 2015). Film and TV work has seen him create work in Ireland, UK, Spain, Budapest, Morocco. Film/TV credits include: Dungeons and Dragons, The Northman, Game of Thrones S1-6, Krypton S2, Outlander S4, Frankenstein Chronicles, Halo-Nightfall, The Golden Compass, City of Ember, The Wolfman, Your Higness, Pirates of the Carribbean 2, King Arthur and Ella Enchanted.

### GARTH MCCONAGHIE
Garth has worked extensively as a Composer, Sound Designer, Musical Director, Arranger and Music Producer for studios, theatre, film and television. Garths work has been performed and broadcast all over the UK, Ireland and internationally as part of theatrical productions, exhibitions, art installations, television and radio.
Recent TV/Radio credits include: Derry Girls (Hat Trick Productions, Channel 4); Flight (BBC 1/BBC 4); My Mother and Other Strangers (BBC 1); Malaria, Comic Relief, Days Like This (BBC NI, nominated for IFTA); Wee Wise Words (BBC NI); Not Now Farley (BBC Learning Zone); On the Air (BBC NI); Ulster Volunteers (RTE); A Year in Sex City (DoubleBand Films/BBC 1).
Recent Theatre credits include: X'ntigone (Prime Cut Productions/ MAC, Belfast); This Sh*t Happens All The Time (Lyric Theatre, Belfast); Tamed (Norwich Playhouse); In The Name of the Son (Grand Opera House, Belfast); Carson and the Lady (Lyric Theatre, Belfast); The Border

*Game* (Prime Cut Productions); *A Night in November* (Soda Bread, MAC, Belfast, Chiswick Playhouse); *Mojo Mickybo* (Bruiser); *A Christmas Carol* (MAC Belfast); *Rebus: Long Shadows* (Birmingham Repertory Theatre); *The Miami Showband Story* (GBL Productions, Grand Opera House, Belfast, Gaiety Theatre, Dublin); *Bouncers* (Big Telly / MAC Belfast); *Spud!* (Lyric Theatre, Belfast); *Freak Show* (Big Telly); *Tamed* (Southwark Playhouse, London); *The Elves and the Shoemaker* (MAC Belfast, Cahoots NI); *A Night In November* (Lyric Theatre, Belfast); *Penguins* (Cahoots NI, Birmingham Repertory Theatre); *Under the Hawthorn Tree* (Cahoots NI, MAC Belfast); *Hansel & Gretel* (MAC Belfast); *Aladdin* (SSE Arena, Belfast); *Nivellis War* (Cahoots NI, New Victory Theater, Broadway, New York, Lyric theatre, Belfast); *The Faerie Thorn* (Big Telly); *Madame Geneva* (Macha Productions); *Pinocchio* (MAC Belfast, Cahoots NI); *Macbeth* (YMT:UK, Lyric Theatre, Belfast, Edinburgh Fringe Festival, RADA Studios and Sadlers Wells Theatre); *Christmas Eve Can Kill You* (Lyric Theatre, Belfast); *Shh! We Have a Plan* (Cahoots NI, touring China, 2019); *Egg* (Cahoots NI touring USA, 2016); *The Scarlet Web* (Big Telly), *Mistletoe & Crime* (Lyric Theatre, Belfast); *Sometimes Theres Light [Sometimes Theres Dark]* (Moving Dust, Asylum, London and touring, 2014); *God of Carnage* (Prime Cut Productions); *Crazy* (GBL Productions); *My English Tongue, My Irish Heart* (Green Shoot Productions), *Forget Turkey* (Lyric Theatre, Belfast).

### CLARE GAULT
Clare is currently the Casting Director for the Lyric Theatre. She has worked in professional theatre and casting for over nineteen years. With a degree in English Literature and Politics, she has an extensive knowledge of Theatre, TV and Film across Ireland and the UK. Clare has worked with a diverse range of directors, writers, and producers. Theatre collaborations include: The Abbey Theatre, Dublin; Traverse Theatre, Edinburgh; Tricycle Theatre, London; Fiery Angel, London; Young Vic, London; Perth Theatre, Scotland; Rough Magic, Dublin; Decadent Theatre, Galway; Prime Cut Productions, Belfast; Bruiser Theatre Company, Belfast; Cahoots NI, Belfast and Commedia of Errors, Belfast. Screen collaborations include: BBC, Ni Screen and Up the Lagan.

### FLEUR MELLOR
Fleur Mellor trained initially as a professional dancer at the London Studio Centre and subsequently worked touring all over the world. With twenty years in the industry, she has been producing & choreographing for commercial theatre for over twelve years in London, Northern Ireland & in The Netherlands. Her emphasis is on live work with a strong dance/theatre element. Working in shows, music, fashion and the corporate and commercial sectors she is passionate about the visual arts.
Theatre credits include: *Stones In His Pockets* (The Barn Theatre, Cirencester) & (GOH, Belfast); *The Showman Is Coming* (NI tour); *Celtic Rhythms* (Netherlands tour); *Archy In Manhattan* (GOH, Belfast); *Annie Get Your Gun* (Theatre At The Mill); *Cats* (SSE Arena); *Thoroughly Modern Millie* (Adelphi Theatre); *Spectacular!* (NI tour); *The Music Box* (NI, various); *The Boyfriend* (Her Majesty's Theatre); *Irish Wings*

(Netherlands Tour); *The Tenderland* (Arcola Theatre); *Crazy For You* (London Palladium).

Commercial credits include: The Fantastic Hairdesser Awards (2016-2019); World Dairy Summit (ICC, Belfast); Alternative Hair Show (Royal Albert Hall); Feelin' Festive, Dream Circus/Masquerade (Best Parties Ever); The Nolan Show (BBC NI).

Fleur was recently movement director for 'Green Space, Dark Skies' at the Giant's Ring as part of the UK wide Unboxed festival curated by Walk The Plank. This was an outdoor project involving hundreds of volunteers in a mass movement arts project designed to highlight the natural beauty of the terrain with low impact geo lights. She looks forward to returning for the finale of this spectacular project.

As a board member of Theatre & Dance NI (one the main resource organisations for the arts & culture sector in NI) & Thrive Audience Development, she is a fierce advocate for dance and a champion for the arts.

### JAMES MCFETRIDGE

James has been working as a lighting designer for over twenty-five years. His earliest designs were in the Lyric Theatre and included Stones in his Pockets, which he re-lit in the West End (firstly in the Ambassadors Theatre, followed by a three-year residency in the Duke of York Theatre) and then on Broadway (John Golden Theatre, New York). His design was also used in various Irish, UK, US and World tours.

He has had one other West End show (*Alone it Stands*, Duchess Theatre), and has lit shows in Canada, Australia, Russia and New York, and his designs have toured all across the UK and Ireland.

James' previous lighting designs for the Lyric include: *Dracula, Dark of the Moon, Dr Scroggy's War, The Heresy of Love, The Patriot Game, Eternal Love, Demented, Can't Forget About You, 55 Days, Brendan at the Chelsea, Our Country's Good, The Civilisation Game, Light Shining in Buckinghamshire*, and *The Jungle Book*.

Other recent lighting designs include: *Mojo Mickybo, The 39 Steps, The Colleen Bawn, The Secret Diary of Adrian Mole, The Complete Works of William Shakespeare (Abridged), Playhouse Creatures, Cabaret, The Nose, The Caucasian Chalk Circle, Spelling Bee*, and *Lady Windermere's Fan* (Bruiser Theatre Company); *The Elves and the Shoemaker, Under the Hawthorn Tree* (Cahoots NI); *Three's A Shroud, The History of the Peace... According to My Ma, Crazy*, and *Baby It's Cold Outside* (GBL Productions); *In The Name of the Son, Two Sore Legs, 1932 – The People of Gallagher Street, Meeting At Menin Gate* (Green Shoot Productions).

### REBECCA MAIRS

Rebecca is the Lyric Theatre's Literary Manager where she's led the New Work department since 2016. She acts as dramaturg on the theatre's slate of commissioned projects as well as managing talent development programmes for young, new, and emerging playwrights and theatre makers. She also works collaboratively with a range of national and international companies, producers, and organisations to promote and support writers.

# LYRIC

The Lyric Theatre in Belfast is a playhouse for everyone to enjoy. It's a creative hub for theatre-making, a safe space for nurturing talent and has an unwavering passion for creating meaningful connections through theatre arts.

We've always done things a little differently at the Lyric. Right from its modest beginnings in 1968, this special place has been a springboard for internationally acclaimed playwrights, poets and actors. As Northern Ireland's only theatre to produce its own productions from page to stage, we care deeply about maintaining a high-quality, diverse and inclusive programme that captures the imaginations of our audiences leaving them changed, charged and empowered.

Great writing is in our bones. Building on the canon of work from previously premiered playwrights like Brian Friel, Christina Reid, Marie Jones and many more, the Lyric continues to nurture creative talent and amplify new voices.

Clare McMahon was part of the Lyric's 2019 New Playwrights Programme where she further developed *The Gap Year* and it was performed as a rehearsed reading in the Naughton Studio. During the pandemic the play was recorded as an audio play as part of the 'Listen at the Lyric' series. We are delighted to be staging this full-scale production in association with Commedia of Errors which showcases the Lyric's focus on innovative new work, world class talent and live theatre, and as part of a vibrant new season.

## BOARD OF DIRECTORS
SIR BRUCE ROBINSON (CHAIRMAN)
STEPHEN DOUDS (VICE CHAIRMAN)
NUALA DONNELLY
PATRICIA McBRIDE
MIKE MULLAN
DR MARK PHELAN

| | |
|---|---|
| **PATRON** | LIAM NEESON OBE |
| **EXECUTIVE PRODUCER** | JIMMY FAY |
| **SENIOR PRODUCER** | MORAG KEATING |
| **CASTING DIRECTOR** | CLARE GAULT |
| **LITERARY MANAGER** | REBECCA MAIRS |
| **PRODUCTION ASSISTANT** | KERRY FITZSIMMONS |
| **HEAD OF FINANCE & HR** | MICHEÁL MEEGAN |

| | |
|---|---|
| **FINANCE OFFICER** | TONI HARRIS PATTON |
| **FINANCE ASSISTANT** | SINÉAD GLYMOND |
| **FINANCE & ADMIN ASSISTANT** | SHIREEN AZARMI |
| **HEAD OF DEVELOPMENT & MARKETING** | CLAIRE MURRAY |
| **MARKETING MANAGER** | RACHEL LEITCH |
| **MARKETING OFFICERS** | KATIE ARMSTRONG |
| | EMMA BRENNAN |
| **MARKETING INTERN** | BEVERLY STEELE |
| **DEVELOPMENT OFFICER** | BEN McDAID |
| **HEAD OF PRODUCTION** | ADRIAN MULLAN |
| **PRODUCTION MANAGER** | SIOBHÁN BARBOUR |
| **TECHNICAL MANAGER** | ARTHUR OLIVER-BROWN |
| **SENIOR PRODUCTION TECHNICIAN** | IAN VENNARD |
| **THEATRE TECHNICIANS** | LIAM HINCHCLIFFE |
| | DECLAN PAXTON |
| | CORENTIN WEST |
| **COMPANY STAGE MANAGER** | AIMEE YATES |
| **STAGE MANAGERS** | STEPHEN DIX |
| | LOUISE GRAHAM |
| **COSTUME SUPERVISOR** | GILLIAN LENNOX |
| **COSTUME ASSISTANT** | NIAMH MOCKFORD |
| **SCENIC CONSTRUCTION MANAGER** | COURTENAY DRAKOS |
| **SCENIC CONTRUCTION APPRENTICE** | JACK MCGARRIGLE |
| **CASUAL THEATRE TECHNICIANS** | MAIRTIN BRADLEY, |

DEBORAH BRANSON, CONAL CLAPPER, DAMIEN COX, JONATHAN DALEY, PATRICK FREEMAN, PHELAN HARDY, ANNE-MARIE LANGAN, BARRY MCCUSKER, SHEILA MURPHY, MATTHEW RICE, MICHAEL STAPLETON, ADRIAN WALL

| | |
|---|---|
| **HEAD OF CREATIVE LEARNING** | PHILIP CRAWFORD |
| **CREATIVE LEARNING MANAGER** | ERIN HOEY |
| **CREATIVE LEARNING ADMINISTRATOR** | CARAGH O'DONNELL DELANEY |
| **HEAD OF CUSTOMER SERVICE** | JULIE McKEGNEY |
| **CUSTOMER SERVICE MANAGER** | ELLA GRIFFIN |
| **ASSISTANT CUSTOMER SERVICE MANAGER** | SEÁN GALLAGHER |
| **DUTY SUPERVISOR** | LUCY ARMSTRONG |
| | MARINA HAMPTON |
| | RONAN McMANUS |
| | GERARD KELLY |
| | TIERNA MCNALLY |
| **BOX OFFICE MANAGER** | EMILY WHITE |
| **BOX OFFICE SUPERVISOR** | PAUL McCAFFREY |
| **HOUSEKEEPING** | DEBBIE DUFF |
| | AMANDA RICHARDS |
| | SAMANTHA WALKER |

Commedia of Errors create art that responds to, challenges and questions the changing times in which we live. It aims to grow, develop and inform audiences, beneficiaries and the arts sector and to broaden and deepen engagement by overcoming barriers to arts participation.

They are an independent theatre company based in Belfast, Northern Ireland. The company was first founded in London by Benjamin Gould in 2013, moving back to Northern Ireland in 2014 where it became a registered charity and Clare McMahon became Co-Creative of the company.

Commedia of Errors operates three main strands of work:

- **Theatre productions**
- **Work for older audiences**
- **Exploring new technologies within live performance.**

| | |
|---|---|
| **ARTISTIC DIRECTOR** | BENJAMIN GOULD |
| **CO-CREATIVE** | CLARE MCMAHON |
| **ASSOCIATE PRODUCER** | CONOR MAGUIRE |
| **ASSISTANT PRODUCER** | MEGAN KELLY |

**BOARD OF DIRECTORS**
MICHAEL WEIR (CHAIR)
DAVID GOULD (VICE CHAIR)
NEIL CAUWOOD (TREASURER)
JENNY COOKE OBE
FIONA MCANESPIE
SALLY CAMPTON
MARK FRANCOS
SALLY VISICK

www.commediaoferrors.co.uk

Principal Funders

# AUTHOR'S NOTES

In 2017 I sent an email: Benjamin and I's company Commedia of Errors would like to bring my first play *Shakespeare's Women* to the Naughton Studio, at the Lyric Theatre, Belfast. And when we met with the Lyric, we could not have dreamed that would be the start of this creative relationship with the theatre we both grew up visiting. I feel truly humbled that five short years later *The Gap Year* will be my main stage debut, and not only that but that I get to take this step with my creative collaborator and supporter Benjamin Gould.

*The Gap Year* was first developed with Fishamble theatre company in partnership with the Lyric in 2018. They wanted a play for Ireland. A weighty want but a challenge that I grabbed with both hands. What could I share that would speak to those from all walks of life on this island? It was an idea about new beginnings, that it was never too late to start again and the power of female friendship. In 2019 I submitted the play for the New Playwrights Programme at the Lyric and continued to develop and explore the script. I remember sitting with the incomparable Rebecca Mairs in the café bar saying, "I just don't know what this play is. I can't be an expert on every county in Ireland." And she kindly told me to wise up, I wasn't writing a guidebook for the tourist board – although if they want to get in touch I do know a fair amount these days. Rebecca asked me what I really wanted to say, and that simple question unlocked it. Most of us have been lucky enough to grow up with a mummy, or a granny or an aunt, who took on the weight of the world to get us through this life. *The Gap Year* is about them getting their turn. It's about hope and heart and new beginnings.

In January 2020 Benjamin and I were invited to take the play to New York for Origin Theatre's 1st Irish Festival. It had a rehearsed reading in the American Irish Historical Society as part of the festival's 'Vital Voices' programme, and hearing the response of the American audience only solidified our belief that it was a play for everyone.

Once the pandemic hit I worried it would sit in the drawer until life returned to some sense of normality. But again the Lyric stepped up, they produced multiple audio plays as part of their Listen at the Lyric programme, and *The Gap Year* was chosen. The feedback from that recording was truly uplifting. As we all lived through fear and tragedy, audiences wanted stories about hope and humanity. They needed heart, and fun and fearlessness; *The Gap Year* could give them that.

It was then Benjamin started discussions with Jimmy Fay and the Lyric about making the play in association with Commedia of Errors. He has been an advocate for this story, and my voice, from the start. His dedication alongside the Lyric's commitment has lead us all to this moment. It takes great faith to put on an ambitious play like this, a new writer, coming out of the pandemic, a largish cast, Jimmy and the Lyric's belief in us has been life-changing. I think together we've made something quite special, and I'm hugely grateful to the amazing cast, creatives, production, and entire staff at the Lyric for making this happen. We may be a small corner of the world but we always punch above our weight.

Finally, I am so proud that this play puts the focus on women over the age of sixty – we all know they long deserve their stories to be told. I can't wait to share it with them. I hope they enjoy seeing themselves in the spotlight for once, as Kate, Oonagh and Roisin go on an adventure of a lifetime.

## DIRECTOR'S NOTE

*The Gap Year* is a timely and exciting new play and a gift for a director. It's full of comedy, heart and warmth – offering actors and directors the chance to explore some truly difficult topics, and universal truths, through a lens of light entertainment. Clare's work rattles at high pace and yet still gives each moment its time in the spotlight. A little like working with Shakespeare, her writing has been finely crafted to give the wily director, or actor, all the clues they need to understand how it should be played. Each punctuation mark, each pause has been carefully thought through. If you can't quite land it right, try something else and once it starts to flow and pop you know you're onto a winner! Don't get me wrong, the process hasn't been without its challenges – it's a big play and there's a lot to do. Spanning across the whole of Ireland and conveying the sense of time and distance travelled are no mean feats, nor is the sheer variety of settings, characters and moments. What we've tried to offer is just a little taste, or a series of 'polaroid snapshots', of a year's worth of moments, feelings and memories to spark audiences' imaginations and allow anyone who watches to piece together the rest for themselves.

It's been a joy to work on this play and to engage with all of the groups and people that have fed into making our production. I'd like to thank them all, as well as The Lyric Theatre and of course Clare for letting me direct it. *The Gap Year* doesn't just offer audiences the chance for discussion, and it's not just the characters whose experiences have fed into rehearsals. Working with our team on this production has changed all of our perspectives at least a little. Shared experience and the discussions it inspires are truly the greatest gifts that theatre can give. *The Gap Year* has certainly been an experience for me and I hope it is for you too. See it, read it, share it, but most of all enjoy it.

# CHARACTERS

**KATE MULGREW** – 63

**OONAGH MADDEN** – 61

**ROISIN MCANESPIE** – 62

**FR DONNELLY** – 50s, local priest

**KIERAN** – 30s, camp activities manager

**CAOIMHE** – young mother

**PAT** – 50s, recovering from a stroke

**JOSIE** – nurse, Pat's daughter

**CAMPERVAN MAN** – late 20s

**SISTER THOMASINA** – young nun

**FIONNTAN** – 30s, hitch-hiker

**EDDIE** – 60s, Oonagh's ex

**ALISON** – 24, drunk partier

**PAUL** – 60s, Roisin's husband

**ETHAN** – 20s, Drag artist

**TOURIST** – 30s

**CATHERINE** – 30, Kate's daughter

**TANGO-DANCER**

# SETTING

Ireland.

# TIME

Present day.

# NOTES ON TEXT

These roles can be played by three female actors (60s), two male actors (50s, 30s) & one female actor (20s/30s).

Punctuation denotes delivery and does not conform to the rules of grammar.

/　　　　an interruption

...　　　　a trailing off

*This play is dedicated to the memory of Kate McManus,*
*Roisin McMahon and Monica Donnelly.*
*Three women who would've loved a wee trip.*

# PROLOGUE

*(June, County Antrim.)*

*(Darkness. A single, flickering, red light towards the back of the stage. The smell of old wood, damp coats and dust. The lights slowly rise, an earthy yellow and burnt orange. Centre an old wooden bench, on it a small congregation, heads bowed.)*

*(Quiet humming of the hymn* ["BE NOT AFRAID"].*)*

**FR DONNELLY.** Joseph Mulgrew was a much-loved husband, father, grandfather, friend and colleague.

*(The humming gets louder, the congregation start singing as they stand.)*

*(They face the audience, sombre.* **KATE** *steps forward.)*

**KATE.** May his soul, and the souls of all the faithful departed, rest in peace/

**ALL.** Amen.

*(The lights blackout and there is a cacophony of sounds; traffic, birdsong, a dog barking, a supermarket announcement, the sound of a hoover and Radio 4's Women's Hour.)*

*(The lights rise. We are in a dainty, floral living room. Everything matches. A vase of rhododendron sits on the coffee table.)*

*(**OONAGH** is on the settee. Her ankles crossed as she plays with her wedding band. **KATE** enters carrying a tray of tea and biscuits.)*

**OONAGH.** Apparently he did it last weekend.

**KATE.** Milk?

**OONAGH.** Just a dash. At the top of the hill.

**KATE.** Sugar?

**OONAGH.** One please. He brought a picnic, the whole caboodle, blanket, Prosecco, sandwiches, and inside one of the Tupperwares/

**KATE.** Biscuit?

**OONAGH.** Please. Not the chocolate one, I'm trying to be good. Inside one of the Tupperwares was an old Polly Pocket. Do you remember those? Those tiny plastic toys. Am sure your girls had them?

**KATE.** Oh hundreds of them, and they still fought over who got the pet shop one.

**OONAGH.** So he gave her an old Polly Pocket of a wedding day – how imaginative – and when she opened it up, there was the ring... I was lucky if I got a packet of Rolos from the garage... so she said yes and that's it. He's marrying the florist. And I'm going to be a divorcee at sixty-one.

**KATE.** I'm sorry, Oonagh.

**OONAGH.** Anthony is going to be his best man. Couldn't make it for my 60th birthday party but is flying back to give his Dad away at the bloody altar.

**KATE.** They're having it in a church?

**OONAGH.** The Church of Ireland are happy to marry them. Did I not tell you? That's the florist's club... but, here, how are you feeling this week?

**KATE.**  Fine.

**OONAGH.**  Did the girls bring you out?

**KATE.**  We went to the new garden centre. Barry got a wee tomato plant, says he's going to grow it. No doubt Catherine will secretly water it when he gets fed up.

**OONAGH.**  She'll have to sellotape a few tomatoes onto it if it doesn't work out.

**KATE.**  Exactly.

**OONAGH.**  Is he still getting upset?

**KATE.**  Every time he comes over. Can barely get him through the door. They're talking about a grief counsellor. It's that funny age you know? He remembers Joe. Would be easier if he didn't... easier for us all really.

>  *(Beat.)*

**OONAGH.**  You don't mean that, Kate.

**KATE.**  ... No. I don't.

**OONAGH.**  Did Father Donnelly call?

**KATE.**  Sat here all evening. A full dinner and nearly a whole pack of biscuits.

**OONAGH.**  That's nice he called.

**KATE.**  Oh yes, exactly what I needed. To entertain the priest.

**OONAGH.**  He's only being thoughtful.

**KATE.**  I could do without it.

**OONAGH.**  Ah it must be lonely for him. I think he's a nice man. And him and Joe got on well.

**KATE.**  I suppose.

>  *(Beat.)*

**OONAGH.** Those flowers are lovely.

**KATE.** Rhododendrons. Joe's favourite.

**OONAGH.** Of course... the summer's here at last.

**KATE.** Will you go away with your sister, or ones from the shop?

**OONAGH.** Sure me and her fight the bit out. And those ones all have their own families... *(She sips.)* I was thinking, maybe, we could go somewhere?

**KATE.** You and me?!

**OONAGH.** Don't sound so appalled.

**KATE.** I'm not, I'm just... I don't think so.

**OONAGH.** Would you not fancy a wee break somewhere? We could go to a spa, or Spain maybe, or even Florida?! I haven't been anywhere since Lanzarote and that was before I got the suite re-covered.

**KATE.** I couldn't.

**OONAGH.** Why not?

**KATE.** I can't leave the girls. It's not even a month since Joe...

**OONAGH.** The girls have their families, they have work, friends. Meanwhile you're sitting here waiting on the one time a week they bring you to the bloody garden centre!

**KATE.** What would it look like, me just heading off on holiday after Joe/

**OONAGH.** Well, what else have you planned? You just going to stew here until it's respectable for you to start living again?!

**KATE.** Oonagh, now I appreciate what you're doing but/

**OONAGH.** If you don't want to sit here and entertain the priest then come on, a week off?! A week, Kate. What's a week? Anywhere you like.

**KATE.** Would be nice to get out of the house.

**OONAGH.** Course it would! I'm sick of this place. I can't walk down the street but for someone asking me about Eddie and his flipping wedding. I'm fed-up of it. A florist called Flora, it's bloody ridiculous.

**KATE.** Where would we go?

**OONAGH.** It's June, we can go anywhere we like in June. The schools aren't off yet.

**KATE.** Nowhere foreign. I couldn't face getting on a plane.

**OONAGH.** I've heard there's a lovely hotel in Fermanagh, lakes and walks and a good restaurant.

**KATE.** That might be nice. A bit of luxury.

**OONAGH.** We'll have ourselves a pamper.

**KATE.** We could ask Roisin?

**OONAGH.** We'd have to prise her away from those boys, but it'd do her good.

**KATE.** It would.

**OONAGH.** That's a yes then?

**KATE.** … Yes. OK. Just a few days, now. A spa or a hotel or something. The three of us. Why not.

> (*The lights change, a school bell rings,* **ROISIN** *stands 'holding' the hands of two boys.*)

**ROISIN.** Hello Matthew, hello Luke. How was school today? No, we're not going to the shop. Oh, don't pull so hard love, Granny's arm will be broke off. You played football, did you? No I don't think Granda could manage football, not with his bad knee. Well golf isn't really that like football. Football is for the young to

6THE GAP YEAR

play. He's the same age as me. You don't think I'm old?
That's very kind of you... no, that doesn't mean we can
go to the shop.

> *(Lights change and we hear birdsong and
> distant roadworks.)*

**OONAGH.** *(On the phone.)* Yes, a family room for three. It's
for my friend, newly widowed, a wee treat. Does that
include breakfast?

> *(Lights change and we hear piano music and
> the ten o'clock news.)*

**KATE.** *(On the phone.)* No, I'm fine Catherine, it's just
Oonagh. She wants to get away for a little break, and I
said I'd go with her. It's hard on her, all this with Eddie.
Yes, and Roisin. It'll be good for them both.

> *(Lights change and we hear children's TV
> and kids playing.)*

**ROISIN.** *(On the phone.)* They've asked me to go with them
and I've said yes. I'm afraid you're just going to have to
think of something, Nuala. Maybe your Dad or / well,
I'm sorry. I am sorry but it's not for me it's for Kate and
Oonagh. They need cheering up and I think I should
go with them. I know I haven't seen them for a while, I
was too busy minding the boys. I know you're grateful,
love... I don't have to ask your father's permission to go
away with my friends! Right, well, I'll see you when I
get back. Yes, I've your washing here. Love you.

> *(Lights change and the three women come
> together centre-stage, the sounds build to a
> cacophony around them.)*

# ACT ONE – SUMMER

## Scene One

*(Donegal, late afternoon.)*

*(Three smallish tents, one green, one purple, one pink, are pitched on the stage.* **ROISIN** *sits in front of the centre tent, on a purple camp chair. She is peeling potatoes into a small purple basin.* **KATE** *stands facing out, in deep reverie. Both are dressed in full camper gear.* **ROISIN** *sings* **[QUE SERA SERA]** *by Doris Day and Frank De Vol.)*

*(***ROISIN** *sings the first four lines.)*

**KATE.**  Those clouds are moving in.

*(***ROISIN** *sings the chorus.)*

**KATE.**  Told you that'd be the case.

**KATE.**  Rosh?

**ROISIN.**  … Hmm?

**KATE.**  Clouds are coming, I'm telling you.

**ROISIN.**  Donegal's green for a reason.

**KATE.**  We should've got the campervan.

**ROISIN.**  We took a vote and tents are more authentic.

**KATE.**  They'll not be so authentic when they're washed into the bloody bog.

**ROISIN.**  We agreed it would be a good experience.

**KATE.**  They'll be digging us out of the turf in two hundred-years. Trying to figure out why three women in their sixties were camping in Donegal.

**ROISIN.**  It'll make a great story for our clog.

**KATE.**  What?

**ROISIN.**  We're going to clog our experiences. Sixty and touring Ireland.

**KATE.**  It's not clog.

**ROISIN.**  It is. You chat and then log it. It's clog.

**KATE.**  It's blog, or vlog, not bloody clog. A clog is a shoe from Amsterdam, nothing to do with the internet, even I know that.

**ROISIN.**  Regardless of what you call it, we are doing Donegal in a tent. That was the agreement.

> *(Pause.)*

**KATE.**  Where is Miss Adventure?

**ROISIN.**  She's away to see the activities manager to find out what's on tonight.

**KATE.**  God help us.

**ROISIN.**  If it's a quiz you need to stop her from drinking vodka, I still haven't got over losing to the over-eighties at the parish fundraiser.

**KATE.**  I might have a quiet night tonight. Make sure the tent survives those clouds.

**ROISIN.**  Kate!

> *(Enter **OONAGH** and **KIERAN**.)*

**OONAGH.** Ladies, look who I finally got my hands on. This is Kieran.

**KIERAN.** Hello. I hope you're settling into your spot OK?

**ROISIN.** It's lovely Kieran, the view is wonderful.

**KATE.** Do you know the forecast for tonight?

**KIERAN.** Do you know, I don't.

**OONAGH.** Guess what ladies? There is an informal music session in the rec room at nine.

**KATE.** Oh Lord above.

**KIERAN.** Oonagh tells me we've a wonderful singer in our midst?

**ROISIN.** Well, I was, in my day, and Kate here can play the piano.

**KIERAN.** Ah will you come down to the rec room and have a go? We have an old piano there.

**KATE.** No, thank you. There'll be young ones, far more capable.

**OONAGH.** Now that is totally against the ethos of this place. Isn't it, Kieran?

**KIERAN.** I'm not sure/

**OONAGH.** Are you seriously going to sit there and say you're too old to sing? On your holiday?

**KATE.** Don't be getting excited Oonagh/

**OONAGH.** It's only a bit of singing. Why does everything have to be such a big deal?

**KATE.** You're being melodramatic now.

**OONAGH.** In Derry, you refused to do anything except look at that bloody wall/

**ROISIN.** Oonagh/

KATE. I like a bit of culture, it's not all about making a fool of ourselves/

KIERAN. I think I'll go on/

ROISIN. No/

OONAGH. Don't you leave just because Miss Prim here is being a party-pooper.

KATE. We can't party every night, Oonagh, we are not in our twenties! That ship has sailed.

OONAGH. I am well aware of how many ships have sailed, Kate Mulgrew. I have a long record of how many bloody ships have sailed out of my harbour. I thought that was the reason we were here? To embark on a few new ships!

KATE. Will you please just give it a rest/

OONAGH. Fine. You stay here and watch the drips roll down your tent. Roisin and I will be engaging with civilization in the rec room.

ROISIN. I'm not sure if/

OONAGH. Let's take the scenic route. There's a few sheep I haven't said hello to yet.

> (ROISIN *looks at* KATE, *smiles anxiously and exits with* OONAGH. KIERAN *stands awkwardly.*)

KATE. Well. *(Beat.)* I'm sorry, Conal.

KIERAN. It's Kieran, but no worries/

KATE. Sorry. Kieran.

KIERAN. Conal's a nicer name, actually. I wouldn't mind it.

> *(Beat.)*

KATE. Would you like a cup of tea?

KIERAN. Ah/

KATE. If you've time?

KIERAN. Sure. That'd be lovely.

> (**KIERAN** *sits on* **OONAGH**'s *pink chair as* **KATE** *readies the stove.*)

Have you been travelling a while then?

KATE. A fortnight.

KIERAN. Ah right, and have you been getting on well? (**KATE** *looks at him.*) I mean, what all have you seen?

KATE. We've done all of the North now. The cathedrals of Armagh, big houses in Down, castles in Antrim, walls in stroke-city, lakes of Fermanagh and then we gave up on the culture and got tipsy in Tyrone.

KIERAN. That's brilliant. When do you go home?

KATE. We're giving it a year.

KIERAN. Sorry?

KATE. We're doing a year. Around Ireland.

KIERAN. The whole of Ireland?

KATE. Yes. You know, one of those 'Gap Years' all you young ones are obsessed with?

KIERAN. A gap year? Around Ireland?

KATE. Yes, Kieran. Does that sound so surprising?

KIERAN. No, no. I just... well, fair play to you.

KATE. We're going to try and do every county. Oonagh's son's getting married next summer so we need to be back by then.

> (**KATE** *gives him the tea and sits beside him on her own green camp-chair.*)

KIERAN.  I went traveling around Australia after my leaving cert. Was a great year.

KATE.  Am sure.

KIERAN.  I've never really done Ireland, though. Wouldn't even have thought. Are your families excited for you?

KATE.  Not sure excited is the word.

KIERAN.  I'd have loved it if my Mum went off adventuring.

KATE.  Roisin's daughters depend on her for childcare. They've had to rearrange things. Oonagh's not got too many commitments now she's retired from the shop, just her son and he's in Spain.

KIERAN.  What did your kids say?

KATE.  My girls reckon I'll be back home soon enough.

KIERAN.  And will you?

KATE.  No. I won't... does your Mum live here in Donegal?

> *(Beat.)*

KIERAN.  I lost my mother. Last year.

KATE.  I'm sorry.

KIERAN.  'Lost' is a funny way to describe it, isn't it? As if I had something to do with it. My first touch with grief. 'Cept for pets, you know? But it's just... always there.

KATE.  Your first time's hard. When my sister died I was bereft... part of me can't believe I've outlived them all. I smoked until I had the girls, loved late night cheese and a large glass of red. My husband. Non-drinker, keen gardener, took our grandson Barry and his dog for a walk every day after school. Then just like that he was gone.

KIERAN.  We're all in the queue.

KATE.  Sorry?

**KIERAN.** Some poet said it. "We're all in the queue." Lucky thing is we don't know who's next.

**KATE.** Jesus, Kieran.

**KIERAN.** Sorry! I'm being depressing… it's great you're doing this, having a new adventure with your friends. All I did was get a bit drunk and go back to work.

**KATE.** I could probably be nicer.

**KIERAN.** Your friend is a force to be reckoned with. She reminds me of my Mum.

**KATE.** All of this is because of her. If you needed her to meet you at the Giant's Causeway in the morning, she'd be there. No questions asked. She's had a rough paper-round herself… suppose I should go have a look at that piano? If I am to redeem myself. I bet it's half out of tune.

**KIERAN.** What will you play?

> *(There is the sound of piano music,* **KATE** *moves centre,* **ROISIN** *and* **OONAGH** *join her.* **ROISIN** *begins to sing four verses of* **[DOWNTOWN]** by Petula Clark.*)*

## Scene Two

*(Sligo. Late July.)*

*(A doctor's waiting room.)*

*(**KATE**, **OONAGH** and **ROISIN** sit on a long metal bench. **OONAGH** fills in a form.)*

**KATE.** Did the nurse say how long it'd be?

**OONAGH.** No, she just told me to fill this in and take a seat.

**ROISIN.** It's very quiet all the same. For a Friday, isn't it?

**KATE.** It's Thursday.

**ROISIN.** It is not?

**KATE.** It is. All day.

**ROISIN.** Jesus, I thought it was Friday. If I'd have known that I wouldn't have had fish for lunch.

**OONAGH.** I can't believe you still carry on with that.

**ROISIN.** It's the least I can do. He did die for our sins. Oh, did you hear who died?

**KATE.** How would we hear who died when we're in the middle of Sligo?

**ROISIN.** Nuala texted me.

**OONAGH.** She's talking to you again?

**ROISIN.** Well, she only puts one x at the end but that's an improvement from a full-stop.

**KATE.** She's a selfish blight being annoyed at you.

**ROISIN.** I spoiled her. No point complaining about it now, it's forty years too late.

**KATE.** Why is it only you who gets the blame? What about Paul? You'd think he was her own personal taxi!

**OONAGH.** So who died?

**ROISIN.** What?

**OONAGH.** You said someone died, who was it?

**ROISIN.** Oh. Bertie McGill.

**OONAGH.** Not Bertie.

**KATE.** Oh dear.

**ROISIN.** Took ill quite quickly, into hospital on Sunday night, gone by Wednesday.

(*There is a bleep.*)

**OONAGH.** Oh, that's me.

(**OONAGH** *exits.*)

(*Beat.*)

**ROISIN.** Did you know she was still on the HRT?

**KATE.** No.

**ROISIN.** I'd have thought they'd have tried to weane her off it.

**KATE.** Especially with her family history.

**ROISIN.** I came off mine straight away.

**KATE.** I didn't take any.

**ROISIN.** You did without?

**KATE.** I did. It only lasted a few months and then nothing.

**ROISIN.** Lucky you. Mine was two years of hot flushes and cold sweats. Paul said he was going to move into the spare room if I kept kicking off the duvet.

**KATE.** What did you say?

ROISIN.  Told him to go right ahead.

> (*A young woman enters, pushing a child in a buggy. She sits down beside them.*)

> (**ROISIN** *smiles down at the buggy. The mother looks up.*)

CAOIMHE.  Don't bother smiling at him, he's a shite.

ROISIN.  Ah, now. Am sure he has his moments.

CAOIMHE.  Moments where he makes me question my feckin sanity! This is the third time we are here for him swallowing or shoving a toy somewhere. He's obsessed. Today it's a crayon. Swallowed it. Straight down. Time before that it was a lip-balm cap. And the first time he shoved his daddy's cuff-link – he'd left it at his backside – up his bloody nose. We were three hours waiting in A&E on a Saturday night.

ROISIN.  Three hours? That's not bad. In Belfast, my grandson waited six hours to check he hadn't broken his toe on the trampoline. Lucky he's only choosing small things, I suppose.

CAOIMHE.  I've told him, that's it, (*To the child.*) the doctor is going to take him off his mammy and he'll have to go live with strangers, and how will he like that?! No amount of tidying does it, he keeps finding something!

ROISIN.  Wonder what started him on it?

CAOIMHE.  I don't know. But I'm mortified going in to see this nurse again. There's only so many times you can say, "my child is a shite", in a polite way. And Josie is lovely, but I do think she'll have to call the services on me this time. (*There is a bleep.*) Oh, that's us. Come on you.

> (**CAOIMHE** *exits.* **ROISIN** *smiles.*)

**KATE.** Isn't it terrible using that language in front of your child?

**ROISIN.** Oh it's not the end of the world.

**KATE.** What sort of example does it set though? We never/

**ROISIN.** If you start saying "In my day" I'm going to buy you denture cream and a subscription to Ireland's Own. *(Pause.)* I miss the boys.

**KATE.** I wonder how Barry's tomato's getting on.

**ROISIN.** It feels a bit wrong to be missing a year of their lives. Doesn't it?

**KATE.** Are you having regrets? You said you wanted to do it/

**ROISIN.** I do. I do. But do you not feel guilty at the same time?

**KATE.** ... No. I don't.

**ROISIN.** Not at all?

**KATE.** I feel too sad to feel anything as easy as guilt.

*(Enter* **OONAGH.***)*

**OONAGH.** Ladies! I've just met the most amazing Nurse, Josie, and she says we can stay the night with her!

## Scene Three

*(Later that day.* **JOSIE***'s living room.)*

*(***KATE*** *sits on the settee beside* **PAT***. He is around 50, smartly dressed, with a thoughtful stare. He is recovering from stroke, experiencing mild Aphasia. He drinks tea with his left-hand.* **KATE** *beside him, keeping a helpful eye.* **ROISIN** *is ironing.)*

*(Enter* **OONAGH***.)*

**OONAGH.** I've found some rice, and an old can of sweet and sour. If there's chicken I could do that? What do you think?

**KATE.** What time did Josie say she'd be home?

**OONAGH.** No idea. It was all so quick.

**KATE.** Pat, do you know what time your Josie's home?

*(***PAT*** *stares at* **KATE***.* **OONAGH** *comes towards* **PAT** *and kneels beside him, speaks slowly.)*

**OONAGH.** Pat, is Josie home by six?

**KATE.** You don't need to speak to him like he's stupid.

**OONAGH.** I'm not! I'm just speaking slowly.

**KATE.** Any slower and you'd be back in Belfast.

*(***PAT*** *looks towards* **OONAGH***, then back to* **KATE***, he smiles.)*

**OONAGH.** Well, you try then.

**ROISIN.** What exactly did Josie say, Oonagh?

**OONAGH.** Just what I told you. That she would be working but we'd be welcome to stay here as long as we didn't mind keeping an eye on Pat.

Maybe we could call the doctors surgery, see if they'd tell us?

**KATE.** Pat, is your daughter home by six?

> (**PAT** *looks at* **ROISIN** – *he smiles.*)

**ROISIN.** Jeepers Pat, don't you start giving me the glad eye. I've enough trouble with my own husband! I don't need another one.

**PAT.** *(Slowly.)* Home. Daughter.

**KATE.** Yes, when is she home?

**OONAGH.** Is it six?

**PAT.** *(Slowly.)* One.

> *(Beat.)*

**OONAGH.** One?

**KATE.** No Pat, it's past one now, it's four o'clock.

**OONAGH.** Sure we'll just call them.

**ROISIN.** He'll have trouble with numbers. Hold up your fingers.

**KATE.** My what?

**ROISIN.** Your fingers. Look. Pat? What time is Josie home? Is it six? *(She holds up six fingers.)*

> *(Beat.)*

**PAT.** *(Nods.)* Yes.

**KATE.** Ah, good man yourself! See Roisin, you've the magic touch. That gives us two hours to get the house nice and dinner made.

**OONAGH.** Will the kids be back before her?

**KATE.** Ask Pat, are your grandchildren home before six?

*(PAT smiles at KATE. He shakes his head.)*

**OONAGH.** I'll get dinner on then.

**PAT.** Yum. Yum. *(He giggles.)*

*(OONAGH exits.)*

**KATE.** Stroke or no stroke Patrick Barr you are the same as every other man. A trouble-maker! And here's me doing my best nurse. Joe always said I had a terrible bedside manner.

**ROISIN.** I'd have thought you'd have made a good nurse?

**KATE.** Sure I haven't your patience. It was always Joe who was the carer. He'd bandage them up when they fell, take their temperature when they were sick. He even sat up with Catherine when she was still at Queens and had partied too hard. Twenty years old, lying on the bathroom floor, with her Daddy sitting on the bath beside her, comforting her. He just has the knack for it... had the knack for it.

**ROISIN.** My Paul wouldn't even know where we kept the Calpol.

**KATE.** Your Paul is a man's man.

**ROISIN.** He's a lazy get.

**PAT.** Lazy. Get. *(PAT giggles.)*

**ROISIN.** I'm watching you, Patrick. Your Josie warned us about you. Her Daddy the charmer. The stroke may have clipped your tongue, but it hasn't stopped your flirting!

**KATE.** I'll help Oonagh with the dinner.

**ROISIN.** No fighting, Kate.

**KATE.** It's never me who starts it/

**ROISIN.** Just no fighting in front of Pat. We're guests.

*(KATE exits. ROISIN continues to iron. PAT looks over to her.)*

Well now. I'm sure you're tired watching all these goings on. Would you like a wee sleep maybe?

*(PAT shakes his head 'no'.)*

It really was very kind of your Josie to let us stay. I was getting a bit stiff in the tents, don't tell Kate, though.

PAT. Jo-sie.

ROISIN. Yes? Josie'll be back at six like you said.

PAT. Sad.

ROISIN. What's that?

PAT. Jo-sie.

ROISIN. Josie what?

PAT. Sad.

ROISIN. Ah now. I'm sure she's not. She's just working hard.

PAT. Daugh-ter. Sad... sad... sad... sad...

*(Beat.)*

*(ROISIN stops ironing and sits beside PAT.)*

ROISIN. When my mother was still alive, I spent so much time running after her. Opticians, podiatrists, Mass. Sometimes I'd forget to look after myself. I was alright, if she was alright, you know? Then when she passed, it was like my arm was cut off. No one to phone after dinner. No one to keep the paper for. No one to tell me who's died... All your Josie wants is to look after you. She wouldn't be happy if it was any other way. Believe me. I know it must hard for you. Seeing her try to manage everything. Not being able to help. I don't think I could bear it.

**PAT.** Car.

**ROISIN.** Hmm?

**PAT.** The car. Broke.

**ROISIN.** The car's broke? Can it not be fixed?

**PAT.** No. Too much. Too – too... *(Shakes his head.)* Sad.

**ROISIN.** Ah dear. If my Paul was here he could have a look at it, or Kate's Joe, God rest him. I'm afraid we're no use to you. All we're good for is the dinner and the washing. We never learnt how to do anything useful. But wait to you see, this'll fairly cheer her up. You can't underestimate the good of an empty laundry basket. She won't have to iron for a week – maybe even a month!

**PAT.** Jo-sie. Sad.

*(The lights change. The three women together.)*

**ROISIN.** I just think, we can't leave her like this, struggling.

**KATE.** Roisin, the whole point of this trip is to get away from caring for everyone else.

**ROISIN.** That woman is at her wits end. They can't even afford to get the car fixed. She's bussing it everywhere, Kate. And in the meantime Pat's stuck at home.

**OONAGH.** We could stay another few nights, just to get all the odd jobs done?

**KATE.** I don't want to be the big bad wolf. I just – both of you – I thought we were doing this for us, to give ourselves time, to not mind or pick up after anyone except ourselves/

**ROISIN.** That doesn't mean we can't help a few people along the way. What's the rush?

**OONAGH.** She's right, Kate.

*(Lights change. **PAT** stands with **JOSIE**, his arm linked to hers. The three women stand with their bags at their feet.)*

**KATE**. We'll hear no arguments about it.

**OONAGH**. We were going to get a campervan anyway. Kate's fed up of the tents.

**ROISIN**. It's yours. For the year. Look after it and get yourself back on your feet. We know what it is like being a carer. And you've children to mind and work to go to. Take the car, pack up everyone and go a drive up the coast. We insist.

**JOSIE**. Oh you're too kind. The three of you. You're like angels sent from heaven. Thank you. Thank you very much.

*(**PAT** slowly steps forward.)*

**ROISIN**. You take care, OK? And keep on doing what they tell you. You'll be back shouting at the football soon enough.

**PAT**. Safe trip.

*(He holds out his hand to **ROISIN**. She takes it and pops a kiss on his cheek. **PAT** smiles. He and **JOSIE** exit.)*

*(The three women wave. And start to walk.)*

*(Pause.)*

**OONAGH**. Is it a long walk to the van place?

**KATE**. About two mile.

**OONAGH**. Jesus, Mary and Joseph. Can't we ask her for a lift?

**ROISIN**. Oonagh, you can't give them the car then ask for a lift.

**OONAGH.** I don't think I've ever walked two miles.

**KATE.** Well, you wanted an 'authentic' Gap Year. Do you think all the young ones get taxis across China?

**OONAGH.** *(Looks behind.)* They're still waving.

**KATE.** Come on, you'll be fine.

**OONAGH.** Least I might lose a bit of weight on this trip.

**ROISIN.** That's true.

**KATE.** You're meant to do ten thousand steps a day.

**ROISIN.** I'd say two miles is more than that.

**OONAGH.** Oh look, a coffee shop. Shall we get something to keep us going?

## Scene Four

*(Lights change. Sounds of Sligo FM and motorway traffic.)*

*(**KATE** meets **CAMPERVAN MAN** who is holding an invoice.)*

**KATE.** I don't care how many miles it has on it. I am not paying that.

**CAMPERVAN MAN.** I'm practically giving it away/

**KATE.** I may be twice your age but I did not come up the Lagan in a bubble.

**CAMPERVAN MAN.** What?

**KATE.** Salesmen are the same whether you're North or South. Monaghan or Mayo. Belfast or Cork. I am not a 'little old lady' ready to be had/

**CAMPERVAN MAN.** Sweetheart, I never said you were/

**KATE.** Asking me if I'm sure I can drive such a big vehicle, showing me the most expensive models, refusing to negotiate. If I was standing here with my Joe you'd be talking only to him. I'd be invisible. That suited me fine and dandy for forty years. I didn't give a damn if the car or boiler or bank was 'a man's job', I had enough to be doing. But I have had the misfortune of losing my husband and now I am standing here on my own and I won't let you treat me like a little old lady. So, *sweetheart*, I will say it one more time, I Am Not. Paying. That.

*(Beat.)*

*(He marks down the invoice and hands it to **KATE**.)*

**CAMPERVAN MAN.** Take this up to the desk.

KATE. Thank you.

> *(Lights change.)*

> *(The three women sit on the bench. It is now the campervan.* **OONAGH** *drives, confidently, haphazardly,* **KATE** *navigates, and* **ROISIN** *prays.)*

> *(Sounds of traffic, radio adverts and the road... then a steady drum-beat.)*

> *(The following is spoken to time, with a steady beat 1 – 2 – 3 – 4.)*

KATE. 1        2            3

> Left, right, not that right/

ROISIN. 4

> Jesus!

OONAGH. 1        2        3

> Left, left, this left?

KATE. 4

> Right!

ROISIN. 1            2

> Hail Mary Full of Grace/

KATE. 3        4

> Slow, slow/

ROISIN.        1                2

> The Lord is with Thee/

KATE.            3

> Would you just/

**OONAGH.** 4

Jesus!

**KATE.** 1 2 3

Left, left, not that way/

**ROISIN.** 4

Mind the hedge!

**OONAGH.** 1 2 3 4

Jesus! Kate, did see you see what he did?

**ROISIN.** 1 2

For the love of God/

**KATE.** 3 4

Lights – use your lights!

**ROISIN.** 1 2 3

Blessed art thou amongst women/

**KATE.** 4

Mind the line!

**ROISIN.** 1 2 3

Blessed art thou amongst women/

**OONAGH.** 4

Don't/

**KATE.** 1 2

It's a solid line/

**OONAGH.** 3 4

I'm doing my best here.

**ROISIN.** 1 2

Blessed is the fruit/

**OONAGH.** 3              4

    I've the hang of it now.

**ROISIN.** 1                2        3

    And blessed is the fruit of thy womb/

**ALL.** 4

    Jesus!

       *(They stop. They breathe.)*

## Scene Five

*(Knock. Early September.)*

*(A soft wind blows. Flickering lights on one side of the stage reveal a large Mary effigy. There is a quiet humming of prayer.)*

*(**ROISIN** and **OONAGH** kneel, praying. A young nun kneels nearby.)*

**ALL.** Our Lady of Knock, Queen of Ireland, you gave hope to your people in a time of distress, and comforted them in sorrow.

**ROISIN.** Bless Paul, let him remember to feed the cat. And to empty the fire grate, he always lets it spill out. And bless his bad knee. I hope it isn't hurting too much.

**SISTER.** Help me to remember that we are all pilgrims on the road to heaven. Fill me with love and concern for my brothers and sisters in Christ, especially those who live with me.

**OONAGH.** Mary, will you keep a wee look out for me, please? Let me get through this trip without annoying or hurting anyone too much. If you could send a bit of patience Kate's way, I'd really appreciate it.

**SISTER.** Comfort me when I am sick, lonely or depressed. Teach me how to take part ever more reverently in the Holy Mass.

**ROISIN.** Bless Nuala and Siobhan. I hope they don't stay angry forever. Bless Matthew and Luke. Give Matthew a bit more time to find his place, it's hard being the youngest. Bless Oonagh. Bless Kate, bless... eh, oh no... isn't that terrible? Kate's husband? Ah bless Kate's husband.

**OONAGH.**  Mary, may I have the confidence to drive that big van and not kill anything along the way. Especially wee animals, I can't bear the thought.

**SISTER.**  Give me a greater love of Jesus in the Blessed Sacrament. Pray for me now and at the hour of my death.

**ROISIN.**  Joseph! Bless Joe. And Mammy, and Daddy, and Graham and Jean.

**OONAGH.**  I must ask Roisin who the patron saint of travel is...

**ROISIN.**  May their souls and the souls of all the faithful departed rest in peace.

**ALL.**  Amen.

> *(Lights  change.*  **ROISIN**  *and*  **SISTER THOMASINA** *exit.* **KATE** *joins* **OONAGH**.*)*

**KATE.**  What do you mean we're giving a nun a lift?

**OONAGH.**  She was going to get the bus so we said we'd drive her as far as Galway.

**KATE.**  I'm not listening to a nun pray the length of Ireland.

**OONAGH.**  She won't be praying in the van/

**KATE.**  She will if you're driving.

**OONAGH.**  Jesus Kate, what's got into you? We're only giving her a lift not doing the Novena. She's the youngest nun I've ever seen.

**KATE.**  No woman needs to be a nun these days, she must be a lunatic.

**OONAGH.**  God forgive you. That girl felt a calling. Who are you to judge?

**KATE.**  I'm not sitting beside her. I'll drive.

## Scene Six

*(Galway. Later that day.)*

*(**KATE** and **SISTER THOMASINA** sit outside a garage.)*

**SISTER.**  Oonagh said you visited Ceide Fields? Is that why you didn't make it to Knock?

**KATE.**  I fancied something different.

**SISTER.**  I've never made it there. It's on my list.

**KATE.**  It's an interesting spot.

**SISTER.**  I'm sure. I loved New Grange.

**KATE.**  Hmm?

**SISTER.**  New Grange? It's in Meath. It's a beautiful spot. Feels very spiritual.

**KATE.**  I'm sure.

*(Beat.)*

**SISTER.**  I am sorry for your loss, Kate.

**KATE.**  Thank you.

**SISTER.**  Oonagh said Joseph was a very kind, caring man.

**KATE.**  Did she.

**SISTER.**  Yes. I'm sure it was really difficult for you. How have you been feeling?

**KATE.**  Thank you for your concern Sister Thomasina, but I'd really rather not talk about it.

**SISTER.**  Would you like to pray with me instead?

**KATE.**  No. Thank you.

*(Beat.)*

**SISTER.**  Would you like me to pray for you?

**KATE.**  That will not be necessary.

**SISTER.**  Honestly, it's no trouble/

**KATE.**  What was your name before?

**SISTER.**  My name?

**KATE.**  Yes, before you took holy orders?

**SISTER.**  Oh. Megan.

**KATE.**  Megan. That's a nice name. And why did you, Megan – if you don't mind me asking – decide to become Sister Thomasina?

>    *(Beat.)*

**SISTER.**  I don't mind you asking, Kate. Just over six years ago I lost my mother, father and two brothers. A lorry driver was texting. He didn't notice the lights had turned red and my Dad had stopped ahead. He drove the truck straight through them. They died instantly. Except my youngest brother, Thomas. He held on a few hours before passing. I even managed to say goodbye to him. I had nothing. I was nothing. Then I felt God. God's presence. God's love. And here I am.

**KATE.**  I'm sorry for your loss... how did you feel God's presence?

**SISTER.**  You'll laugh.

**KATE.**  I'm not asking to laugh at you. I'm trying to understand.

**SISTER.**  I felt, in all that pain, and grief and brutality, His love. He was there with me. When I had to identify them, when I had to stand at the funeral, surrounded by people and yet entirely alone. When I had to go home to an empty house. He was there. It didn't make me feel any less sad – sad isn't a strong enough word – but I didn't feel quite so alone. God was with me.

**KATE.** Could you not have just given out Communion or joined the choir? You're so young. You're going to miss out on so much, you'll spend the rest of your life living under the rules of the Catholic Church.

**SISTER.** You think I'm wasting my life? Is that it? Why would a young person like me dedicate themselves to God?

**KATE.** Not just to God, to the church. I just think/

**SISTER.** I fought it. With every fibre of my being, I fought it. You know how much effort it takes to ignore God. You know it Kate, I'm sure. I drank – a lot – went travelling, met people and made a mess of most things. When I finally came home I just drove up to the Sisters of Mercy and asked them to accept me. I felt God's calling. *(Beat)* He is with you. If you can only let Him in.

**KATE.** Please don't.

**SISTER.** Pray with me, Kate. Pray that God will care for your dear Joseph/

**KATE.** Don't! You have my sympathy, you really do. But take it from someone much older. You turned to God to escape. And fine, that's working for you. But your loving God let a man drive a truck through your family. He let my Joe die alone on a cold hard floor. I went to Mass, prayed, raised my children in the Church. I did everything I was meant to do. Look where it's got me? God is either cruel or non-existent because my Joe deserved better and look how your God left him to die.

    *(OONAGH enters.)*

**OONAGH.** You could catch a venereal disease in those toilets – Oh! Sorry Sister, I thought you were still inside.

**SISTER.** No problem. I'll use the bathroom next.

*(SISTER leaves.)*

**OONAGH.**  Have you upset her?

**KATE.**  I doubt it.

**OONAGH.**  She's a very sweet young woman, Kate.

**KATE.**  I'm sure she is.

**OONAGH.**  Why are you giving her such a hard time?

**KATE.**  Please, I don't want to argue/

**OONAGH.**  I'm not arguing with you, I'm embarrassed by you. You're struggling, I get it, but stop taking it out on her. It's not her fault Joe died.

**KATE.**  It's not just about Joe.

**OONAGH.**  What is it about then? You should be using your faith to get you through. It can help, trust me.

**KATE.**  Do you not think I wish I could? Do you think I'm glad I've lost my faith as well as my bloody husband?!

**OONAGH.**  Kate/

**KATE.**  But they're not making it easy for me. It isn't just the younger generations Rome has lost, it's anyone with two eyes in their head. Long before Joe died I was struggling. Paedophile priests, cover-ups, mother and baby homes and God knows what else!

**OONAGH.**  You don't go to Mass for the priest. You go to talk to God.

**KATE.**  MAYBE I DON'T WANT TO TALK TO GOD!! MAYBE I THINK GOD'S A SELFISH BASTARD WHO LET MY JOE DIE ON A SUPERMARKET FLOOR/

*(KATE bursts into a rage of tears.)*

**OONAGH.**  Kate! Katie, come on, come on now. You're OK. You're OK. I'm sorry. Shh. Shh.

(**ROISIN** *enters holding two ice creams.*)

**ROISIN.**  Ah dear. There-there now Kate, there-there. Here. Take this. There's nothing a wee ice cream can't help.

(**KATE** *takes the ice cream.*)

# ACT TWO – AUTUMN

## Scene One

*(The Ring of Kerry. October.* **OONAGH** *is driving the campervan.)*

**ROISIN.** So I said to Nuala, I don't care if it's your Daddy's birthday I won't be home for it. She went mad: I was being selfish; her and Siobhan couldn't believe I was behaving this way at my age. I said to her it was damned lucky – I said damned – that I was behaving this way, because if I hadn't I'd have been dead and buried before any of them took a blind bit of notice.

**KATE.** About time Rosh.

**ROISIN.** Going on and on about me missing Paul's birthday. I wanted to remind her of my 60th and how he had a golf tournament in Antrim that he "just couldn't miss". And how I told him it was no problem, that he should go and enjoy himself. Which he did. More fool me.

**KATE.** When I was still working in the school Joe forgot my birthday. When he came home after work I made no dinner for him, got the girls to bed early, and then I let rip. The one date the length of the year he had to remember. I did everything else, the girls' birthdays, his birthday, his Mother's birthday. All I needed was a card. I didn't even need a present, just a card, an acknowledgement of the day.

**OONAGH.** Am sure he felt awful.

KATE. Didn't he tell me there were cuts going on at work. He was worried he'd be made redundant and he was so sorry it'd just slipped his mind. I felt awful. We made up and he drove into town and got us a fish supper.

ROISIN. Ah that's lovely. Do you know who's dead?

KATE. Who this time?

OONAGH. I think by the time we get home there's going to be more dead than living.

ROISIN. Bertie McGill.

*(Beat.)*

KATE. Sure you told us that in Sligo.

ROISIN. Did I?

KATE. Yes. In the doctors.

ROISIN. What doctors?

KATE. Josie's place, when Oonagh was getting her HRT.

ROISIN. Oh, right. I forgot.

OONAGH. Is it this left? *(Beat.)* Roisin?

ROISIN. Hmm?

OONAGH. Here, this left, is this the one?

ROISIN. I don't know.

OONAGH. You're meant to be navigating!

ROISIN. What?

OONAGH. Am I taking it or not?

KATE. Take it! Sure it says Kerry.

ROISIN. Jesus!

OONAGH. Will you please stop Jesus-ing! You're meant to be keeping me right/

**ROISIN.** I'm sorry, I didn't/

**KATE.** Oonagh! MIND THAT MAN!

> (**FIONNTAN,** *a man with a backpack appears,*
> *then dives out of the way.*)

> (*They swerve and scream then crash.*)

**ROISIN.** Holy Mary mother of God/

**OONAGH.** Oh no, oh no, oh no/

**KATE.** Did you hit him? Did he get hit?

**OONAGH.** I don't know. Oh Kate. What if I've hit him? What if I've killed him? I knew I should have lit another candle in Roscommon. I only had three euros, and they were a euro each, and I was going to ask, because it wasn't enough for four candles/

**KATE.** Give over about the candles and go see if he's OK!

**OONAGH.** I can't. What if he's dead? I can't do it. I couldn't even see if Mummy was dead, I had to call the nurse. I just can't/

**ROISIN.** I will.

**KATE.** Rosh?

**ROISIN.** I don't mind.

> (**ROISIN** *gets out of the van.*)

**OONAGH.** That's her nurses training. I always think what a waste it was she didn't practice once she married.

**KATE.** Please would you just shut up for a second.

> (**ROISIN** *goes to* **FIONNTAN** *who is slowly*
> *getting to his feet.*)

**ROISIN.** Are you OK?

**FIONNTAN.**  Yes, just a bit muddy. Sorry, I must have surprised you.

**ROISIN.**  We didn't see you. Sorry.

**FIONNTAN.**  No harm done. I'm Fionntan.

**ROISIN.**  Roisin. What are you doing on the road?

**FIONNTAN.**  Thumbing a lift. You wouldn't be able to give me a ride, would you?

*(Lights change.)*

## Scene Two

*(Dingle. Evening. A bar.)*

**OONAGH.**  When I was nineteen I met Eddie Dunlop. Eddie was mysterious, handsome. An accountant. Which in 1980 Northern Ireland was very attractive. He lived in south Belfast. We went out to dances, and the cinema. It was difficult to make time to meet, what with the roadblocks and riots going on around us. But it didn't stop us. May 1st '81 we married. My mother didn't go. She felt betrayed, I think. Eddie was from the other side. I didn't care, I just had to have him and he me. Those first few months... I moved into his flat and had Anthony ten months later. I fell pregnant a few times after that. But it never worked out. Shame, I always wanted a full house. So, I dedicated all my energy to my boys. I remember Eddie telling Anthony to think of his mother and put the seat down. He was always quite thoughtful. Until, he wasn't. After nearly twenty years of marriage he started to come home late from work. Left early in the morning. I was clueless, thought he was just distracted, you know? It was just a phase. He needed some space, maybe. Two years. He dragged it out for two years. In the end it was her who made him act. She was fed up being his bit on the side. He either had to leave me and have it with her, or she was dumping him. I often think that was a bit of a gamble, for her, you know? Like if it was me, I wouldn't want to risk losing him... I begged, begged on my hands and knees. I wanted to keep my husband, my marriage. I was prepared to forgive to keep what I had. He left and I pieced myself back together. I didn't have the energy to move home, town, newsagents. So I've spent years seeing what I lost. They walk past me on the street. Say a polite hello. Hold hands in the ice-cream shop. Eventually I was OK. I joined clubs. I went back to Mass. I filled the void. Stuffed it full. And now

I'm sixty-one. My son's in Spain, he won't be coming home. And Eddie wants to marry the florist

*(The lights change.* **OONAGH** *sits beside* **FIONNTAN.** *Traditonal music plays.)*

**FIONNTAN.** You're beautiful.

**OONAGH.** Jesus, Fionntan.

**FIONNTAN.** You are.

**OONAGH.** I like this band. They're very good.

**FIONNTAN.** Do you not know you're beautiful?

**OONAGH.** I'm sixty-one.

**FIONNTAN.** Like a fine wine.

**OONAGH.** That drink must be strong.

**FIONNTAN.** Tell me about yourself.

**OONAGH.** You first. Why are you hitch-hiking around Ireland? Were all the flights to Australia booked?

**FIONNTAN.** I don't like to stay anywhere for too long.

**OONAGH.** Where were you last?

**FIONNTAN.** Limerick.

**OONAGH.** Did you chase women there too?

**FIONNTAN.** I had a girlfriend. I was there a year.

**OONAGH.** A woman in every county.

**FIONNTAN.** Just Limerick. Just Savita. I don't know how to root down and stay in one place. Don't know how anyone does... it's your turn.

**OONAGH.** What do you want to know?

**FIONNTAN.** What did you want to be when you grew up?

**OONAGH.** That's a long time ago now.

**FIONNTAN.** I wanted to be in the army.

**OONAGH.** The Irish Army?

**FIONNTAN.** Whatever army Action Man was in.

**OONAGH.** My son loved him.

**FIONNTAN.** How old is your son?

**OONAGH.** Forty. How old are you?

**FIONNTAN.** I'm not telling you.

**OONAGH.** You're too young to be worrying about your age.

**FIONNTAN.** If I tell you, you won't let me kiss you.

**OONAGH.** You don't want to kiss me.

**FIONNTAN.** I want to do more than kiss you.

**OONAGH.** Fionntan!

**FIONNTAN.** It's the truth. I haven't just stayed around to hitch a lift. You're funny, and fun and bleedin' beautiful. Oonagh Madden, I'm mad for you. Mad to kiss and hold and touch you.

**OONAGH.** Bloody hell, Fionntan. I'm old enough to be your mother. What age are you?

**FIONNTAN.** Why does that matter? It doesn't matter to me. I haven't felt like this in months... and you never answered my question.

**OONAGH.** I wanted to be Grace Kelly.

**FIONNTAN.** You'd suit being a Princess. Or a movie star.

**OONAGH.** Lines like that might have worked in Limerick but you can't pull the wool over my eyes. Am I an experiment, is that what this is?

FIONNTAN. Maybe I've been imagining things. Picking up the wrong signals. But you can't look me in the eye without blushing.

OONAGH. Is this a joke? The night you kissed an old woman in Dingle.

FIONNTAN. So we are going to kiss?

OONAGH. You're impossible! Like a child. A grown child. How old are you?

FIONNTAN. I'm thirty-five.

OONAGH. There you go. See! You're far too young to be interested in a woman like me.

FIONNTAN. And yet I am sitting here in front of you telling you I'd like to kiss you. If you'll let me.

OONAGH. I'm too old, too tired. It's too much to even think of.

FIONNTAN. Then how about a dance?

OONAGH. I am not dancing.

FIONNTAN. You're meant to be on an adventure! One dance. (FIONNTAN *holds out his hand.*) To save my pride?

> (OONAGH *hesitates, then downs her wine and takes his hand.*)

OONAGH. One dance.

> (*They move centre, the band starts playing a steady, fierce jig.* FIONNTAN *starts to tap around* OONAGH, *she slowly moves around him, they gaze at each other, circling. As the music builds so too does* OONAGH's *confidence. The intensity builds between them. On the climax of the music she takes off, leaping around, jigging like a girl of*

*ten, her hair flying behind her.* **FIONNTAN** *is mesmerised and claps along. She finally leaps towards him and he throws his hands around her, they spin as she firmly, determinedly, passionately kisses him.)*

*(Lights.)*

## Scene Three

*(Kerry campsite. Early morning.)*

*(**KATE** stands holding a cup of tea, staring out. **OONAGH** enters, same clothes as before.)*

*(**OONAGH** stops when she sees **KATE**.)*

**OONAGH.** Oh.

**KATE.** Oh?

**OONAGH.** Hello.

**KATE.** Hello.

**OONAGH.** You're up early.

**KATE.** I'm up early?

**OONAGH.** Why are you repeating everything I say?

**KATE.** Why do you think?

**OONAGH.** Don't start that Irish Ma stuff with me, Kate, I invented the half of it.

**KATE.** Where have you been?

**OONAGH.** At the pub, where do you think? If you weren't such a party-pooper you could've been there too.

**KATE.** You don't stay at the pub until six in the morning.

**OONAGH.** You do in Kerry.

**KATE.** So that's where you were? All night?

**OONAGH.** Kate, I don't know why you think you are the Queen Bee. We're old friends but you're not the boss of me.

**KATE.** Just answer my question, were you in the pub all night?

**OONAGH.** Yes, I told you.

**KATE.** Liar.

**OONAGH.** Excuse me?

**KATE.** I walked to the bloody pub. It was shut at two a.m. So where have you been for the last four hours?

**OONAGH.** What is it to you where I've been? I'm not your daughter, you don't get to bark me around.

**KATE.** Selfish Oonagh, always satisfying herself. Just another time on this bloody trip where you act like you're the only one here.

**OONAGH.** How dare you! I am entitled to occasionally do whatever the hell I like and not offer it up to a democratic vote.

**KATE.** No Oonagh, you're not. Not when you're here with two other people. That is the reality of being a woman with responsibilities. You haven't had to think about anyone except yourself for twenty years. Roisin and I would never dream of not coming back to the van, in case you were sat here worried. But no, you need to go and have your own adventure, just to remind us that you are a lone-wolf and we don't matter a jot.

**OONAGH.** How dare you! How many years have I been made to feel less because I'm not Kate Mulgrew? Martyring yourself for everyone. At least Roisin doesn't even realise she does it. But you – you make yourself feel better by lording it over everyone, showing us how much you're needed. I had no choice but to look after myself. Who else was going to? No Eddie, no Anthony, no mother, half the time no friends and I made the most of my lot. You can't be angry at me because you dedicated your life to everyone except yourself.

*(Enter **EDDIE**. **KATE** sees him first.)*

**KATE.** Eddie.

**OONAGH.** You're going to take Eddie's side now?!

**KATE.** No, *Eddie.*

**EDDIE.** Hello Oonagh.

> (**EDDIE** *is a smartly dressed, retiree from South Belfast. He speaks with a soft, serious tone.*)

> (**OONAGH** *turns to see him.*)

**OONAGH.** Eddie!

**KATE.** What are you doing here?

**EDDIE.** You couldn't get me a cup of coffee, Kate love? I've been driving all night.

> (**KATE** *looks to* **OONAGH,** *then leaves.*)

You're a hard woman to track.

**OONAGH.** I don't understand how you're here.

**EDDIE.** That's a lovely way to greet me after all these months. Roisin's Nuala told me so I jumped in the car. It's a long drive. Flora will be worried. I need to let her know I made it.

**OONAGH.** I'm sure Flora the Florist is weeping with worry.

**EDDIE.** Don't do that.

**OONAGH.** I'll do what I like.

**EDDIE.** You always do.

**OONAGH.** Don't you start.

**EDDIE.** You know why I'm here, Oonagh.

**OONAGH.** Missed running into me in Tesco's? Missed smiling at me in The Anchor? Missed having someone around town to remind you of what a total shit you are?

**EDDIE.** I've apologised to you for twenty years. I can't do anything more.

**OONAGH.** That doesn't mean it's all wiped away, doesn't mean I get my life back the way I wanted.

**EDDIE.** You could have had a new life same as me. It was your choice to stay in no-man's land and blame Flora and I for the rest of your life/

**OONAGH.** Don't you/

**EDDIE.** And now you're just making a fool of yourself. Do you think you can just ignore it? I need you to sign the papers.

**OONAGH.** Oh you need me, do you?

**EDDIE.** You don't want it going to court. It would be easier for us all if you signed them and that was it. This is silly. No one from the solicitors has been able to get a hold of you for months. Flora and I are going to be married and you need to just get over it/

**OONAGH.** I will not!

*(Enter **KATE**.)*

**KATE.** Oonagh, have you seen Roisin? She's not inside.

**OONAGH.** What do you mean?

**KATE.** She's not in the van, she's not there.

**OONAGH.** Well, she's not out here.

**KATE.** Oh God.

**OONAGH.** She'll be OK.

**KATE.** She must have went out when I went looking for you.

**EDDIE.** She's a grown woman, she'll be around here somewhere.

**KATE.** What if something's happened? What if she's wandered off the edge of a cliff somewhere?

**OONAGH.** We'll find her. We'll go look for her now. I'll call Fionntan and he can help.

**EDDIE.** Are you trying to get away from me?

**OONAGH.** For God's sake this is not about you.

**EDDIE.** I don't understand what the big deal is, the woman's entitled to go for a walk.

**OONAGH.** She's doting!

**KATE.** What if, oh God, what if/

**OONAGH.** We'll find her. We have to.

(*They exit.* **EDDIE** *follows.*)

## Scene Four

*(The ring of Kerry countryside.)*

**KATE.**  Roisin!

**OONAGH.**  Rosh! Roisin?

**KATE.**  I'm sorry.

**OONAGH.**  No I'm sorry. I should've told you I was staying out. Not that I knew I was staying out, it was just/

**KATE.**  You don't need to tell me/

**OONAGH.**  I slept with Fionntan.

*(Pause.)*

**KATE.**  You what?

**OONAGH.**  I had, you know, *(Whispers.)* sex, with Fionntan. Last night. Or this morning. Well both really.

**KATE.**  Right.

**OONAGH.**  Ah don't start disapproving now, we've only just made up/

**KATE.**  I'm not! I didn't/

**OONAGH.**  I can tell by your face.

*(Lights change. **FIONNTAN** and **EDDIE**.)*

**EDDIE.**  Mrs McAnespie!

**FIONNTAN.**  Roisin?! ... So you're Eddie.

**EDDIE.**  I am.

**FIONNTAN.**  Heard a bit about you.

**EDDIE.**  Don't believe everything a scorned woman tells you, son.

**FIONNTAN.** I don't think Oonagh is scorned. Scarred maybe.

**EDDIE.** No offence but what business is it of yours anyway? Who are you?

**FIONNTAN.** I suppose you'd call me her 'bit on the side'?

*(Lights change.* **OONAGH** *and* **KATE.***)*

**OONAGH.** Roisin!

**KATE.** And was it, did you... how did it go?

**OONAGH.** Oh, it was... it was lovely.

**KATE.** Good.

**OONAGH.** Good?

**KATE.** You deserve a bit of lovely.

**OONAGH.** I mean it's impossible. He's half my age.

**KATE.** Why's that impossible?

**OONAGH.** What would people say?

**KATE.** Who cares what people say! We're three women in our sixties taking a gap year around Ireland. Sleeping with a younger man is only a small part of the scandal we've created.

*(Lights change.)*

**EDDIE.** Mrs McAnespie!

**FIONNTAN.** Roisin?!

**EDDIE.** So you're a Dub?

**FIONNTAN.** I am.

**EDDIE.** And have you a job?

**FIONNTAN.** I do bits and bobs. Travel around.

**EDDIE.** You a Traveller?

**FIONNTAN.** No. Just, not one for staying still.

**EDDIE.** Sounds like a Traveller to me.

**FIONNTAN.** And what do you do?

**EDDIE.** I was an accountant. Retired now.

**FIONNTAN.** Rosin!

**EDDIE.** She's been doting they say.

**FIONNTAN.** Has she?

**EDDIE.** So they say. Not good.

**FIONNTAN.** Roisin!

*(Lights change.* **OONAGH** *and* **KATE.***)*

**OONAGH.** Roisin? …she's been getting worse.

**KATE.** I know.

**OONAGH.** Leaving the milk out, her purse open.

**KATE.** The tap running.

**OONAGH.** What if we can't find her/

**KATE.** We have to find her. We just have to.

**OONAGH.** But what if we can't. What if we're too late. Oh Kate/

**KATE.** We'll not be too late. She'll have just gone for a walk/

**OONAGH.** It'll be my fault. If I wasn't out all night you wouldn't/

**KATE.** It is neither of our faults. Listen. No listen to me. We will find her/

*(Enter* **FIONNTAN** *and* **EDDIE.***)*

**FIONNTAN.** Oonagh! Look! What's that down there on the side of the rocks?

**OONAGH.** Where?

**EDDIE.** Look, there a purple coat!

**KATE.** A coat?

**FIONNTAN.** I think it is.

**KATE.** Oh God.

**OONAGH.** It's moving!

**KATE.** The coat's moving?

**OONAGH.** ROISIN?!

**EDDIE.** It's her.

**FIONNTAN.** She's waving.

**KATE.** Oh thank God.

**OONAGH.** Oh Rosh – stay there! We'll come to you.

**EDDIE.** What's that she has in her hands?

**OONAGH.** It's/

**KATE.** A rhododendron.

> *(Lights change.* **ROISIN** *stands alone on stage.)*

**ROISIN.** When I was a little girl all I wanted was to be a nurse. I read as many books I could get my hands on, from the library mostly. That's what I worry about young people these days, where do they go to dream if they're not going to the library? I got my place and off I went to college. I lived in halls with girls from all over the North. The matron kept a close eye on us, but it was the most freedom I'd ever had. I cooked my own meals, saved up and went to the cinema. In my first year I met Paul. Paul McAnespie, a charming, handsome young man. It was 1978 and the world as we knew it was going mad. Paul worked in the City hospital as a porter, a server, then as a driver. He had three brothers and a mother who thought the world shone out of his you know what. We were young and in love and everything just happened so quickly. By '81 I was married, pregnant and living with Paul and his mother in a terrace house. Paul's mother had been there for twenty years, the neighbours knew her, were kind to her, but over the next few years it changed. Less Christmas cards, the veg man stopped calling, her bin got burnt out, and eventually Paul told us we were moving into a semi-detached on the Shore Road. I was so green at the time I did whatever he said. I never thought to say, "Can your mother maybe go live somewhere else?" or "I'd quite like to go back to work" or even, "Love, this rhythm method doesn't seem to be working shall we try abstinence?" I loved him and I was young. It's not like he took advantage, he was just doing what he thought was best, what he'd seen men do before him. And I was too ignorant to ask for anything better. We went on like that for a lifetime. Had our family, got them through school. Cared for – then buried – his mother, and mine. Suddenly we were at our sixtieth birthdays, our ruby wedding anniversary, Paul's retirement party. And then I... I forgot to collect the boys. The two of them standing there, waiting for their Granny... that did it really... and I'm terrified, some of the time. Terrified of being on my own, terrified I've hurt my family, terrified I've ran out of time for myself.

## Scene Five

*(Evening. Back at the campervan.* **OONAGH**
*is sitting on her pink camp chair, drinking*
*a glass of wine. Beside her a bottle and a few*
*glasses.* **EDDIE** *enters.)*

**EDDIE.** May I join you?

**OONAGH.** Why not.

*(***EDDIE*** *sits on* **KATE***'s green chair. After a*
*moment he pours himself a glass of wine.)*

**EDDIE.** That was some day.

**OONAGH.** It was.

**EDDIE.** Have all the counties held that much adventure?

**OONAGH.** We've not done too badly.

**EDDIE.** I wouldn't have the energy.

**OONAGH.** Sometimes we take it easy. Go to the pub.

**EDDIE.** Is that where you met that Fionntan lad?

**OONAGH.** No. We nearly ran over him.

**EDDIE.** Wouldn't blame you. He's a lively enough sort.

**OONAGH.** You two seemed to be getting on OK on the way
back.

**EDDIE.** He's a Dub, I'm a Nordie. We soon put the world to
rights... he says you and he are a thing.

**OONAGH.** Does he now.

**EDDIE.** Are you not?

**OONAGH.** What do you care?

**EDDIE.** Just curious.

**OONAGH.** He's a friend.

**EDDIE.** Just a friend?

**OONAGH.** What is it to you, Eddie? *(Beat.)* Jesus, you are as clear as a window. If I had been with Fionntan you could go back to the lawyer and say I'd been unfaithful too? Is that what's going on?

**EDDIE.** I was just thinking how happy it would make me to see you find someone. You deserve someone who'll appreciate you. Even if he is a Free-Stater *(Beat.)* Will you sign the papers? Let me go, love.

**OONAGH.** Don't call me love.

**EDDIE.** We were young. It is mad to think we'd stay together another twenty years. You can't pretend you were happy? It wasn't just me who was miserable.

**OONAGH.** I didn't know we weren't happy! It was you who made that choice, Eddie. It had nothing to do with me. You made a choice for the both of us. And after everything we'd been through. A bloody lifetime. I lost my mother to be with you. I walked away from it all. I would never choose to walk away from you.

**EDDIE.** I'm sorry I didn't do it the right way, I should have talked to you, I know that. But now I need you to choose to let me go.

**OONAGH.** Do you know it's still there? The void you left in me? And yes, I didn't help it heal, I should've left the town or got a new job or done anything to start again. But the emptiness was so big it took all my energy not to just disappear inside it. It would envelop me. The pain of it. All I could do was keep going. Keep pushing on.

**EDDIE.** What else can I say but sorry?

**OONAGH.** You could say why you stopped loving me. You could say why you allowed a gap in your heart for her to fill. You could say you wished it was different and if you could go back and change everything or anything you would. We could be sitting here over forty years married, planning a cruise and arguing about binday. You could say anything except "sorry". I can't do anything with "Sorry".

(*Pause.*)

Have you them here?

**EDDIE.** What?

**OONAGH.** The divorce papers.

> (**EDDIE** *takes rolled up papers from his coat pocket. He pulls a pen from his top pocket.*)

**EDDIE.** You serious?

**OONAGH.** Just because I've more past than future doesn't mean I have to stay there.

> (*She signs, stands and holds them out to* **EDDIE.** **EDDIE** *stands, takes them, for a moment she doesn't let go, then simultaneously as she releases them he moves to hug her. They stand there, together, still for a moment.*)
>
> (*They break.*)
>
> (*Lights.*)

## Scene Six

*(The next morning.* **FIONNTAN** *stands with his bag packed.)*

**OONAGH.** Well, that was a quare few days.

**FIONNTAN.** "Quare"?

**OONAGH.** Never mind.

**FIONNTAN.** I can't convince you to change your mind?

**OONAGH.** No. I'm sorry.

**FIONNTAN.** I guess I should be grateful we had what we had.

**OONAGH.** It was... lovely.

*(He moves towards her, kisses her gently, then less gently. She is overcome for a moment.)*

You're a bad influence.

**FIONNTAN.** Best thing anyone's ever said about me. Goodbye Oonagh Madden.

**OONAGH.** Goodbye, Fionntan. Thanks for... well.

**FIONNTAN.** You know, if I had you in my life, there wouldn't be a moment wasted. You're a very special woman.

*(He exits.)*

*(Pause.)*

*(***KATE*** and ***ROISIN*** enter.)*

**KATE.** Well, is that him away?

**OONAGH.** It is.

**ROISIN.** Are you OK?

**OONAGH.** I'm fine. More importantly, what about you? How're you feeling?

**ROISIN.** Oh fine. I'm fine. I'm sorry I worried you.

**KATE.** I think I'm ready to leave Kerry.

**ROISIN.** Yes, me too.

**KATE.** I will miss those views though.

**ROISIN.** And the lake.

**OONAGH.** And Fionntan's bum.

*(They laugh, then exit.)*

# ACT THREE – WINTER

## Scene One

*(Waterford.* **KATE,** **OONAGH** *and* **ROISIN** *are in the van. The radio plays Christmas adverts.)*

**KATE.** I called Catherine when we were in Cork.

**OONAGH.** Did you?

**KATE.** She sounded genuinely pleased to hear from me.

**ROISIN.** Of course she was.

**KATE.** She says she might come down after Christmas.

**ROISIN.** We're inspiring women everywhere!

**OONAGH.** Three women in their sixties taking a stand*! (Beat.)* Do you think 'feminist' is a dirty word?

**ROISIN.** I'm still not sure what it really means.

**KATE.** It's just about women being treated the same as men.

**ROISIN.** That's fine, but there are some things men are better at.

**OONAGH.** Like what?

**ROISIN.** Like lifting things.

**KATE.** I know plenty of women who could lift double than my Joe.

**OONAGH.** Depends on the woman.

**KATE.** And the man.

**ROISIN.** Well there are some things women are better at than men.

**KATE.** My mother's generation would say cooking and cleaning and caring.

**OONAGH.** Agh, Kate.

**KATE.** A girl I worked with in the primary school refused to let her daughters play with kitchens and ironing boards and babies. She thought it was a way of conditioning them to stay at home.

**ROISIN.** Little children, boy or girl, like copying what they see adults do. You want the girl to think she can do anything? Let her see the Da hoover the stairs.

**KATE.** I suppose men are better at farming.

**ROISIN.** Do you think?

**KATE.** They're more stubborn than any woman would be and they'll work the land until it gives them what they want. A woman would just find another field.

*(Pause.)*

**ROISIN.** Do you ever wish you'd had boys?

**KATE.** It would've been nice for Joe. He had a lot to handle there for a few years in the hormone stage. And with all the weddings.

**OONAGH.** I'd have loved another, a girl maybe. My Anthony was never really a needy child. And I need to be needed by someone.

**ROISIN.** Your Anthony's found someone now. You might be a grandmother yet.

*(Beat.)*

**OONAGH.** Maybe... I hear a lot of gay men are adopting or using a surrogate these days. I'm not sure what it's like in Spain.

*(Pause.)*

**ROISIN.** Oh. Sorry, I/

**OONAGH.** I know. I didn't... it's fine.

**ROISIN.** All this time on the road and we're still discovering new things.

**OONAGH.** I probably should have mentioned it earlier. Anthony is marrying Alex. A lovely man from Madrid.

**KATE.** Indeed.

**OONAGH.** Indeed? Is that all you've to say?

**KATE.** What else do you want me to say?

**OONAGH.** You just don't seem very surprised, that's all.

**KATE.** I'm not really.

**OONAGH.** Excuse me?

**KATE.** Maire told me.

**OONAGH.** Told you what?!

**KATE.** She told me, that Anthony was gay.

**OONAGH.** When?

**KATE.** Oh about twenty years ago.

**OONAGH.** Twenty?!

**KATE.** I thought you'd bring it up in your own time. It wasn't for me to force you.

**OONAGH.** And how did Maire know?

**KATE.** Apparently, she tried to give him a lumber and he did a runner.

**OONAGH.** *(Begins to laugh.)* He did a runner?

**KATE.** She was quite affronted, he told her she just wasn't his type.

**OONAGH.** And, you've kept that to yourself, all these years?

**KATE.** I have. We shouldn't be too far away now.

**ROISIN.** It is much colder now, isn't it?

**KATE.** It is.

**ROISIN.** When we get home do you think anything will have changed?

**OONAGH.** I'll need to score a few names off my Christmas card list.

**KATE.** Barry will be nearly finished his first year of school.

**ROISIN.** I'll have to tell them all.

> *(Beat.)*

**KATE.** You didn't tell anyone?

**ROISIN.** ... I couldn't face it.

**KATE.** You've plenty of time. Just do it quicker than Oonagh telling us about Anthony.

**OONAGH.** Shut you up. Just you take your time, Roisin.

**ROISIN.** The doctor said it could be a year, before I really start declining.

**KATE.** A year from now or a year from when we left?

**ROISIN.** I can't remember.

**OONAGH.** We'll manage it together.

**ROISIN.** Yeah.

**KATE.** Unless...you want to go home?

**ROISIN.** No I/

**KATE.** Because that's ok/

**OONAGH.** Oh yes, we can if you want to/

**ROISIN.** No! No, thank you. I want to carry on.

**KATE.** OK then. We'll carry on.

> *(Pause.)*

**KATE.** Is this it on the right?

**OONAGH.** It is.

**ROISIN.** The nights are getting much colder now.

> *(Lights.)*

## Scene Two

*(Tipperary. Christmas Eve. A pub bathroom.)*

*(In the background Abba's* [DANCING QUEEN] *plays.)*

*(A young girl (*ALISON*) is reapplying some very smudgy makeup.)*

*(*KATE *comes out of a toilet. The young girl sniffs.* KATE *begins to wash her hands. The young girl fixes her skirt.* KATE *fixes her hair. The young girl sniffs again.* KATE *turns to look at her.)*

KATE. Are you OK?

ALISON. Fecking bastard.

KATE. Oh.

ALISON. Why do we do it? Why? I mean I'm twenty-four. He has robbed me of the best years of my life.

KATE. Now, I don't think – you've plenty of/

ALISON. He's a cheating, lying bastard.

KATE. Are you here with friends? Can I get someone?

ALISON. He can go to hell in a horse-cart. I'm not going to be putting up with it. I saw my mother treated like dirt for twenty years before he did us all a favour and pissed off. I'm not going to join that club. I can find someone else... you single?

KATE. No.

ALISON. Married?

KATE. Yes.

ALISON. Is your husband decent? Or is he a bastard?

KATE. He... he's wonderful.

ALISON. Then you need to write a book or something 'cause we don't have a clue. How do you find a man? Why are they all bastards?

KATE. They're not all bastards. They're just... young.

ALISON. Some of them are old and they're still bastards. I caught crabs from a thirty-one-year-old from Athlone.

KATE. Oh. Well, I don't/

ALISON. How'd you meet your husband? In the village hall? No swiping right for you.

KATE. I – I met him at my cousin's wedding.

ALISON. Weddings. They're the key. Only everyone is waiting ages to get married now. My sister, she's thirty and she's going to all her friend's weddings and the fellas are already in long-term relationships or there's a reason they're single!

KATE. There'll be someone out there for you. You just have to stop looking. My daughter, Catherine, was Miss Career. Wasn't interested in any of it. We had to get her second cousin to go with her to the formal.

ALISON. The formal?

KATE. The end of year thing, you know at school?

ALISONI. Oh, the Debs?

KATE. She was no more interested than the man on the moon. Off she went to uni, still no sign. Then in her third year she appears with the softest, gentlest man, Brian. She met him at a *Game of Thrones* pub quiz. And he brought out a side of her we'd never seen. She was smitten.

ALISON. So just wait it out, is that it? Watch *Game of Thrones*?

**KATE.** Concentrate on you and someone will come along when you stop looking.

**ALI.** You remind me of my Nan. You're just like her. Except you know, not dead. *(ALI leans in to hug KATE.)* Happy Christmas to you. You tell that husband he's a very lucky fella, to have a legend like you to curl up with, OK?

**KATE.** I will.

> *(ALI exits.)*
>
> *(Pause.)*
>
> *(KATE stands still. She strokes her handbag. ROISIN enters.)*

**ROISIN.** Kate, are you ready to go? My head's thumping with all that loud music and there's a hen party from Carlow in.

**KATE.** Coming now.

> *(KATE tries to conceal her upset.)*

**ROISIN.** Are you OK?

**KATE.** Fine, fine.

**ROISIN.** Come on we head to the van and have a cup of tea and toast. Does that sound good?

**KATE.** It does.

**ROISIN.** He'd be very proud of you, you know? Having this adventure.

**KATE.** I wish he could see it.

**ROISIN.** Sure he can, you must believe that, he's here with you.

**KATE.**  It's just, the first Christmas, the first New Year. Maybe, maybe it's harder to be away from everyone, no normality.

**ROISIN.**  Of course it's hard. You've spent your whole life sharing it with Joe. And now it's you, and us. We're here with you. We're making a new tradition. Christmas in Tipperary. And wait to you see the blog this week! Us squeezed in the van with crackers and hats! Now pull your socks up. You can't mope your way around Ireland. As the shepherd said to the sheep?

**KATE.**  *(Smiling.)* Let's get the flock out of here.

## Scene Three

*(Wicklow. A campsite. A Saturday in March.)*

*(**PAUL** is standing opposite **ROISIN**. He is a gentle, quiet man. He is dressed in his best casuals and holding an old battered sports-bag.)*

*(Beat.)*

**PAUL.** Hello love.

**OONAGH.** Hello, Paul.

**KATE.** Shall I put the kettle on?

**PAUL.** That'd be lovely thank you.

*(**KATE** exits.)*

**OONAGH.** Was the drive down OK?

**PAUL.** Not too bad.

**OONAGH.** It's lovely weather today, Spring is on its way. Is it as nice at home?

**PAUL.** It's alright. Would you mind giving us a moment, please?

**OONAGH.** Oh, is that OK? I'll go help Kate?

*(**ROISIN** nods, **KATE** exits.)*

*(Beat.)*

**PAUL.** You aren't speaking to me then? Nine months isn't long enough to thaw the cold? *(Beat.)* I've been practising what I was going to say. *(Pause.)* I guess the first thing to say is that I love you. Very much. I have for all our years together, please don't ever doubt that I didn't. I'm sorry I didn't show it, more clearly, in the last

few years. At the start, when it was all to play for, I was
so delighted you were in my life, and we could share
responsibilities, and chores, and – well no I suppose
not chores, that sounds – what I mean is we were in it
together. I went to work and came home and there was
always dinner on the table. And that was grand, great,
for me, but these past few months I've been thinking
that maybe that was a tad selfish. Maybe, I should have
let, or not let because I hope to God I never forced you
against your will, but maybe I should have encouraged
you to think of your own needs too. It suited me to
have you at home. It was sensible with the money and
the childcare, but maybe you would have liked to have
your own career? I know I liked having mine. Or even,
after I retired, I took it as my time for a holiday, I'd
worked hard, I deserved it, but you, you've never had
a holiday, not from your work at home. I should have
thought about us enjoying time off together. I'm sorry
you've had to come away with the girls for me to realise
any of this. *(Pause.)* And the final thing I have to say is;
will you come on holiday with me?

> *(Beat.)*

ROISIN. Will I come on holiday with you?

PAUL. I bought a van.

ROISIN. A van?

PAUL. A campervan. It's parked at the town hall. Took me
forever to find two spaces together.

ROISIN. Why have you bought a van?

PAUL. For us, to... to have an adventure.

ROISIN. Paul/

PAUL. No listen, please. It doesn't mean everything
would be forgotten. I have to really make up for lost
time together, but I bought it so we could start, a new
chapter, so to speak. Just you and me. I told the girls,

they... they understood, eventually. They have to work things out for themselves, we're not here to be their skivvies. They've had their children and now is the time to manage it themselves. I can't stand by and see you come home for the rest of your sixties to mind weans. So what do you think?

ROISIN.  Paul, I have Alzheimer's.

   *(Beat.)*

PAUL.  Sorry?

ROISIN.  I have Alzheimer's. It's still early days, but, even these past few months, I'm getting worse.

PAUL.  You, you have... when did you find out?

ROISIN.  Just before I left.

PAUL.  You knew before you left? Is that why you left?

ROISIN.  One of the reasons. I was feeling... I wanted to take some time, to myself.

PAUL.  Do the girls know? Oonagh and Kate?

ROISIN.  They suspected for a while. Now they know.

PAUL.  And you couldn't tell me?

ROISIN.  No, I couldn't. I'm sorry.

PAUL.  Oh God, Roisin.

ROISIN.  Don't you pity me. I don't want pity. That's why I didn't tell any of you.

PAUL.  But love, we can, we can fight it together/

ROISIN.  Paul it is what it is. There is no fight.

PAUL.  Roisin/

ROISIN.  You get in your van and head home. There's no new chapter for us, no time to start again. We've had our time together. I'll be home once we finish all the counties, then we can look at a nursing home.

**PAUL.** No.

**ROISIN.** What do you mean 'no'?

(*Enter* **KATE** *and* **ROISIN** *with a tray of tea.*)

**KATE.** Well I've club biscuits and some digestives, unless you'd like a wee sandwich, Paul?

**PAUL.** I mean no. I will not go home. How can you think I would after telling me that?

**KATE.** Oh dear.

**OONAGH.** Maybe we should/

**PAUL.** And you two never thought to lift the phone and let me know?

**KATE.** It's not up to us/

**ROISIN.** Don't you start blaming them, I am my own woman Paul McAnespie and I/

**PAUL.** What are we going to do?

**ROISIN.** You aren't going to do anything. Nuala's told me you've been golfing and touring all around the country. Living the life of the single man, just like you wanted but were too scared to admit. You go ahead home and live your life. I won't be a burden to anyone. You aren't capable of minding me, nor are the girls, and you know what? I don't want you to.

(*Beat.*)

**OONAGH.** I'm just going to, get some sugar and... gin.

**PAUL.** Tough luck, Roisin. No.

**ROISIN.** No?

**PAUL.** No. No wallowing, no rejection, no giving up. I have said my piece about how I am sorry for my past behaviour, I can't change it, but in terms of our future, that I can still change. So, no. The van is stocked and ready to go. I am inviting you to join me. I'll come back tomorrow morning at nine. You can tell me your decision then.

(PAUL *nods to* OONAGH *and* KATE, *and exits.*)

KATE.  I don't think I've heard your Paul talk that much in forty years.

OONAGH.  Rosh?

ROISIN.  I/ He/ He's lost his marbles.

OONAGH.  I'd say he's finally found them.

KATE.  He seems pretty determined.

ROISIN.  That's just his pride talking, he won't be back. He'll realise he likes the easy life and head home.

(ROISIN *exits.*)

KATE.  Do you think that's true?

OONAGH.  Oh, don't ask me. What would I know?

KATE.  We'll see in the morning I suppose. Let's find that gin.

## Scene Four

*(The next morning.)*

*(**ROISIN** stands centre stage, holding a mug of
tea and staring out.)*

*(Enter **KATE**.)*

**KATE.** It's a beautiful view. Will be a shame to move on.

**ROISIN.** Ireland's filled with beautiful views.

**KATE.** How are you feeling?

**ROISIN.** When we first left, I was empty. Now, I've filled
the tank a little. Let's just hope I can remember it.

**KATE.** Sure you've the blog to read, and all the photos. And
us.

**ROISIN.** I do.

**KATE.** Are you glad you came away?

**ROISIN.** If I hadn't, you and Oonagh would have destroyed
each other by Donegal.

*(**KATE** laughs. Enter **OONAGH**.)*

**OONAGH.** No sign of him?

**ROISIN.** Who?

**KATE.** *(Gently.)* Paul. He was going to call back?

**ROISIN.** Paul who?

**OONAGH.** Oh God.

**KATE.** Shh. Paul, your husband, he was here yesterday, he/

*(**ROISIN** bursts out laughing.)*

**ROISIN.** Ahhh, you, I got you both, the look on your faces/

KATE.  You little/

OONAGH.  It's no laughing matter. I thought we'd/

ROISIN.  If you can't laugh about it what are you going to do?

KATE.  An absolute disgrace.

ROISIN.  Shall we get packed up then?

KATE.  You don't want to wait 'til nine?

ROISIN.  He'll have gone home.

> *(Paul starts to sing the opening line of* **[IF YOU LEAVE ME NOW]** *by Chicago.)*

OONAGH.  Is that?

KATE.  It is, it is. Roisin?!

> *(Enter* **PAUL,** *singing. He is dressed in an old battered wedding suit. He holds a veil and a bunch of flowers.)*

ROISIN.  Oh my God.

> *(Paul sings the second verse of* **[IF YOU LEAVE ME NOW]** *by Chicago.)*

PAUL.  Roisin McAnespie, will you do me the honour of continuing to be my wife, and join me on a second honeymoon to Cherbourg?

ROISIN.  Cherbourg?

PAUL.  The ferry from Dublin is booked for two thirty. I would love it if you joined me.

> *(He goes down on one knee.)*

ROISIN.  Jesus Paul, mind your knee.

PAUL.  It's worth it for you, Roshie.

OONAGH.  I think I might cry.

*(Pause.)*

ROISIN. Would you two, would you mind if I ...

KATE. Course not!

OONAGH. We're fed up looking at you anyway.

ROISIN. What about the last few counties?

KATE. We'll do them without you. We haven't a man on one knee looking to take us to France.

OONAGH. Go for it, Rosh.

*(ROISIN smiles. She moves to PAT and helps guide him up.)*

*(The girls cheer. PAT grins, and leans in and kisses her. She takes the veil and flowers.)*

ROISIN. You're an absolute glype.

KATE. You better go pack, if you've to make the ferry!

OONAGH. Do you want a hand?

PAUL. I'll help.

ROISIN. You'll help with the packing?

PAUL. If you'll let me.

*(ROISIN and PAUL exit.)*

KATE. Jesus.

OONAGH. I know.

KATE. So we're doing the last bit just us?

OONAGH. Seems that way.

KATE. Do you think we'll be OK?

OONAGH. Oh yes.

KATE.  How can you be so certain? We can't even make one
journey without arguing about the directions.

OONAGH.  I've a plan.

KATE.  A plan?

OONAGH.  Yes, I'm going to find you a nice young man in
Dublin. You need to let off a bit of steam.

KATE.  Oh Oonagh, would you ever/

(**OONAGH** *laughs and exits,* **KATE** *follows.*)

# ACT FOUR – SPRING

## Scene One

*(Dublin, midnight.)*

*(There is the sound of loud music, a crowd, a flash of neon.* **KATE** *and* **OONAGH** *stand at a bar. It's dark, and red and buzzing. The barman wears a black tank top with a red 'P', he serves them two large cocktails.)*

**KATE.** What did you order?

**OONAGH.** A 'Ginger Minge'.

**KATE.** Jesus, Mary and Joseph.

**OONAGH.** Now don't you start being a little old lady/

**KATE.** I'm here, aren't I?

**OONAGH.** You're sat there like Mother Theresa.

**KATE.** I have never been somewhere like this before. How does your Anthony know bars in Dublin, when he's been in Spain the past ten years?

**OONAGH.** He flies into Dublin, sometimes he stays down the weekend before coming up the road. The few times he even bothers himself to come home.

*(There is a blast of music. Bonnie Tyler's* **[HOLDING OUT FOR A HERO]** *begins.)*

**KATE.** What would Joe say?

**OONAGH.** Oh he'd probably order their pale ale and sit here happily.

*(***KATE** *looks to* **OONAGH.** **OONAGH** *raises her glass.)* To new adventures!

*(Lights change.)*

*(Outside, at the back of the bar. A young man stands smoking.* **KATE** *approaches.)*

**KATE.** Do you have a light?

**ETHAN.** Sure. *(She holds a cigarette out, he lights it.)*

**KATE.** I'm not actually a smoker.

**ETHAN.** You in denial?

**KATE.** Reliving my youth. I got this from that man in the cowboy hat.

*(A girl passes them.)*

**DRUNK GIRL.** *(On her phone.)* No, I'm round the back. ROUND THE BACK!

*(To* **KATE.***)* What's road's this on, pet?

**KATE.** Pardon?

**DRUNK GIRL.** *(On her phone.)* I'm askin! Hold On! *(To* **KATE.***)* The bar, this bar we're stood in, what road's it on?

**KATE.** Oh. It's Capel street/

**DRUNK GIRL.** The elderly woman says it's/

**KATE.** Excuse me!

**DRUNK GIRL.** *(To* **KATE.***)* Hold on, sweetie, I'm on the phone/

**KATE.** I am not/

**DRUNK GIRL.** Yes, I'm coming now. *(To* **KATE.***)* Thanks so much. You are so cute.

*(She teeters off.* **KATE** *fumes.* **ETHAN** *smiles.)*

**ETHAN.** I'm surprised you didn't go for her.

**KATE.** You're my witness.

**ETHAN.** You showed great restraint.

**KATE.** Yeah well. Maybe she's right. I feel elderly tonight. I just didn't need reminded.

**ETHAN.** What brings you here then? A hen do? A dare?

**KATE.** No, my friend, Oonagh.

**ETHAN.** And where is she?

**KATE.** Inside doing the Macarena.

**ETHAN.** Ah, she's your friend? She's a character.

**KATE.** She is. I bet you're wondering why she's friends with an old fart like me?

**ETHAN.** I'm just impressed an old fart like you stepped over the threshold. I'm Ethan.

**KATE.** Kate. We were told of all the bars in Dublin this was the one to see so here we are.

**ETHAN.** And what do you think so far?

**KATE.** Not bad.

**ETHAN.** We'll put that in the google review. Kate from the North says "Not bad." You just down for the weekend?

**KATE.** A few days here. We're trying to do all the counties in Ireland. We're nearly there.

**ETHAN.** That's amazing. Where have you still to do?

**KATE.** Longford, Offaly, the midlands really.

**ETHAN.** *(Laughs)* You saved the best 'til last! All the counties? What made you do that?

**KATE.** My husband dropped dead in the bread aisle of Lidl.

**ETHAN.** Fuck.

**KATE.** Yeah. I wish it had happened at home. In the garden even, and not on that cold floor. People walking round him, me at home waiting, annoyed he was taking so long... So, there you have it.

> *(Pause.)*

**ETHAN.** I'm sorry.

**KATE.** Nothing to do with you, Ethan.

**ETHAN.** I know. But that's fucking awful.

**KATE.** It is.

**ETHAN.** Would you like another cigarette?

**KATE.** Why not.

**ETHAN.** Has the trip helped?

**KATE.** Sorry?

**ETHAN.** Has the tripped helped? You grieve?

**KATE.** Do you know, in ten months you're the first person to ask me that.

**ETHAN.** I'm sorry.

**KATE.** Stop saying sorry. "It gives away your power", as my youngest daughter would say.

**ETHAN.** You've a daughter?

**KATE.** Two, four grandchildren. *(Beat.)* It has helped me. At the start I thought I'd leave the feeling behind. But you just bring your problems with you. I don't know who I am. Without him. He was part of me. Part of my bones and blood and brain. And now he's gone.

He's been gone for ten months. But it doesn't feel real. It feels like he's just gone. Or I'm just gone. Like I've stepped into another world. A world where I'm on holidays and when I get home he'll be there waiting with all the news for me. And now the trip is almost over and I still have to go back to an empty house. Still have to face that he isn't there. Face that that part of me still missing. I don't know if I'll cope.

**ETHAN.** Not without support.

**KATE.** Support? My daughters are barely speaking to me. Sure I did a bunk.

**ETHAN.** Did you tell them why?

**KATE.** What's the point, sure.

**ETHAN.** The point is you're not giving them a chance.

**KATE.** They should know/

**ETHAN.** How you feel?

**KATE.** Yes.

**ETHAN.** Well they clearly don't. You need to help them understand/

**KATE.** Oh, you've experience in that do you?

**ETHAN.** You think because I'm not you I can't relate?

**KATE.** No, no of course not I/

**ETHAN.** Because let me tell you, you'd be hard pushed to find anyone in this bar tonight who hasn't stood in your shoes at some point. Maybe not the dead husband part, but certainly the being truthful about who they are and how they feel to their loved ones.

**KATE.** I'm sorry/

**ETHAN.** Stop saying sorry, it gives away your power. (*KATE smiles.*) Listen, I'll not do the full sob story. But you've shared so I think I need to share. I grew up concealing who I was for fear of hurting those I loved. I was protecting myself by not being honest about who I was. A gay lad reared by two law-abiding Catholics from Cavan. Once I told them, yeah they took time to *process* as the Americans say. But now? Now my Mum is my biggest fan, my Dad? He shows the fella's at the pub my drag performances on YouTube. My brother? The rugby loving, IT consultant with two kids and a semi-detached, he built my website. And my sister? Well my little sister brought her girlfriend, Aisling, home to watch *Dancing with the Stars* last week and my Nan didn't bat an eye. And it's not perfect, it's not without its drama. But it's better than it was. I'm glad I told them. You need to talk to your daughters.

KATE.  You're probably right. You've a sensible head on your shoulders. So, you're a drag queen?

ETHAN.  A drag artist.

KATE.  Are you on tonight?

ETHAN.  No my friend's on tonight, I'm just here enjoying myself.

KATE.  Oh.

ETHAN.  Why, what were you thinking?

KATE.  Well what's the chances of your friend doing two old farts a favour?

ETHAN.  I'm sure I could have a word with her.

KATE.  Would you mind?

ETHAN.  For you, Kate, anything.

      *(Pre-recorded film is projected on stage.)*

      (**ETHAN** *holds* **KATE**'s *phone, filming the action.)*

*(The intro of Donna Summer and Barbara Streisand's* [NO MORE TEARS (ENOUGH IS ENOUGH)] *begins.)*

*(Drag queen, Cherrie Ontop enters centre stage, she begins to sing.)*

*(Then* OONAGH *enters, lip-syncs her opening line.)*

*(*KATE *enters, lip syncs her opening line.)*

*(The trio perform, Cherrie singing, the women miming, it is wonderful, transformative, effervescent.)*

*(They come together, sharing the spotlight, building to the big finish.)*

## Scene Two

*(Louth. Early May. Carlingford Lough.)*

**CATHERINE.** Hi Mum.

**KATE.** Catherine! You made it?

**CATHERINE.** You've missed me then?

**KATE.** Course I have. *(She hugs her.)* How are the boys? Maire? Molly?

**CATHERINE.** Everyone's fine. Everyone misses you, the whole parish is asking how your trip's been going.

**KATE.** Have you been showing them our blog?

**CATHERINE.** They especially liked the picture of you kissing the blarney stone.

**KATE.** My back wasn't right for a week, Oonagh had to do most of the driving.

**CATHERINE.** Where is Oonagh?

**KATE.** She went for a walk around the castle. She really loves castles. I think after this she could write a book about every castle in Ireland. *(Beat.)* Are you staying?

**CATHERINE.** I thought I'd stay a few days. It's a long weekend.

**KATE.** Will Brian be OK with the boys?

**CATHERINE.** Of course he will. Why wouldn't he be?

**KATE.** I didn't mean/

**CATHERINE.** It's fine.

*(Beat.)*

**KATE.** Did you like my video?

**CATHERINE.** It was... surprising.

**KATE.**  Did you show it to Barry?

**CATHERINE.**  Of course I didn't.

**KATE.**  Why not?

**CATHERINE.**  I'm hardly going to show him a video of his Nana dancing with a drag queen in Dublin.

**KATE.**  Drag artist. I thought he might like it.

**CATHERINE.**  Why? What do you mean by that?

**KATE.**  I don't mean anything, just what I say.

**CATHERINE.**  Sure.

**KATE.**  Barry always loved singing and dressing up.

**CATHERINE.**  Yes, when he was younger. He's grown out of that now, not that you'd know.

**KATE.**  Oh here we go.

**CATHERINE.**  Forget it.

**KATE.**  No, tell me how awful I've been go on.

*(Enter* **OONAGH.***)*

**OONAGH.**  Catherine! You made it!

**KATE.**  Catherine is staying the weekend.

**OONAGH.**  Oh brilliant! You can take Roisin's old spot. As long as you don't mind listening to your Mum's snoring.

**KATE.**  I do not snore/

**OONAGH.**  I swear your Daddy must've been half deaf listening to her.

**CATHERINE.**  He put up with a lot.

*(Beat.)*

**OONAGH.**  We could go shopping tomorrow if you like?

**CATHERINE.**  We could.

**OONAGH.** Or, maybe we could go for lunch? We have this book that has all the best coffee shops in Ireland in it, maybe there's one in Carlingford.

**CATHERINE.** Maybe.

**KATE.** Or maybe, you're just going to stand here and stew until you come out with whatever it is you want to say to me?

**CATHERINE.** I don't have anything I want to say to you/

**KATE.** I know you, Catherine. You never could hide your sulking, you've something on the tip of your tongue so just get it over with.

**CATHERINE.** You always do this, this demand thing, insist people tell you what you imagine they're thinking.

**OONAGH.** Now let's just/

**KATE.** I've obviously somehow upset you, so I'd rather just get to it. You know for a solicitor you're rarely very direct.

**CATHERINE.** "You've *somehow* upset me?" My father died and my mother ran away. How could that not upset me?

**OONAGH.** Now Catherine/

**KATE.** I did not run away.

**CATHERINE.** So what do you call this?

**KATE.** I call this taking a break, with my friends. No different than you did at nineteen, Catherine. Only you went to New Zealand and picked strawberries, all we have to pick is which coffee shop to try or the best route to Kildare. Did you know there was an Avoca on the ring of Kerry? We were over the moon, weren't we Oonagh.

**OONAGH.** I should probably just/

CATHERINE.  You taking a trip with your friends directly after Dad died is totally un-related then? Staying on the road for almost a year?!

KATE.  I needed time to think. To, get away from it all.

CATHERINE.  But what about us, Mum? Maire and me? And your grandchildren? Barry already lost his best-friend, then he had to say goodbye to his Nana as well?

KATE.  I never liked being called Nana. I'd prefer to just be Kate, or Katie maybe.

CATHERINE.  You're ridiculous.

KATE.  I'm sorry my leaving has upset you, and Maire, and the children. I am.

CATHERINE.  But you're still glad you did it? You'd do it again?

KATE.  Yes. I would.

CATHERINE.  Unbelievable, you're so selfish. We lost someone too, you know? We lost Dad, my Dad, and then we lost you. We just said goodbye to one parent and the other abandons us in the time we need them the most. We needed you to show us how to be OK.

KATE.  I didn't know how to! Do you think I was OK? I'm sorry your Dad died. I'm sorry you feel abandoned. But I could not stay in that house a day longer. It was too hard. It would have destroyed me. You and Maire popped in once, twice a week. I was stuck there. In that house, without him. I lost my best friend, my heart, myself for Christ's sake. Sorry I couldn't make it better for you. I did want to make it better for you, I just didn't know how you, Cat.

     (Beat.)

CATHERINE.  I'm going to unpack.

*(*CATHERINE *exits.* OONAGH *walks to* KATE
*and places a hand on her shoulder.)*

OONAGH.  It'll get sorted.

## Scene Three

*(The next day. A coffee shop.)*

**CATHERINE.** Thanks for inviting me along.

**OONAGH.** No problem.

**CATHERINE.** Mum didn't feel like doing much.

**OONAGH.** Is it little wonder.

**CATHERINE.** What's that supposed to mean?

**OONAGH.** You've been punishing her, I haven't see her this stern since we left Donegal.

**CATHERINE.** I haven't been punishing her.

**OONAGH.** What would you call it then?

**CATHERINE.** Me and Mum are just... working things out.

**OONAGH.** You've had eleven months to work things out. Your showing up here was meant to be a chance to reconnect and give your Mum some support/

**CATHERINE.** Me give her support? She's the parent, she's meant to/

**OONAGH.** You are thirty years old. Don't you think you've had enough support? When's your Mum's turn?

**CATHERINE.** That's not fair. Dad died and Mum/

**OONAGH.** Abandoned you? Your Dad died and instead of sitting in an empty house, feeding the priest once a week, waiting on you to fit her in, she packed a bag and went on a trip. Is that so awful?

**CATHERINE.** It's not just a trip. It's a year. The first year, no Dad or Mum/

**OONAGH.** And you wanted her to dedicate her time to caring for you and your grief/

CATHERINE.  No, of course not, I just wanted/

OONAGH.  For her only to live for her daughters, or her grandchildren?

CATHERINE.  No! I just/ We needed her. I needed her.

OONAGH.  Did you ever tell her that? Or did you just assume she'd know?

CATHERINE.  Of course she knows.

OONAGH.  You and Maire have your husbands and your jobs and your kids, and your youth for God's sake. Your mother cannot be at your beck and call until the day she drops dead.

CATHERINE.  It's just... everyone keeps asking, how she's doing and what a wonderful thing it is, and how proud we must be and I just feel... I just feel. Jealous! Jealous and forgotten and hurt. I needed her and she left. I missed her and she didn't come back. And I had to learn to be OK without her.

OONAGH.  And are you OK? Did you learn to be OK?

CATHERINE.  *(Beat.)* Yes. I did.

OONAGH.  Then, why are you spending the time you do have with her acting like a spoilt child?

CATHERINE.  ...

OONAGH.  Go talk to her. Spend time with her. She's missed you too you know.

*(Lights change.)*

## Scene Four

*(KATE stands alone, holding her bag.)*

KATE. I always found it hard to put me first. You would tell me, go have a lie down, don't be worrying, sure the washing would wait for another day. Now I suppose it'd be on you to do more of those types of jobs. If we were married today I mean. I didn't really mind being the home-maker. When you died, I just, suddenly, I put me first. Only me. I'm so sorry for hurting the girls. I understand of course, why they're mad. But, but when you died Joe, I felt a tidal wave of fear. Fear it was, I think. Fear of being alone. Fear of being left with myself for company. Fear I'd wasted the time we did have on hoovering and washing and everything else. I wish I'd said, 'mon we go a wee drive. Forget all the jobs we have today, we'll go to Strangford, or Newcastle or Carnlough. I was never spontaneous, I didn't cherish you enough. And when you died, I felt as close to breaking as I've ever felt. It reminded me of that time after I'd had Catherine. Something just didn't line up the way it was meant to. I was barely able to get out of bed. And you carried me through it all. I always think you and Catherine had a special bond because of that. And my lack of bond with her reminds me of my failing then. Oh I know, I'm not meant to blame myself or feel responsible, Joe. But that's how I feel. I couldn't cope with the basic thing a mother should do. And here I am again, she needed me and where was I. I left. I left her again and I feel like a failure once again, Joe. And you're not here to carry me.

*(Lights change, CATHERINE enters.)*

CATHERINE. Hi Mum.

KATE. How was your coffee?

CATHERINE. Lovely.

**KATE.**  Expensive?

**CATHERINE.**  Ten euros.

**KATE.**  For two coffees? Carlingford's wild/

**CATHERINE.**  Mum/

**KATE.**  It's the Boyne tomorrow.

**CATHERINE.**  Yes.

**KATE.**  We're almost done.

**CATHERINE.**  It's some achievement.

**KATE.**  What time will you head home?

**CATHERINE.**  I ... I wanted to talk to you about that.

**KATE.**  Hmm?

**CATHERINE.**  I called Brian, and work, and Maire. I'd... I'd like to stay, if you didn't mind.

**KATE.**  Stay?

**CATHERINE.**  For the last few stops? Would that be OK?

**KATE.**  Why?

**CATHERINE.**  Because... because I've been...

**KATE.**  Look, don't worry about it. I know you're busy and you don't need to/

**CATHERINE.**  Listen Mum. I want to stay, with you and Oonagh. Do the last stops/

**KATE.**  But why?

**CATHERINE.**  Oh, I just do!

**KATE.**  Alright, alright don't shout/

**CATHERINE.**  I'm not shouting. I just. I want to do this with you. The last few stops. I want / I've been. I've been so hard on you and I think, I just think it's inspiring. Putting yourself first. You were right to put yourself first. And I'd like to do that, just for a few more days. Brian agrees. I want to finish this with you, Mum. Then we'll go home together. And we'll, you'll be OK. We'll find a way through. You could re-decorate, or move in with us, or get a new place/

KATE. No, no, you've said it now, I'll move in.

CATHERINE. Yes, sure if that is what you want/

KATE. Ah whisht, Catherine. Don't worry. I won't be living with you and Brian. Can you imagine?

CATHERINE. Well the offers there if you want.

KATE. Thank you, love.

CATHERINE. So, can I join you?

KATE. It would be an honour.

## Scene Five

*(Meath. Newgrange. June 21st.)*

**OONAGH.** Before the pyramids,

**CATHERINE.** Before Stonehenge,

**KATE.** Before the wheel. There was Newgrange.

**OONAGH.** How old did you say it was?

**KATE.** Five thousand years old.

**OONAGH.** Unbelievable

**CATHERINE.** To think men and women transported those stones all the way from the Wicklow mountains.

**OONAGH.** And the Mournes. A north south effort.

**KATE.** Two-hundred thousand tonnes of stone.

**OONAGH.** I wish the fella who did my conservatory would take a page out of their book. Lazy so and so.

**CATHERINE.** Ireland feels ancient, standing here.

**OONAGH.** The High Kings of Ireland are meant to be buried here.

**KATE.** To feel so dedicated to your dead, you make this. It's wonderful, isn't it?

*(Beat.)*

**OONAGH.** Shall we go in?

**CATHERINE.** We didn't come all this way not to.

**KATE.** I'll join you in a moment.

**CATHERINE.** You OK, Mum?

**KATE.** Yes, love, just need a minute.

**CATHERINE.** OK. Come on Oonagh.

**OONAGH.** It might be a bit claustrophobic.

**CATHERINE.** I'll be grand.

**OONAGH.** Sure take my arm.

*(They exit.)*

*(**KATE** takes a small urn from her handbag.)*

**KATE.** Well, Joe. This is it. The last county. Meath. Or *Meathe* as they call it here. An ancient spot full of history and folklore, life and death. To think the Irish made this. It's impressive, isn't it? We do do some things right... I like that it's here. Joseph you were as fine as the High Kings... although we'll not mention it was near the Battle of the Boyne to the neighbours, can you imagine their faces? We've seen it all now, all the counties, all the craic and drama. That was Ireland in our sixties... I'm sorry you didn't get to see it yourself. I'm sorry you worked all those years not to enjoy your retirement. I'm sorry I sent you out for bread... but listen, you're not to worry, OK? I'm OK. I'll be OK... And maybe I'll see you again. Oh I think I probably will. See you love. Thank you for everything. Goodbye for now.

*(**KATE** looks to the entrance of the tomb. She walks slowly towards it. **OONAGH** appears.)*

**OONAGH.** You coming, Kate?

**KATE.** I am.

# EPILOGUE

(**KATE** *sits playing the piano.*)

(**CATHERINE** *comes in with a tray full of tea and sandwiches.*)

(**ROISIN** *sits in front of a large purple tent, sipping a Margarita.*)

(**PAUL** *kneels beside her in a tropical shirt, frying sausages on a gas stove.*)

(**OONAGH** *is in a smart dress and ballroom dance shoes.*)

(*A young man comes towards her. They start to dance traditional Tango.*)

(*The lights change, the music fades, there is the sound of birds, trees in the wind, laughter.*)

(*The three women turn to face the audience.*)

(*They smile.*)

(*Blackout.*)

## NOTE

It is important to honour the art of drag – should the
actor playing Ethan have experience in the Drag form
then the following is proposed.

# ACT FOUR

### Scene One

KATE.  Are you on tonight?

ETHAN.  Yes, at midnight.

KATE.  How would you feel about doing two old farts a
favour?

ETHAN.  For you, Kate, anything.

> (ETHAN *and* KATE *move centre stage.*
> OONAGH *joins them. She hands* ETHAN *a wig
> and heels.*)

> (*Donna Summer and Barbara Streisand's*
> [NO MORE TEARS (ENOUGH IS
> ENOUGH)] *begins.*)

> (KATE *and* OONAGH *stand back to back, with*
> ETHAN *behind them. They begin to mime,
> move, dance, it is effervescent. They step out
> to reveal a wonderous* ETHAN.*)

# THANKS

A lone writer is never alone.

With heartfelt thanks to Fishamble: New Play Company for first selecting this idea with the Lyric Theatre, Belfast for their *A Play for Ireland* programme, 2018. Sincere thanks to the Arts Council of Northern Ireland for its continued support, especially through the Support for Individual Artist award, the New Playwrights Programme 2019 and 1st Irish Festival, New York 2020. Huge thanks to Rebecca Mairs for continually believing in me and these women's stories, to Jimmy Fay for his endless hard-work, and the whole Lyric Theatre team for making it happen. Thank you to Paula McFetridge for her continued support. Thank you to George Heslin and Origin Theatre Company. Thanks to all the wonderful actors who contributed to the research and development stages including: Seamus O'Hara, James Doran, Laura Hughes, Carol Moore, Libby Smith, Julia Dearden, Maria Quinn, Cathan McRoberts, Terry Donnelly, Polly McKie, Bernadette Quigley, David O'Hara, Paul O'Brien, Jack McLaughlin, Grainne Duddy and Tim Palmer. Thank you to Siobhan Kelly & Rosie McClelland who read a very early idea aloud even though it had no end.

Thank you to all those I spoke to during my research of Ireland, especially Julie Kinsella, Grainne (who's surname I didn't catch), Eileen Kilkenny, Paddy & Breda Clarke, Aileen Hennessey, Maura Leavy, Dympna and Philip Cribbin, Briege and Eleanor at Ashford, Lawrence & Kate McMahon and everyone I met along the road.

Thank you to the Stroke Association and their members for their time and thoughts, thanks to Ruth McCarthy at Outburst, thanks to Abbeyfield & Wesley, Radius Housing and all those I have worked with who manage their Alzheimer's with fight and grace. Thank you to Matthew Cavan, Marcus Hunter-Neill, The Vault and Eastside Arts.

Sincere thanks also go to the Lir Academy, Trinity College especially Graham Whybrow, Loughlin Deegan and the family of Patricia Leggett to whom I will always be grateful. Thanks to the board at Commedia of Errors, especially outgoing member Sally Visick, for her support and belief over the years.

Heartfelt gratitude as always to my wonderful in-laws June and David, life-long supporters of the arts. Thanks to my brother Aidan, partner Danielle and to my extended family and friends who always support and champion me.

I am eternally grateful to my ever-supportive parents Owen and Cecilia, who have always encouraged me to dream big and not take no for an answer. Through the many, many junctures of this career I chose, they have had unceasing faith in me. And that belief made me believe. Thank you.

Finally, thank you to my unceasing supporter, friend and inspiration, Benjamin. You inspire me each and every day and your belief in me and my plays have been life-changing. I will always be grateful to have met you in the stage left wing of the NTL studio theatre, 1999. You handed me my prop baton as I readied to chase Fagan's gang, and sometimes I got distracted talking to you, but you always made sure I didn't miss my cue. Even then you were a director. Thank you.

# ABOUT THE AUTHOR

Clare McMahon grew up in Carrickfergus, County Antrim. She first discovered theatre and the performing arts through the Speech & Drama festival at the town hall. At thirteen she joined The Rainbow Factory, Youth Action and spent most weekends rehearsing plays. At eighteen she attended Central School of Speech & Drama and graduated with BA Hons Acting. Clare has worked as an actor in theatres across the UK & Ireland including: *The Cripple of Inishmaan* (West End); *A Midsummer Nights Dream* (The Almeida); *Northern Star* (Finborough) and *The Cherry Orchard* (Greenwich). At home she has worked with the Lyric, Mac, Kabosh, Tinderbox, Cahoots and Bruiser. In 2017 her debut play *Shakespeare's Women* sold out its run at the Lyric before an NI Tour. In 2018 she was awarded the Patricia Leggett Scholarship to attend The Lir Academy and achieved a distinction in her MFA Playwriting. In 2018 she was one of Fishamble Theatre's *A Play for Ireland* artists in conjunction with the Lyric and in 2019 was one of The Lyric's New Playwrights Programme chosen writers. Her play *The Gap Year* was presented in New York as part of 1st Irish Festival 'Vital Voices' programme, 2020. It was also presented for the Lyric Theatre's Listen At The Lyric programme, 2020. Clare recently wrote *LILY* a 360 virtual-reality film for Commedia of Errors, allowing users to experience living with early-onset Alzheimer's. She is one half of Commedia of Errors Theatre Company and her most recent play *I Am Maura* debuted in the Lyric Theatre in May 2019. She is currently under commission with Kabosh, Commedia of Errors and is one of the Abbey Theatre's commemoration awardees. She lives in Belfast with her husband and her plants.

Lightning Source UK Ltd.
Milton Keynes UK
UKHW020617270822
407756UK00009B/239